GW00383476

ENVIRONMENTAL SCIENCE, ENGINEERING AND TECHNOLOGY

WETLANDS IN CENTRAL FLORIDA: AN ECOLOGY AND HYDROLOGY PRIMER

ENVIRONMENTAL SCIENCE, ENGINEERING AND TECHNOLOGY

Additional books in this series can be found on Nova's website under the Series tab.

Additional E-books in this series can be found on Nova's website under the E-books tab.

ENVIRONMENTAL SCIENCE, ENGINEERING AND TECHNOLOGY

WETLANDS IN CENTRAL FLORIDA: AN ECOLOGY AND HYDROLOGY PRIMER

SAMANTHA L. ELLIOT
EDITOR

Nova Science Publishers, Inc.
New York

NOTICE TO THE READER

The Publisher has taken reasonable care in the preparation of this book, but makes no expressed or implied warranty of any kind and assumes no responsibility for any errors or omissions. No liability is assumed for incidental or consequential damages in connection with or arising out of information contained in this book. The Publisher shall not be liable for any special, consequential, or exemplary damages resulting, in whole or in part, from the readers' use of, or reliance upon, this material. Any parts of this book based on government reports are so indicated and copyright is claimed for those parts to the extent applicable to compilations of such works.

Independent verification should be sought for any data, advice or recommendations contained in this book. In addition, no responsibility is assumed by the publisher for any injury and/or damage to persons or property arising from any methods, products, instructions, ideas or otherwise contained in this publication.

This publication is designed to provide accurate and authoritative information with regard to the subject matter covered herein. It is sold with the clear understanding that the Publisher is not engaged in rendering legal or any other professional services. If legal or any other expert assistance is required, the services of a competent person should be sought. FROM A DECLARATION OF PARTICIPANTS JOINTLY ADOPTED BY A COMMITTEE OF THE AMERICAN BAR ASSOCIATION AND A COMMITTEE OF PUBLISHERS.

Additional color graphics may be available in the e-book version of this book.

LIBRARY OF CONGRESS CATALOGING-IN-PUBLICATION DATA
Wetlands in central Florida : an ecology and hydrology primer / editor,
Samantha L. Elliot.
p. cm.
Includes index.
ISBN 978-1-61728-600-1 (hardcover)
1. Wetlands--Florida. 2. Wetland ecology--Florida. 3.
Florida--Environmental conditions. I. Elliot, Samantha L.
GB625.F6W48 2010
577.6809759--dc22
2010025954

Published by Nova Science Publishers, Inc. ✝ New York

CONTENTS

PREFACE

Freshwater wetlands are an integral part of central Florida, where thousands are distributed across the landscape. However, their relatively small size and vast numbers challenge efforts to characterize them collectively as a statewide water resource. Freshwater wetlands and their interaction with ground water play a pivotal role in the water resources of Florida. Understanding the long-term effects of wetland augmentation and other mitigation practices on wetlands in Florida requires systematically comparing the hydrology, water quality, and ecology of both natural and augmented systems. This book provides an overview of the ecology and hydrology of the freshwater wetlands in Central Florida.

Chapter 1 - Freshwater wetlands are an integral part of central Florida, where thousands are distributed across the landscape. However, their relatively small size and vast numbers challenge efforts to characterize them collectively as a statewide water resource. Wetlands are a dominant landscape feature in Florida; in 1996, an estimated 11.4 million acres of wetlands occupied 29 percent of the area of the State. Wetlands represent a greater percentage of the land surface in Florida than in any other state in the conterminous United States (Dahl, 2000; 2006). Statewide, 90 percent of the total wetland area is freshwater wetlands and 10 percent is coastal wetlands (Dahl, 2005). About 55 percent of the freshwater wetlands in Florida are forested, 25 percent are marshes and emergent wetlands, 18 percent are scrub-shrub wetlands, and the remaining 2 percent are freshwater ponds.

Freshwater wetlands are distributed differently in central Florida than in other parts of the State. In the panhandle and in northern Florida, there are fewer isolated wetlands than in the central and southern parts of the State, and few of those wetlands are affected by activities such as groundwater withdrawals. In southern Florida, the vast wetlands of the Everglades and the Big Cypress Swamp blanket the landscape and form contiguous shallow expanses of water, which often exhibit slow but continuous flow toward the southwestern coast. In contrast, the wetlands of central Florida are relatively small, numerous, mostly isolated, and widely distributed (Figure 1). In many places, wetlands are flanked by uplands, generating a mosaic of contrasting environments—unique wildlife habitat often adjacent to dense human development. As the population of central Florida increases, the number of residents living near wetlands also increases. Living in close proximity to wetlands provides many Floridians with an increased awareness of nature and an opportunity to examine the relationship between people and wetlands. Specifically, these residents can observe how wetlands are affected by human activities.

Chapter 2 - This appendix includes maps showing the distribution of wetlands by type and pie diagrams showing the percent of each wetland type in each county of central Florida.

Chapter 3 - Comparing altered wetlands to natural wetlands in the same region improves the ability to interpret the gradual and cumulative effects of human development on freshwater wetlands. Hydrologic differences require explicit attention because they affect nearly all wetland functions and are an overriding influence on other comparisons involving wetland water quality and ecology. This study adopts several new approaches to quantify wetland hydrologic characteristics and then describes and compares the hydrology, water quality, and ecology of 10 isolated freshwater marsh and cypress wetlands in the mantled karst landscape of central Florida. Four of the wetlands are natural, and the other six have water levels indirectly lowered by ground-water withdrawals on municipally owned well fields. For several decades, the water levels in four of these altered wetlands have been raised by adding ground water in a mitigation process called augmentation. The two wetlands left unaugmented were impaired because their water levels were lowered. Multifaceted comparisons between the altered and natural wetlands are used to examine differences between marshes and cypress wetlands and to describe the effects of augmentation practices on the wetland ecosystems.

In the karstic geologic setting, both natural and altered wetlands predominantly lost water to the surficial aquifer. Water leaking out of the wetlands created water-table mounds below the wetlands. The smallest mounds radiated only slightly beyond the vegetated area of the wetlands. The largest and steepest mounds occurred below two of the augmented wetlands. There, rapid leakage rates regenerated a largely absent surficial aquifer and mounds encompassed areas 7-8 times as large as the wetlands.

Wetland leakage rates, estimated using a daily water-budget analysis applied over multiple years and normalized as inches per day, varied thirtyfold from the slowest leaking natural wetland to the fastest leaking augmented wetland. Leakage rates increased as the size of the flooded area decreased and as the downward head difference between the wetland and the underlying Upper Floridan aquifer increased. Allowing one of the augmented wetlands to dry up for about 2.5 months in the spring of 2004, and then refilling it, generated a net savings of augmentation water despite the amount of water required to recreate the water-table mound beneath the wetland. Runoff from the surrounding uplands was an important component of the water budget in all of the unaugmented wetlands and two of the augmented wetlands. At a minimum, runoff contributed from half (45 percent) to twice (182 percent) as much water as direct rainfall at individual wetlands.

Wetland flooded areas, derived using wetland water levels and bathymetric data and presented as a percentage of total wetland area, were used to compare and contrast hydrologic conditions among the 10 wetlands. The percentages of the natural wetland areas that flooded during the study were comparable, despite differences in the sizes of the wetlands. The percent flooded area in each wetland was calculated daily over the study period and monthly for up to 16 years using historical water-level data. Historical flooding in the natural wetlands spanned a greater range in area and had more pronounced seasonality than historical flooding at either the impaired or augmented wetlands. Flooding in the impaired and natural wetlands was similar, however, during 2 years of the study with substantially reduced well-field pumping and above average rainfall.

Comparisons indicated several hydrologic differences between the marsh and cypress wetlands in this study. The natural and impaired marshes leaked at about half the rate of the natural and impaired cypress wetlands, and the marshes collectively were underlain by geologic material with lower vertical leakance values than the cypress wetlands. The natural marshes had higher evaporation rates compared to cypress wetlands, and their more isotopically- enriched surface waters indicated longer water residence times than the cypress wetlands. Over the same 8-year period, marshes spent from 16 to 30 percent more time (or about 15 to 29 months more) than cypress wetlands with greater than half of their total areas flooded. Cypress wetlands were nearly dry a greater percentage of time than marshes; however, more than 80 percent of their area was flooded a greater percentage of time than marshes. The water quality of natural marsh and cypress wetlands was similar, with a low pH, low conductivity, minimal alkalinity, and low concentrations of major ions; therefore, periphyton communities in natural marsh and cypress wetlands also were similar. Vegetation is inherently different between marsh and cypress wetlands, and among wetland sites of the same type there was a large variety and small overlap of vegetation species. Macroinvertebrate taxa richness and density were generally greater in natural marshes than in natural cypress wetlands.

The hydrology and water quality of augmented wetlands differed substantially from natural wetlands, but ecological differences were less apparent. Augmentation preserved between 40 and 80 percent of the original surface areas of four wetlands. The water levels in augmented wetlands, however, fluctuated less than in natural wetlands and augmented wetlands dried out far less frequently, accelerating sediment accumulation. Year-round augmentation of the deepest and fastest leaking wetland, Duck Pond Augmented Marsh, required a volume equivalent to a 60-foot column of water over an area of about 3 acres. The bottom sediments in augmented wetlands did not show enrichment of radium-226, as has been reported in augmented lakes in the area. Augmentation shifted wetland water quality from an acidic, dilute, and sodium-chloride dominated chemistry to a calcium-carbonate rich water with much higher alkalinity, specific conductance, and pH. The abundance of periphyton species known to prefer higher pH, conductivity, and nutrient concentrations was greater in augmented wetlands.

"Freshwater wetlands and their interaction with ground water play a pivotal role in the water resources of Florida"

Plant species richness and biomass were higher in the augmented wetlands than in unaugmented wetlands, most likely in response to more prolonged flooding and greater availability of nutrients released by accumulated decaying plant material. The natural variability of macroinvertebrate communities in marsh and cypress wetlands in this study exceeded the differences attributable to augmentation, although the presence of gastropods at augmented wetlands of both types was due to inherent water-quality differences. The comparisons of macroinvertebrate communities between natural and augmented wetlands would be more useful if a larger population of wetlands was available for study.

Quantifying wetland hydrology along with water quality and ecological indicators makes the results from the comparative analyses of these 10 wetlands generic. The approaches used in this study can be applied to future studies and those results can be compared to this initial study population, allowing the comparative analyses to describe an increasing number of wetlands.

In: Wetlands in Central Florida: An Ecology and Hydrology...   ISBN: 978-1-61728-600-1
Editor: Samantha L. Elliot   © 2010 Nova Science Publishers, Inc.

Chapter 1

HYDROLOGY AND ECOLOGY OF FRESHWATER WETLANDS IN CENTRAL FLORIDA: A PRIMER

United States Geological Survey

INTRODUCTION

Freshwater wetlands are an integral part of central Florida, where thousands are distributed across the landscape. However, their relatively small size and vast numbers challenge efforts to characterize them collectively as a statewide water resource. Wetlands are a dominant landscape feature in Florida; in 1996, an estimated 11.4 million acres of wetlands occupied 29 percent of the area of the State. Wetlands represent a greater percentage of the land surface in Florida than in any other state in the conterminous United States (Dahl, 2000; 2006). Statewide, 90 percent of the total wetland area is freshwater wetlands and 10 percent is coastal wetlands (Dahl, 2005). About 55 percent of the freshwater wetlands in Florida are forested, 25 percent are marshes and emergent wetlands, 18 percent are scrub-shrub wetlands, and the remaining 2 percent are freshwater ponds.

Freshwater wetlands are distributed differently in central Florida than in other parts of the State. In the panhandle and in northern Florida, there are fewer isolated wetlands than in the central and southern parts of the State, and few of those wetlands are affected by activities such as groundwater withdrawals. In southern Florida, the vast wetlands of the Everglades and the Big Cypress Swamp blanket the landscape and form contiguous shallow expanses of water, which often exhibit slow but continuous flow toward the southwestern coast. In contrast, the wetlands of central Florida are relatively small, numerous, mostly isolated, and widely distributed (Figure 1). In many places, wetlands are flanked by uplands, generating a mosaic of contrasting environments—unique wildlife habitat often adjacent to dense human development. As the population of central Florida increases, the number of residents living near wetlands also increases. Living in close proximity to wetlands provides many Floridians with an increased awareness of nature and an opportunity to examine the relationship between people and wetlands. Specifically, these residents can observe how wetlands are affected by human activities.

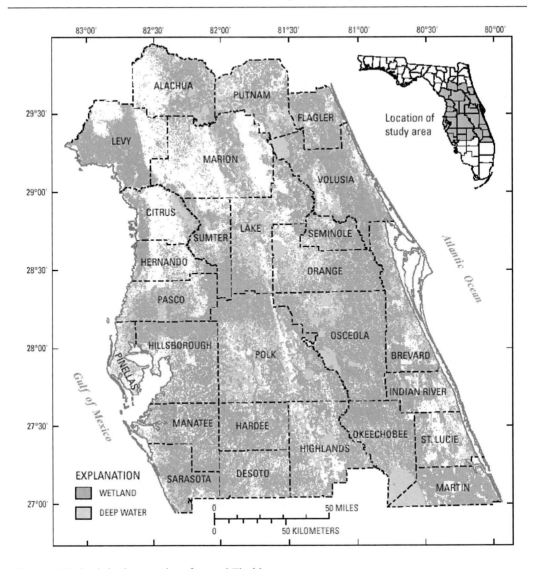

Figure 1. Wetlands in the counties of central Florida

Freshwater wetlands are unique and complex ecosystems defined by characteristic properties. Wetlands usually have standing water during at least part of the year, although water depths can vary from a few inches to as much as several feet from one wetland to another. The hydrologic behavior of wetlands is influenced by drainage basin characteristics, as well as by natural variations in climate. Wetlands in central Florida (especially forested wetlands) often have acidic waters that are darkly stained from organic substances released by decomposing leaves and other plant material. Wetlands are characterized by biogeochemical cycles in which vital elements such as carbon, nitrogen, phosphorus, and others are transformed as they move between wetland soils and sediments, the open water, and the atmosphere. Wetlands are populated with plants that can thrive under conditions of saturated soils and low dissolved-oxygen concentrations. The bottoms of many wetlands, especially marshes, are covered with decayed plant material that can accumulate over time to form brown peat or black muck soils. Wetlands are inhabited by animals that need standing water to complete some or all of their life cycles, and they also provide periodic food, water, and shelter for many other animals that spend most of their lives on dry land. The complex and interrelated components of wetlands directly affect one another and there are numerous feedback mechanisms (Figure 2).

PRIMER FACTS

The U.S. Geological Survey reports on the state of the Nation's terrestrial, freshwater, and coastal/marine ecosystems, including wetlands, and studies the causes and consequences of ecological change, monitors and provides methods for protecting and managing the biological and physical components and processes of ecosystems, and interprets for policymakers how current and future rates of change will affect natural resources and society.

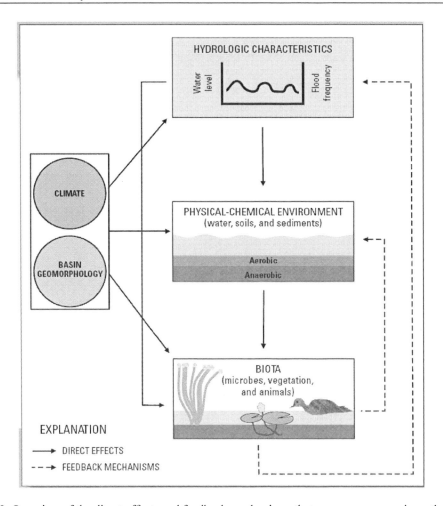

Figure 2. Overview of the direct effects and feedback mechanisms that govern processes in wetlands. (Modified from the National Academy of Sciences, 1995, and published with permission.)

Wetland ecology is directly linked to the extent and duration of wetland flooding and the quality of the water. The vegetation and wildlife associated with wetlands are largely adapted to the changes in water availability associated with seasonal fluctuations between wet and dry conditions, and seasonal patterns are evident to residents living nearby. For example, isolated wetlands are most lush and most densely vegetated during the wet season from summer to early fall. Frog eggs may hatch in abundance during an early wet summer, and frogs adapted to moving from wetlands into upland trees can instead appear on the windows of nearby homes. Colorful dragonflies and damselflies are important predators that feed on swarming mosquitoes and other flying aquatic insects. The burnt-orange fall color of cypress trees in November is one of the few conspicuous indicators of the approach of winter and seasonal dry conditions in central Florida. Many shorebirds overwinter in Florida wetlands, and feed on the aquatic insects and other invertebrates that are abundant. December and January are the best times for watching waterfowl on marsh wetlands when the grassy vegetation dies back as wetland flooded areas diminish. Extreme wet or dry conditions can cause some patterns in plant and animal communities to change, and often these changes are noticeable to people living and working near wetlands. Heavy rains and flooding in isolated wetlands in central Florida during the winter bird migration can bring herons, ibis, and other waterfowl wandering through nearby suburban yards. During drought years, central Florida residents may encounter alligators or turtles crossing roads as they migrate between wetlands in search of water.

Wetlands covered an estimated 50 percent of the State before land use changes and other human activities began to cause wetland losses in Florida (Dahl, 1990). Historically, wetlands were viewed as inhospitable places, and their connection to the landscape was not appreciated. Wetlands were often seen as obstacles to agriculture and there was widespread ditching and draining of Florida wetlands as farming expanded, especially cattle grazing and citrus cultivation (Renken and others, 2005). By 1906, when the first systematic inventory of the Nation's wetlands was conducted, there were an estimated 19.8 million acres of wetlands remaining in Florida (Shaw and Fredine, 1956), excluding tidal and coastal wetlands. Wetlands losses continued as human development expanded in Florida, and by the 1950s about 15.3 million acres of wetlands remained (Shaw and Fredine, 1956).

Why have wetlands been eliminated at a rapid rate even though they confer substantial benefits to society? The answer to this paradoxical question is that the majority of wetlands are privately owned and the nature of wetland benefits is such that the owners of wetlands typically cannot capture the benefits for their own use (Florida Department of Environmental Protection, 2008a). For example, flood protection benefits affect people downstream from a given wetland; wildlife species that breed in a wetland often migrate and are enjoyed by other residents; and groundwater recharge provides no immediate commercial benefit to the landowner. Therefore, for a wetland owner to directly benefit from the resource, usually the owner has to alter it, convert it, or develop it (Florida Department of Environmental Protection, 2008a). Fortunately, the public perception of wetlands has changed over time. Substantial losses of wildlife, periodic flooding, widespread water shortages, and pervasive water-quality problems throughout the State have resulted in a new appreciation of wetland values and their benefit to the environment. Today, wetlands are considered important multi-use resources, and are increasingly viewed from a drainage-basin perspective. Wetlands are protected by Federal, State, and local laws designed to preserve their hydrologic and ecological values (Darst and others, 1996).

Increasing the public awareness of wetland hydrology is important because wetlands in Florida are at the center of numerous environmental issues related to freshwater quantity and quality. Unlike rivers that carry floodwaters downstream, or a lake basin that collects and accumulates rainfall and runoff at a single point, wetlands in central Florida distribute seasonal rainfall into thousands of shallow depressions across the local landscape. The water is temporarily held in these wetlands and then slowly released into the groundwater aquifer. Although wetlands retain water in the local landscape, when their capacity for storing water is exceeded, especially during times of heavy rainfall, additional water flows across the adjacent landscape and can cause local flooding. In an undeveloped setting, runoff flows through a network of shallow inconspicuous surface channels that convey flow into and out of a succession of wetlands positioned at progressively lower elevations in the landscape, until the flow exits the drainage basin by way of a stream or river. As the landscape continues to be altered by development, understanding the natural seasonal and annual flooding cycles in the freshwater wetlands of central Florida is increasingly important to residents.

Because wetlands are an important part of the landscape to central Florida residents, and because these ecosystems are complex and change over time, this chapter was prepared by the U.S. Geological Survey (USGS) to address the need for a broader understanding of the interactions between wetland ecosystems and surface-water and groundwater resources in central Florida. The purpose of this wetland primer is to describe the general hydrology of freshwater wetlands in central Florida, the interactions between wetlands and groundwater/surface-water resources, and how hydrology and water quality are related to the biological communities and ecology of these wetlands. Rather than report the results of new investigations, this primer summarizes existing data and interpretations in a format readily accessible to residents and the water-resources community in central Florida. The report was prepared in cooperation with the St. Johns River Water Management District, the Southwest Florida Water Management District, and Tampa Bay Water.

In collaboration with others, the USGS reports on the state of the Nation's terrestrial, freshwater, and coastal/marine ecosystems, including wetlands, and studies the causes and consequences of ecological change, monitors and provides methods for protecting and managing the biological and physical components and processes of ecosystems, and interprets for policymakers how current and future rates of change will affect natural resources and society (U.S. Geological Survey, 2008a). The USGS has collected hydrologic data in central Florida since the 1920s in response to the requests of those local and regional agencies charged with managing the groundwater and surface-water resources of the region, including wetlands. Beginning in the 1990s, the USGS has undertaken interpretive hydrologic studies of isolated wetlands in the region and published reports and fact sheets about the hydrologic factors that affect wetland water levels and the implications of those factors for wetland ecology.

This primer describes the continually changing hydrologic status of isolated freshwater wetlands along a continuum from dry land to flooded water body, including: (1) the seasonal flooding cycle in natural wetlands and in those affected by human activities; (2) how flooding and drying cycles change the percentage of the total wetland area inundated at any given time, and the depth of the water throughout the wetland; (3) annual flooding cycles in wetlands during decade-long time periods that are used to compare the percentages of time that deeper and shallower areas of the wetland bottom remain flooded; and (4) how State and regional agencies monitor the hydrologic condition of central Florida wetlands and assess them as a collective water resource. Viewing the hydrologic condition of wetlands over both short and long time periods allows resource managers to assess current conditions and to predict regional trends in wetland resources.

Wetlands are most lush and densely vegetated during the wet season. Photographer credit: Michael Hancock, Southwest Florida Water Management District.

As the landscape is altered, understanding the natural flooding cycles in wetlands like this cypress dome is increasingly important to residents. Photographer credit: Kim Haag, U.S. Geological Survey.

This primer also describes various aspects of wetland ecology, including (1) an overview of wetland water quality and how water quality and soils affect plant and animal communities in wetlands; (2) a survey of the types of bacteria, algae, and plants that live in central Florida wetlands, how they influence environmental processes in wetlands, and how they change over time with changing hydrologic conditions; (3) a description of the animal communities that populate central Florida wetlands, how they vary seasonally, and how they change in response to changes in the plant community; (4) a discussion of the effects of human activities on the plants and animals that live in central Florida wetlands; and (5) a brief summary of the implications of climate change for wetland ecology.

In addition to describing wetland hydrology and ecology, this primer incorporates 11 features throughout the text that present additional topics of special interest or highlight wetland communities of unique character in central Florida. The appendix at the end of the report contains county maps showing the distribution of wetlands in each county and a pie chart indicating the relative proportions of individual wetland types. Cities, towns, and location names referred to in this chapter are shown on the county maps as well. Finally, throughout this chapter the reader is directed to selected wetland publications and websites that can provide further detailed information.

Wetlands can provide food, water, and shelter for wildlife such as these sandhill cranes (Grus canadensis). Photographer credit: Dave Slonena, Pinellas County Utilities Department.

Living in close proximity to wetlands provides many Floridians with an increased awareness of nature. Photographer credit: Michael Hancock, Southwest Florida Water Management District.

CLASSIFICATION AND DISTRIBUTION OF WETLANDS IN THE CENTRAL FLORIDA LANDSCAPE

The wetlands in central Florida can be classified according to a number of commonly observed criteria. Some of the earliest classification systems placed wetlands in categories based on their location—near rivers, near lakes, or in uplands (Wright, 1907). Later wetland classification schemes were based on the amount of time a wetland was inundated—permanently, seasonally, or temporarily. Other classifications were implemented in response to national planning needs, or for ecological reasons. For example, a 1950s classification framework was developed for a national inventory to assess waterfowl habitat (Martin and others, 1953). Eventually, more than 50 wetland classification schemes were in use across the United States. Despite the proliferation of classification schemes, most were based upon only a few prominent wetland characteristics related to hydrology, vegetation, and soils. In 1974, the U.S. Fish and Wildlife Service convened a group of wetland scientists to develop a new wetland classification system that (1) was based on the concept of the ecosystem; (2) would facilitate resource management decisions; and (3) would provide uniformity in terminology throughout the Nation so that wetlands could be compared from one region to another and be better understood as a collective national resource. This classification of wetlands and deepwater habitats has become a recognized national standard for identifying and classifying wetlands (Cowardin and others, 1979). The Cowardin classification has five major systems: marine, estuarine, palustrine, lacustrine, and riverine. Within each system are other categories including classes, subclasses, and dominance types. The other categories may or may not be present in all systems.

Freshwater wetlands in central Florida described herein are classified in the Palustrine, Lacustrine, and Riverine Systems (Cowardin and others, 1979). The majority of wetlands in central Florida are in the Palustrine System. The Palustrine System includes all non-tidal wetlands dominated by trees, shrubs, persistent emergents, emergent mosses or lichens, farmed wetlands, and all such wetlands that occur in tidal areas with salinity less than 0.5 ppt. It also includes wetlands lacking such vegetation, but with all the following characteristics: area less than about 20 acres; water depth in the deepest part less than about 6.6 ft; salinity less than 0.5 ppt; and active wave formed or bedrock shoreline features lacking.

Wetlands associated with deepwater habitats include lacustrine and riverine wetlands. Wetlands in the Lacustrine System are situated in a topographic basin; lack trees, shrubs, and persistent emergent vegetation with more than 30 percent areal coverage; exceed 6.6 ft in depth in the deepest part of the basin; and have salinity less than 0.5 parts per thousand. In central Florida, lacustrine wetlands frequently form fringes around lakes. The fringing wetlands often obscure the lake shoreline and provide rich habitat for waterfowl and other wildlife. Wetlands in the Riverine System are contained within a channel of periodically or continually moving water, are bounded by the upland and by the channel bank, and have salinity less than 0.5 ppt. Wetlands in the flood plains adjacent to rivers that are inundated by seasonal over-bank flow are not considered part of the Riverine System. The water in flood-plain wetlands may pond in low areas and also may move very slowly in a downstream direction in shallow channels called sloughs. Lacustrine and riverine wetlands are not as abundant as palustrine wetlands in central Florida.

Rainfall beneath the tree canopy in a pond cypress (Taxodium ascendens) wetland can be 5-15 percent less than outside the canopy. Photographer credit: Michael Hancock, Southwest Florida Water Management District.

Central Florida wetlands in the Palustrine, Lacustrine, and Riverine Systems can be grouped into classes based on the nature of the wetland bottom (substrate) and the vegetation defining their general appearance. Seven classes of palustrine wetlands are present in central Florida: rock bottom, unconsolidated bottom, aquatic bed, unconsolidated shore, emergent wetland, scrub-shrub wetland, and forested wetland. Lacustrine and riverine wetlands may include the following classes: rock bottom, unconsolidated bottom, aquatic bed, rocky shore, unconsolidated shore, and emergent wetland. Classes can be further divided into subclasses (for example, persistent and nonpersistent emergent wetlands) and dominance types (individual wetland plant species that are predominant) (Cowardin and others, 1979). In central Florida, for example, the pond cypress (*Taxodium ascendens*) is dominant in some forested wetlands, the buttonbush (*Cephalanthus occidentalis*) is common in scrub-shrub wetlands, maidencane (*Panicum hemitomon*) is widespread in many emergent marsh wetlands, and water lilies (*Nymphaea odorata*) are present in many pond and aquatic bed wetlands. In contrast, slash pine (*Pinus elliotii*) and longleaf pine (*Pinus palustris*) are common upland trees that are often found in the pine flatwoods that surround or separate many of the wetlands.

White water lily (Nymphaea ordorata). Photographer credit: Michael Hancock, Southwest Florida Water Management District.

Meadow beauty (Rhexia salicifolia) growing in flooded pine flatwoods. Photographer credit: Dan Duerr, U.S. Geological Survey.

Freshwater wetlands are present in every county throughout central Florida (Figure 1). The distribution of wetlands in each of the counties of central Florida is shown in detail in the appendix, along with associated pie diagrams that show the relative proportions of each wetland class. The distribution of wetlands is not uniform across the region. Polk, Osceola, Volusia, and Lake Counties have the greatest total acreages of wetlands in the region. Wetlands in these counties account for 30 to 35 percent of the total land area of each county. The lowest acreages of wetlands are found in Pinellas, St. Lucie, Hernando, and Citrus Counties, where wetlands do not exceed 10 to 15 percent of the total county area. The uneven distribution of wetlands in central Florida reflects the influence of regional physiography, hydrogeology, historical wetland destruction, and other factors.

Wetlands distributed across the central Florida landscape form a mosaic of communities, and it is notable that the patterns of wetland distribution change over different timescales. Over long time periods, changes in climate, erosion of rivers, and sea level changes can each bring about wetland change (van der Valk, 2006). During relatively short periods of time (decades), the acreage of wetland classes fluctuates in response to cyclical changes in precipitation, from drought to above-average rainfall, and to disturbances such as fire. A wide variety of human activities also cause changes in wetland distribution and vegetation. Trends and changes in wetlands within Florida (and across the United States) are documented by the U.S. Fish and Wildlife Service over short timescales (10 years). Wetland areas are categorized by distinguishing features, typically the nature of the wetland bottom (substrate) and the dominant vegetation type defining their general appearance (Cowardin and others, 1979). Wetland areas are then mapped and numbered in the National Wetlands Inventory (Feature A—Wetland Mapping and the National Wetlands Inventory). The county maps included in the appendix herein are based on the National Wetlands Inventory (U.S. Fish and Wildlife Service, 2009a).

A. WETLAND MAPPING AND THE NATIONAL WETLANDS INVENTORY

Mapping is necessary for virtually all activities involving wetlands. For example, wetland maps are essential tools for wetland management, protection, and restoration; land-use planning as it relates to wetlands; and regional analysis of wetland status and trends. Wetland maps are used by local, State, and Federal agencies as well as by nongovernmental organizations, businesses, and private residents. Consistent and reproducible methods for mapping are vital for comparison purposes and indispensible for aggregation of regional maps into a national framework.

Background

The U.S. Fish and Wildlife Service within the U.S. Department of the Interior has primary responsibility for mapping all wetlands in the United States. As part of the National Wetlands Inventory, the U.S. Fish and Wildlife Service has developed a series of maps to show wetlands and deepwater habitats. The goal of the National Wetlands Inventory is to provide current geospatially referenced information on the status, extent, characteristics, and functions of wetland, riparian, deepwater, and related aquatic habitats in priority areas to promote the understanding and conservation of these resources.

Although several other Federal agencies have historically mapped wetlands and continue to do so for various purposes related to their missions (U.S. Department of Agriculture; Natural Resources Conservation Service; U.S. Department of Commerce, National Oceanic and Atmospheric Administration), they typically collaborate with the U.S. Fish and Wildlife Service in their efforts. In addition to State and local agencies, many nongovernmental organizations have become interested in mapping wetlands specific to localized areas of the country or to individual projects, often at more refined scales than are available from the National Wetlands Inventory. Clearly, it is desirable to have a wetland mapping standard that everyone can use to map wetlands, and that would facilitate sharing wetland data in digital format. To that end, in 2007–08 the Federal Geographic Data Committee developed a standard to support a consistent and seamless transition from paper-based map products to technology-based map products. The Federal Geographic Data Committee standard also serves as the national standard for wetland mapping inventories for inclusion in the National Spatial Data Infrastructure. The mapping standard will: (1) streamline mapping efforts for greater consistency and efficiency; (2) enable any entity to map wetlands using the standard and submit data to construct or update the National Wetlands Inventory geodatabase and the National Map; and (3) facilitate consistent mapping layers that can be used across geopolitical and watershed boundaries.

National Wetlands Inventory Mapping

The National Wetlands Inventory maps are prepared from conventional photointerpretation and analysis of mid- to high-altitude (20,000 ft) stereoscopic color-infrared aerial photographs. The source imagery is collected and archived by the Federal Government's National Aerial Photography Program at a 1:40,000 scale. Flight lines for the National Aerial Photography Program are flown in a north-to-south direction through the east and west halves of 7.5-minute quadrangles. All photography is cloud-free, with strict specifications regarding sun angle and minimal haze. Because they are centered on the quarters of the quadrangles, these photographs are sometimes referred to as "quarter quads." Each 9 × 9-in. photo covers an area of about 5 mi on a side (3.75 minutes), and the photographs are indexed on 1:100,000- scale U.S. Geological Survey maps. National Aerial Photography Program images have a 1-meter resolution.

Wetland mapping is most accurate when based on color infrared photography, because the color, texture, and pattern of wetland vegetation, water, and soils in this type of photograph facilitate precise interpretation. For example, wetland vegetation is typically denser and more lush than upland vegetation. Areas covered with water or even saturated soils appear darker than dry soils because of the lack of infrared reflectance. Vegetation factors critical to accurate photo interpretation and wetland mapping include leaf size, shape, structure, and arrangement; branching patterns; height; and growth habit.

PRIMER FACTS

The U.S. Fish and Wildlife Service within the U.S. Department of the Interior has primary responsibility for mapping all wetlands in the United States. The goal of the National Wetlands Inventory is to provide current geospatially referenced information on the status, extent, characteristics, and functions of wetland, riparian, deepwater, and related aquatic habitats in priority areas to promote the understanding and conservation of these resources.

Aerial photograph of forested wetlands in Pasco County. Photograph credit: Southwest Florida Water Management District.

The production of National Wetlands Inventory maps involves many steps, including stereoscopic photo interpretation of spatially referenced photographs of the study area, delineation of wetland boundaries, detailed on-the-ground inspection of wetland plants and soils, quality-control checks of photo interpretation, including consultation of collateral information, and extensive review. The final product consists of wetland boundaries (polygons) added to a black-and-white 1:24,000-scale U.S. Geological Survey topographic base map. The wetland polygons are classified using the categories published by Cowardin and others (1979), and identified using an alphanumeric code identified in the map explanation. After the maps are finalized, they are digitized and made available to the public. National Wetlands Inventory maps in digital format can be readily used in Computer Aided Design (CAD) and Geographic Information System (GIS) software applications. Important metadata for the National Wetlands Inventory maps include (1) the year the aerial photographs used for map creation were taken, which is necessary for subsequent analyses of change in wetland area over time; (2) the season, which affects wetland plant development and ease of identification; and (3) the size of the target mapping unit (the smallest area consistently mapped), which ranges from 0.5 to 1.0 acre in many areas of the country.

Other Photography Useful in Wetland Mapping

Digital orthophoto quadrangles (DOQs) are computer-generated images of aerial photographs in which the image displacement caused by uneven terrain and camera tilt have been removed (Figure A–1). The value of a DOQ is that it combines the image characteristics of the original photograph with the geometric qualities of a map. The DOQs can be either black and white, natural color, or color-infrared images. A standard DOQ covers an area of 3.75 minutes latitude by 3.75 minutes longitude (a quarter "quad"), and the image also is commonly called a "DOQQ" (for digital orthophoto quarter quadrangle). All DOQs are referenced to the North American Datum of 1983 and are positioned on the Universal Transverse Mercator map projection. All DOQs have a 1-m ground resolution, and typically have 50 to 300 m of over-edge image beyond the latitude and longitude corner crosses that are imbedded in the image (Wilen and others, 1996). This margin facilitates "edge matching" of multiple adjacent images to create a much larger image. Each image is accompanied with data for identifying, displaying, and georeferencing the image. The users can spatially reference other digital data with the DOQ, and a DOQ can be incorporated into any GIS that can manipulate raster images. There are many uses for these DOQs relating to wetlands, including vegetation assessment, analysis of changes in land use, and groundwater and watershed analysis.

Selected References about Wetland Mapping

Cowardin, L. M., Carter, V., Golet, F. C. & LaRoe, E. T. (1979). Classification of wetlands and deepwater habitats of the United States: Washington D. C., U. S. Fish and Wildlife Service report FWS/OBS-79/3 1.

Tiner, R. W. (1999). *Wetland indicators—A guide to wetland identification, delineation, classification & mapping: Boca Raton,* Fla., Lewis Publishers, 392 p.

U.S. Fish and Wildlife Service. (2008). National Wetlands Inventory 905 FW 1 Habitat Mapping, accessed June 2, 2008, at http://www. fws. gov/policy/905fw1. html.

U.S. Fish and Wildlife Service. (2008). *Wetlands Geodatabase*, accessed June 2, 2008, at http://www. fws. gov/wetlands index. html.

U.S. Geological Survey. (2001). Digital orthophoto quadrangles: U. S. Geological Survey Fact Sheet 057-01, 2 p.

U.S. Geological Survey. (2008). National Aerial Photography Program (NAPP), accessed June 29, 2008, at http://edc. usgs. gov/guides/napp. html.

U.S. Geological Survey. (2008). National Color Aerial Photography (NAIP), accessed July 11, 2008, at http://www. usgsquads. com/aerialphotos. htm.

U.S. Geological Survey. (2009). *The National Map – Orthoimagery layer*, accessed June 10, 2009, at http://egsc. usgs. gov/isb/pubs/factsheets/fs20073008/fs20073008. pdf.

Wilen, B. O., Carter, V. & Jones, J. R. (1996). Wetland mapping and inventory, *in National Water Summary on Wetland Resources: U. S. Geological Survey Water-Supply Paper 2425,* p. 73-78.

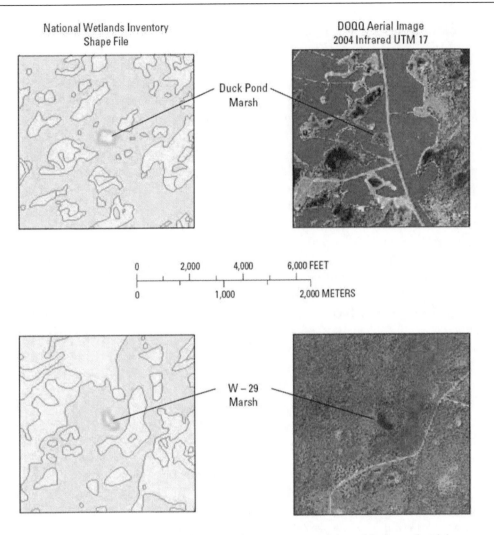

Figure A–1. Digital orthophoto quadrangles (DOQs) are computer-generated images of aerial photographs in which the image displacement caused by uneven terrain and camera tilt have been removed

Palustrine forested wetlands are the most abundant wetland class in central Florida. For example, the ratio of forested wetlands to emergent marsh wetlands in central Florida is about 3:1 (Dahl, 2005). The most familiar dominant plant communities in this class include mixed hardwood swamps, cypress domes, hydric hammocks, and wet pine flatwoods. The greatest acreages of forested wetlands are located in Volusia, Polk, Levy, Osceola, and Lake Counties. From 1985 to 1996, forested wetlands in Florida increased in total area (Dahl, 2005), reversing a long-term trend of wetland loss since the 1950s. Most of this gain is attributable to the natural maturation of shrub-scrub wetlands to wet forests. Forested wetlands remain vulnerable to loss from rural and urban development, such as expansion of paved roads and related infrastructure.

Palustrine shrub-scrub wetlands are characterized by woody vegetation less than about 20 ft tall. The counties with the greatest acreages of shrub-scrub wetlands are Polk, Indian River, and Brevard. From 1985 to 1996, shrub-scrub wetlands in Florida increased in acreage. Drier conditions throughout much of the State may have contributed to the increase in conversion of marshes to shrub-scrub wetlands as shallow- water lakes experienced shorter hydroperiods that are conducive to invasion by shrub-scrub species. Many emergent wetlands subjected to disturbance, nutrient inputs, and lack of fire also tend to develop into shrub-scrub wetlands. Numerous shrub-scrub wetlands have experienced invasions by woody exotic species such as Brazilian pepper (*Schinus terebinthefolius*) and melaleuca (*Melaleuca quinquenerva*), which displace native species and alter habitat for waterfowl and other animals.

Palustrine emergent wetlands include communities such as marshes and wet prairies. Emergent wetlands in central Florida are populated by a wide variety of plant species. Some common emergent species include pickerelweed (*Pontederia cordata*), arrowhead (*Sagittaria latifolia*), and maidencane (*Panicum hemitomon*). The counties having the greatest acreages of emergent wetlands include Brevard, Polk, and Osceola. Emergent wetlands declined in acreage by about 9 percent from 1986 to 1996. This rate of loss was greater than the loss rate during the late 1970s and early 1980s. Some emergent marshes were converted to shrub-scrub wetlands as woody species became established following prolonged periods of drought. Agriculture, urban expansion, and rural development also were responsible for a substantial proportion of the loss (Dahl, 2005).

Palustrine aquatic bed wetlands are characterized by floating and submerged vegetation, whereas palustrine unconsolidated bottom wetlands (open water ponds) have a bottom composed of sand, mud, and/or organic material. Characteristic plants in freshwater ponds that support vegetation include duckweed (*Lemna minor*), bladderworts (*Utricularia* spp.), and water lily (*Nuphar luteum*). Freshwater ponds increased in acreage throughout Florida from 1985 to 1996. The newly created ponds included retention basins in urban areas, ornamental landscape features in office and housing developments, and water traps on golf courses. Retention ponds often are chemically treated to eliminate any aquatic vegetation. Highly urbanized Hillsborough County has a relatively high percentage (13.0 percent) of excavated or impounded wetlands, many of which function as retention ponds in residential developments. The relatively high percentage of excavated wetlands in Polk County (14.4 percent) is a result of widespread phosphate mining. Other counties with a large proportion of excavated or impounded wetlands include Okeechobee and St. Lucie Counties, where freshwater ponds have been created to support agricultural activities.

Aerial view of isolated cypress domes in Sumter County. Photographer credit: Paul Fellers, Lake Region Audubon Society.

PHYSICAL SETTING OF CENTRAL FLORIDA WETLANDS

The abundance of freshwater wetlands in central Florida is mostly due to plentiful rainfall and the low, flat terrain. The physiographic features of the landscape, the underlying geology, and the hydrogeology in the region all provide the context for understanding wetland hydrology and the factors that affect wetland water levels in central Florida.

Physiographic Features and Wetland Physical Characteristics

The physiographic features of the landscape in central Florida determine, to a substantial extent, the distribution of wetlands in the counties across the region. Central Florida can be divided into physiographic regions (Figure 3) based on surface features such as ridges, uplands, plains, lowlands, and valleys. Higher areas in the western part of the region include the Brooksville Ridge, Polk Upland, and Sumter Upland. The relatively small number of wetlands in Hernando and Citrus Counties, for example, is due largely to the thick layer of well-drained sands that overlie permeable limestone within the Brooksville Ridge. In contrast, the Gulf Coastal Lowlands and the Western Valley are at lower elevations in the western part of the peninsula, where wetlands are interspersed with pine- palmetto flatwoods. The Western Valley separates the gently rolling Polk Upland from the Brooksville Ridge, creating a broad flat lowland that merges at the Zephryhills Gap with the Gulf Coastal Lowlands.

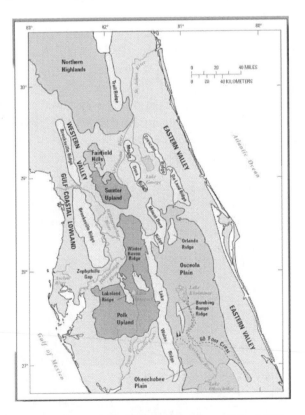

Figure 3. Physiographic regions of central Florida (modified from white, 1970)

Landforms underlain by limestone that contains solution cavities are collectively known as karst, and are well developed throughout much of central Florida. Karst features are particularly abundant along the northern limit of the Polk Upland within the Gulf Coastal Lowlands, and within the Brooksville and Lake Wales Ridges. Sinkholes develop in the porous limestone and result in shallow depressions that often fill with water to become isolated wetlands. The Lake Wales Ridge lies in the approximate geographic center of the peninsula, and has a maximum elevation of about 290 ft above NGVD 29. To its north are the Mount Dora Ridge, Trail Ridge, and Northern Highlands. To the east of the Lake Wales Ridge, the relatively flat Osceola Plain contains the Kissimmee River and associated lakes and wetlands. Farther east, the Eastern Valley is a broad expanse of lowland along the Atlantic coast that includes the St. Johns River and numerous wetlands. Landforms such as sinkholes and shallow basins are common in the Eastern Valley and they often contain isolated wetlands.

Palustrine emergent wetland with maidencane, arrowhead, and pickerelweed. Photographer credit: Kim Haag, U.S. Geological Survey.

Palustrine aquatic bed wetlands support floating aquatic plants including water lilies (Nymphaea sp.) and water shield (Brasenia schreberi). Photographer credit: Dan Duerr, U.S. Geological Survey.

A sinkhole in Hernando County. Photographer credit: Dan Duerr, U.S. Geological Survey.

Regional physiographic features also help determine wetland physical characteristics such as shape, size, depth, and total volume. The typically round to oval shapes of many wetlands in central Florida that occupy depressions, as seen in aerial infrared photography of the central Florida landscape (Feature A—Wetland Mapping and the National Wetlands Inventory), are similar to the shapes of many lakes in the area, and are indicative of their similar sinkhole origins. The small depressional features in the bottoms of many wetlands, which are revealed by detailed bathymetric measurements (Haag and others, 2005), provide further evidence of karst subsidence. The deepest areas in wetlands may overlie sand columns or "piping features" created by localized karst subsidence activity under the wetlands. The extent of localized subsidence, both recent and relict, has contributed to the drying out of some wetlands in west-central Florida when sinkholes breach the underlying clay layer. Breaches create a more direct connection between surface-water and groundwater systems that make some wetlands more susceptible to lower groundwater levels. In these areas, the potential for downward drainage may increase, especially when subsurface cavities are filled with coarser sediments that have high hydraulic conductivity.

Most wetlands in shallow depressions are relatively small. Although central Florida wetlands range in size from less than an acre to more than 100 acres, many are at the lower end of this size range. Throughout Florida, forested wetlands generally are larger than shrub or emergent wetlands, with the exception of the Everglades. For example, forested wetlands average about 20 acres in area, emergent wetlands about 10 acres, shrub wetlands about 7 acres, and freshwater ponds less than 2 acres (Dahl, 2005). Many central Florida wetlands are only 1 to 2 ft deep (Michael Hancock, Southwest Florida Water Management District, written commun., 2009).

Wetlands that do not occupy depressions in the landscape, and that are present on slopes, near lakes, and in river channels, have different shapes than depressional wetlands and are less numerous in central Florida. Seepage wetlands, which are often found on slopes, tend to be small (Feature B— Seepage Wetlands). Other types of nondepressional wetlands can cover large areas. Fringing wetlands, which exist around impoundments, natural lakes, and ponds, can be extensive, depending on the lake size and the slope of the shoreline. Flood-plain wetlands can be very wide if they are associated with the extensive flood-plain valleys of major rivers, whereas riverine wetlands in stream channels typically exist only as narrow strips.

B. Seepage Wetlands

Seepage wetlands differ from other types of forested palustrine wetlands in that they seldom or never experience inundation or flooding, although their soils remain saturated for extended periods. Anywhere that the water table intersects the land surface, shallow groundwater can discharge or seep out to the surface and maintain wet soils, but lateral drainage prevents water from ponding.

Many seepage wetlands form at the base of hillsides (Figure B–1). Rainwater percolates through sand, and when it encounters a less permeable layer such as clayey sand, clay, or rock, the water flows laterally until it encounters the land surface and collects in a topographic depression. Seepage wetlands also may form in shallow depressions on flat sites where the bottom of the wetland is lower than the elevation of the adjacent water table. Other seepage wetlands are present within the flood plains of large rivers. Although seepage wetlands are defined by their hydrology, they are sometimes also named by the dominant vegetation type. In central Florida, the most common types of seepage wetlands are bay heads or bay swamps, hydric hammocks, and flood-plain seepage swamps. Cutthroat seeps, named after the dominant cutthroat grass (*Panicum abscissum*), are a less common and threatened type of seepage wetland in central Florida.

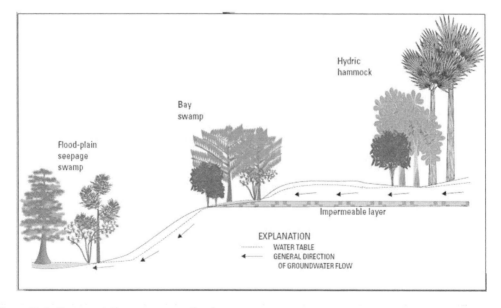

Figure B–1. Representative seepage wetlands

Moss growing in the understory of a seepage wetland. Photographer credit: Michael Hancock, Southwest Florida Water Management District.

Bay Heads

Bay heads (also called bay galls, bay swamps, or seepage swamps) are densely forested, peat-filled depressions. These features may be found at the base of slopes where groundwater **seepage** keeps the soils moist. Bay heads also are found in shallow depressions in areas with abundant cypress wetlands, such as the Green Swamp. In these areas, bay heads represent an advanced stage of wetland succession in which the acidic (pH 3.5–4.5) peat soils accumulate in the absence of severe fire (Florida Natural Areas Inventory, 2006). The hydrologic regime is maintained by the capillary action of the peat soils that draw groundwater up from a shallow water table below the wetland. Substantial surface flooding is rare, and these systems are more hydrologically stable than many other types of wetlands. Fire frequency is highly variable in these systems; shrub-dominated bay heads may burn every 3 to 8 years, whereas a woody bay may burn every 50 to 150 years. After a typical fire, the bay trees usually germinate from seeds and replace those lost (Florida Department of Natural Resources, 1990).

Bay heads are dense evergreen forests or shrub thickets with an understory of moss and ferns. The canopy is composed of densely-packed stands of fragrant sweetbay (*Magnolia virginiana*), swamp bay (*Persea palustris*), red bay (*Persea borbonia*), and loblolly bay (*Gordonia lasianthus*).

Bay seepage swamp in Putnam County. Photographer credit: Mark Minno, St. Johns Water Management District.

The understory is mostly open with shrubs and ferns predominating. Other plants typically found include dahoon holly (*Ilex cassine*), fetter bush (*Lyonia lucida*), wax myrtle (*Myrica cerifera*), cinnamon fern (*Osmunda cinnamomea*), chain fern (*Woodwardia* spp.), and lizard's tail (*Saururus cernuus*).

Hydric Hammocks

Hydric hammocks most often develop as patches on low, flat sites where limestone is at or near the surface and shallow groundwater seepage is present. Soils are usually sandy and contain considerable amounts of organic material. Hydric hammocks have soils that are generally saturated, and these wetlands are inundated only for short periods (seldom more than 60 days per year) following very heavy rainfall. If the water table is lowered by drought or human activities, hydric hammocks gradually change to mesic (drier) forests. If flooding is more frequent, the trees are replaced with species that are more tolerant of standing water.

Hydric hammocks are typically open forests. Cabbage palms (*Sabal palmetto*) and laurel oaks (*Quercus laurifolia*) are mixed with hardwoods such as red maple (*Acer rubrum*), water oak (*Quercus nigra*), dahoon (*Ilex cassine*), gallberry (*Ilex coriacea*), and wax myrtle (*Myrica cerifera*). There is usually minimal understory and little herbaceous vegetation on the forest floor.

Hydric hammocks rarely burn, due to their continuously damp soils and sparse herbaceous ground cover. However, in communities with abundant cabbage palms (*Sabal palmetto*), periodic fires of the flammable palm fronds favor survival of this generally fire-resistant species over other herbaceous vegetation and maintain the palm-dominated hammocks in prairie landscapes (Florida Department of Natural Resources, 1990).

Flood-Plain Seepage Swamps

Flood-plain seepage swamps are present on flood plains of larger rivers, where lateral inputs of **surface runoff** and groundwater seepage are more important than riverbank over-flow. River overflows, when they do occur, are shallow and gentle, and carry little sediment or leaf litter.

Flood-plain seepage swamps in central Florida are bay swamps with additional tree species. Other common tree species are bald cypress (*Taxodium distichum*) and black gum (*Nyssa sylvatica* var. *biflora*). There may also be sweetbay (*Magnolia virginiana*), loblolly pine (*Pinus taeda*), and slash pine (*Pinus elliottii*). *Ilex ambigua* is a holly that grows more often in flood-plain seepage swamps than in other kinds of bay swamps (Livingston, 1991).

Cutthroat Seeps

Cutthroat seeps are communities where shallow groundwater flows downslope at or near the soil surface for several months each year, maintaining a thick bright green carpet of cutthroat grass (*Panicum abscissum*). These communities also may support a few widely scattered slash pines (*Pinus elliottii*) or longleaf pines (*Pinus palustris*), particularly as they grade into more mesic wet flatwoods. In central Florida, cutthroat seeps are common on side slopes of the Lake Wales Ridge in Highlands and Polk Counties. Cutthroat seeps are dependent on frequent fires to maintain their community integrity. Without fire, shrub species such as fetter bush (*Lyonia lucida*), wax myrtle (*Myrica cerifera*), and gallberry (*Ilex glabra*) begin to invade these communities, and trees such as loblolly bay (*Gordonia lasianthus*) begin to dominate within a 10-year period. Cutthroat seeps have been reduced in number since the 1940s, primarily because of long-term fire suppression (U.S. Fish and Wildlife Service, 1999).

Occurrence and Protection

A number of conservation areas protect seepage wetlands in central Florida (U.S. Fish and Wildlife Service, 1999). For example, the Green Swamp has hydric hammocks that drain into the Withlacoochee River (Feature I—The Green Swamp and Use of Wetland Conservation Partnerships). Natural areas in Highlands County contain seepage slopes and hydric hammocks. Some managed areas including the Avon Park Air Force Range also contain seepage wetlands.

Cutthroat grass (Panicum abscissum) communities require frequent fire for maintenance of their community integrity. The greatest threats to cutthroat grass communities are continued fire-suppression and drainage effects. Photographer credit: Steve Morrison, The Nature Conservancy.

Another area with seepage wetlands is in Putnam County south of Welaka (Laessle, 1942). Much of the land is flat, and lateral water movement is slow. The water table is close to the surface, and as organic material accumulates in a wet environment, a hardpan commonly forms. This hardpan layer of dense soil is largely impervious to water. Along the St. Johns River, there are extensive areas rich in peaty organic material. Seepage wetlands form in these areas along the slope between the flatwoods and river. Water moves laterally under the flatwoods and above the hardpan. The hardpan ends at the crest of the slope, where lateral movement provides a surface seep and supports bay head vegetation. Somewhat steeper topography and extensive sands permit rapid percolation and lateral water movement. At the base of the slope just above the water table, hydric hammocks develop where the soils are nearly saturated with moisture due to seepage of groundwater from upslope areas. Accumulated organic material results in soils that have a low pH and are quite peaty. Characteristic trees in the bay heads of the area are loblolly bay (*Gordonia lasianthus*), sweetbay (*Magnolia virginiana*), and swamp bay (*Persea palustris*). Understory shrubs include gallberry, fetter- bush, and wax myrtle. Hydric hammocks are populated with water oak, sweet gum, and American elm. Live oak, loblolly bay, and cabbage palm are also found. Common shrubs are wax myrtle, large gallberry (*Ilex coriacea*), and saw palmetto, and herbaceous vegetation is sparse.

Because seepage wetlands depend on a high water table and seepage flow, they are quickly affected by changes in local or regional hydrology. Development which increases the amount of impermeable surface (roads, parking lots, roofed buildings) can increase the amount of runoff, shifting the hydrologic regime from saturation to inundation, and fostering a change to hardwood swamps. Alternatively, drought and well-field drawdown can lower water tables and reduce or eliminate soil saturation. Under excessively dry conditions, the threat of severe fire is substantial. If the ground surface is lowered from fire damage to the peat, then willows (*Salix caroliniana*) may invade, and a cypress-dominated community can develop. Recurrent fire may result in conversion to a shrub bog. The invasion of exotic species is an increasing problem in seepage swamps, and problematic species include melaleuca (*Melaleuca quinquenervia*), Brazilian pepper (*Schinus terebinthifolius*), Japanese climbing fern (*Lygodium japonicum*), and skunk vine (*Paederia foetida*) (Florida Department of Natural Resources, 1990).

Selected References about Seepage Wetlands

Clewell, A. F. (1991). Vegetational mosaic in Livingston, R.J., ed., *The rivers of Florida: New York*, Springer-Verlag, 289 p.

Duever, L. C. (1984). *Natural communities: Seepage communities: The Palmetto*, v. *4*, no. 1, p. 1-2, 10-11.

Florida Department of Natural Resources (1990). Guide to the natural communities of Florida, 116 p., accessed June 12, 2009, at http://www.fnai.org/PDF/Natural _Communities_ Guide.pdf.

Florida Natural Areas Inventory (2006). Natural Communities, accessed March 30, 2006, at http://www.fnai.org/descriptions.cfm.

Laessle, A. M. (1942). The plant communities of the Welaka area: University of Florida *Biological Science Series*, v. *4*, no. 1, 143 p.

Livingston, R. J., ed. (1991). *The rivers of Florida: New York*, Springer-Verlag, 289 p.

U.S. Fish and Wildlife Service, (1999). Multispecies Recovery Plan for South Florida: Ecological communities, accessed May 1, 2006, at http://www.fws.gov/verobeach/ index.cfm.

Wetlands in central Florida contain a substantial amount of surface water, but this fact has gone largely unappreciated because wetlands have been viewed more as a landscape feature and less as a water resource, and also because more attention has been focused on lakes and rivers as the principal water bodies in the State (Livingston, 1990; Schiffer, 1998). The volume of a particular wetland, also called its storage capacity, can be estimated if the bathymetry of the wetland has been determined. In addition to bathymetry, this storge capacity is determined collectively by the geology, soils, groundwater levels, and vegetation.

Some wetlands that are isolated most of the time may have flow to and from other wetlands, lakes, and rivers during wet years, and continue to flow repeatedly during a series of wet years. Flood-plain wetlands experience "flood pulses" during which floodwaters redistribute nutrients and sediment, and for this reason they are more easily colonized by a wider variety of aquatic organisms than isolated wetlands.

Geologic and Hydrogeologic Framework

The geology of the Florida peninsula provides a framework for the hydrogeologic units that hold water beneath the land surface (Figure 4). The movement of water on and below the surface of the central Florida landscape and the erosion of the karst terrane form wetlands and lakes in this region (Figure 5).

The foundation of the Florida peninsula is composed of igneous and metamorphic rocks overlain by successive layers of sedimentary carbonate rock (limestone and dolomite). Most of the carbonates were deposited during a 100-million-year period when Florida was below sea level. Deep oceans covered the Florida peninsula during the first part of that period; those oceans were less deep during the last 25 million years, forming a shallow reef across the peninsula. Subsequently, sea level rose and receded cyclically so that carbonates alternately were deposited and eroded. During the last 5 million years, eroded sediments originating from the land surface (quartz sand, clay, and silt) were deposited. These unconsolidated terrestrial deposits were then eroded, transported, and redeposited during successive periods of global warming and cooling.

APPROXIMATE NUMBER OF YEARS AGO	SYSTEM	SERIES		GEOLOGIC UNIT	DESCRIPTION	HYDROGEOLOGIC UNIT	
Present to 2,000,000	Quaternary	Recent and Pleistocene		Undifferentiated deposits	Unconsolidated materials including sand, clay, marl, shell, and phosphorite	Surficial aquifer system	
2,000,000 to 65,000,000	Tertiary	Pliocene		Undifferentiated deposits	Silty to sandy clay, thin shell beds, and basal limestone beds of variable thickness, phosphatic	Intermediate confining unit or intermediate aquifer system	
		Miocene		Hawthorn Group	Dolomite, sand, clay, and limestone; silty, phosphatic		
		Oligocene		Suwannee Limestone	Limestone, phosphatic (discontinuous)	Floridan aquifer system	Upper Floridan aquifer
		Eocene	Late	Ocala Limestone	Limestone, chalky, foraminiferal, dolomitic near bottom		
			Middle	Avon Park Formation	Limestone and hard brown dolomite		Middle semiconfining unit
			Early	Oldsmar Formation	Dolomite and limestone with intergranular gypsum		Lower Floridan Aquifer
		Paleocene		Cedar Key Formation	Dolomite and limestone with beds of anhydrite	Sub-Floridan confining unit	

Figure 4. Generalized geology and hydrogeology of central Florida (modified from Metz and Sacks, 2002)

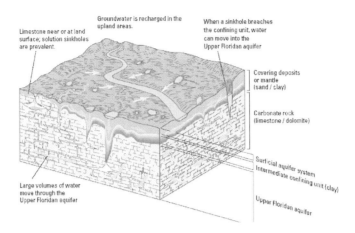

Figure 5. Landscape features, covering deposits, and the hydrogeologic framework of karst terrane that gives rise to wetlands in central Florida (modified from Tihansky, 1999)

The thickness and composition of one particular geologic unit, the Hawthorn Group, varies across central Florida and influences the formation of lakes and isolated wetlands and their ability to hold water. The Hawthorn Group has a complex depositional and erosional history occurring in open marine, coastal marine, estuarine, and riverine environments (Gilboy, 1985). The thickness varies in part because the limestone formation over which the Hawthorn Group was deposited was eroded unevenly in geologic time. In parts of Volusia County, the unit was eroded entirely and is absent from the underlying strata. The composition varies because the lower layers of the Hawthorn Group are marine derived and are relatively porous. The upper layers are mostly land derived and contain clay, fine sands, and silt, which tend to restrict the downward movement of groundwater. Where the Hawthorn is thin, vertical water movement is less restricted and percolation can dissolve the underlying limestone, allowing depressional features and sinkholes to develop. Where the Hawthorn is thick, sinkholes are less common.

The three major aquifer systems (layers of permeable rock or other porous materials that hold water) in central Florida, from shallowest to deepest, are the surficial aquifer system, intermediate aquifer system, and Floridan aquifer system. The thickness, degree of confinement, and capacity to yield water of these three aquifer systems varies spatially throughout the study area (Gilboy, 1985; St. Johns River Water Management District, 2008; U.S. Geological Survey, 2008b).

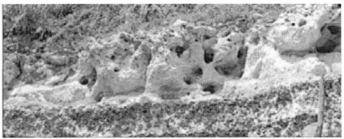

Limestone outcrop of the Hawthorn Group along the Peace River in Polk County. Photographer credit: Patricia Metz, U.S. Geological Survey.

The surficial aquifer system, which is composed of unconsolidated materials including sand, clayey sand, clay, marl, and shell, is nearest to the land surface. The sand and shell layers vary in thickness across central Florida. Typically, the clay layers are not sufficiently thick to slow the downward movement of water. The water in the surficial aquifer system is unconfined in most areas and its level is free to rise and fall. The level of the water in the surficial aquifer system is called the water table, and below the water table all openings or spaces in the soil or rock are filled with water (saturated). The water table may be as much as 50 to 100 ft below land surface in ridge areas, and at land surface in other places. In lakes and wetlands, the surface of the water is an expression of the adjacent water table.

The surficial aquifer system is recharged principally by rainfall. However, lakes, streams, wetlands, irrigation ditches, stormwater retention ponds, and septic tanks also can recharge the surficial aquifer system. Water leaves the surficial aquifer system by evaporation from soil, transpiration by plants, seepage to lakes and wetlands, discharge to streams and wetlands, and downward leakage to underlying aquifers. The surficial aquifer system is tapped by private wells for irrigation of lawns and gardens in many areas. In Duval, St. Johns, Brevard, and Indian River Counties in the eastern part of central Florida, the surficial aquifer system also is used for public drinking-water supply.

The intermediate aquifer system lies directly below the surficial aquifer system in the southwestern part of central Florida. It consists of thin discontinuous layers and undifferentiated deposits of Pliocene and phosphatic sands, silts, and clays, as well as limestone and dolomite of the Hawthorn Group of Miocene age. The thickness of the intermediate aquifer system generally decreases from south to north, ranging from more than 400 ft south of DeSoto County to less than 50 ft in Hillsborough County (Southwest Florida Water Management District, 2009a). The aquifer system is absent north of Hillsborough County and in the eastern part of central Florida, where the geologic units that make up the intermediate aquifer system act as confining layers to the Upper Floridan aquifer. Water in the intermediate aquifer system is confined in some areas, principally by clays in the overlying Pliocene sediments and the Hawthorn Group. The aquifer system can yield small amounts of water sufficient for private use, particularly in areas where the lower part of the aquifer system consists of highly fractured limestone and dolomite, although in Sarasota County it is tapped for public supply (Fernald and Purdum, 1998). The intermediate aquifer system can be recharged from both the overlying surficial aquifer system and the underlying Floridan aquifer system.

PRIMER FACTS

In central Florida, wetlands overlie areas where the Upper Floridan aquifer is confined, unconfined, and thinly confined.

The Floridan aquifer system is composed of a thick sequence of limestone and dolomite. It is effectively divided vertically into three zones based on differences in permeability. The lower and upper zones of the Floridan aquifer system are more permeable than the middle unit. The middle (semiconfining) unit is composed of less-permeable dolomitic limestone, and it restricts movement of water between the upper (mostly freshwater) and lower (primarily saline water) zones of the Floridan aquifer system (Figure 4).

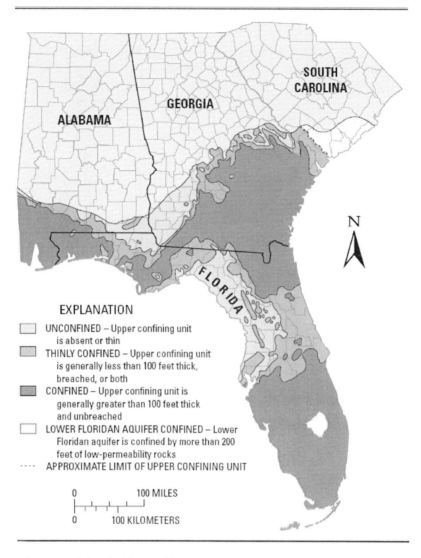

Figure 6. Confinement of the Floridan aquifer system (reprinted from Fernald and Purdum, 1998, and published with permission)

The Upper Floridan aquifer provides most of the drinking water for central Florida residents, and its thickness increases from north to south, ranging from several hundred feet to more than 1,400 ft in parts of Manatee and Sarasota Counties (Southwest Florida Water Management District, 2009a). The top of the Upper Floridan aquifer is closest to land surface in the eastern part of central Florida (east Marion, Lake, central Volusia, west Orange, and west Seminole Counties), where it can be at or slightly above sea level. The lower zone of the Floridan aquifer system in some areas of central Florida contains water that is too high in dissolved constituents (magnesium, calcium, and sulfur-containing compounds) to be used for drinking water. The Upper Floridan aquifer is confined in many parts of central Florida (Figure 6) because in these areas it is overlain by layers of clay, silt, and limestone beds of the Hawthorn Group. These clay-containing layers form a confining unit that is not very permeable and restricts water movement across it. The Upper Floridan aquifer is unconfined, however, in the northern part of west-central Florida, including parts of Alachua, Marion, Lake and Sumter Counties. Moreover, the western boundary of the St. Johns River drainage basin is underlain by the Ocala Limestone, part of the Upper Floridan aquifer. Surface waters percolate through the porous deposits and into the limestone. The high permeability of the Ocala Limestone results in extensive lateral movement of groundwater. This groundwater discharges to numerous springs within the drainage basin, many within the riverbed itself (DeMort, 1991).

HYDROLOGY OF CENTRAL FLORIDA WETLANDS

The movement of water from the atmosphere to land and back again in a series of continuous processes collectively is called the hydrologic cycle. The processes in the hydrologic cycle that are important to wetland water levels in central Florida are precipitation (rainfall), evapotranspiration, runoff, and infiltration (Figure 7). Hydrologic processes fundamentally influence the formation, size, persistence, and functioning of freshwater wetlands (Carter, 1996).

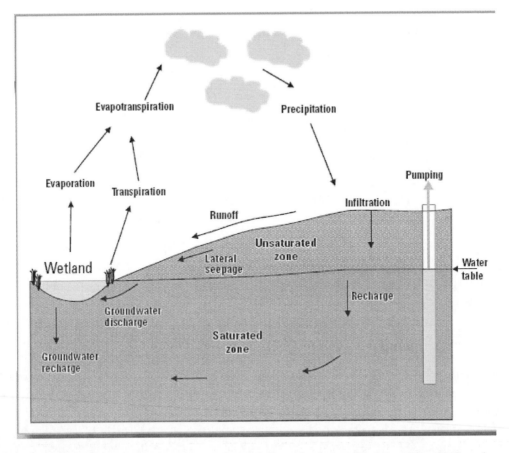

Figure 7. Hydrologic processes that affect water levels in wetlands (modified from Fitts, 2002, and published with permission)

These processes can vary substantially over time and they are related to wetland water levels in complex ways. The cycles of above- and below-average rainfall that occur in central Florida directly affect wetland vegetation patterns and the abundance of wetland wildlife. Changes in runoff and surface-water flow patterns in drainage basins may have substantial effects that are not immediately evident to property owners, but become apparent when rainfall patterns change. Infiltration, groundwater movement, and groundwater/surface-water interactions change in intensity under different rainfall conditions, and processes such as sinkhole development may be exacerbated under both wet and dry conditions. Understanding the influence of these hydrologic processes is important for residents and for those involved with wetland resource management.

Cyclical Changes in Rainfall and the Influence of Evapotranspiration

Rainfall is the primary source of water in many central Florida wetlands. The average annual rainfall in the central Florida region is between 48 and 56 in/yr (Fernald and Purdum, 1998). The National Climatic Data Center of the National Oceanic and Atmospheric Administration summarized long-term regional rainfall averages for 1895– 2005. The long-term regional average is 52.26 in/yr for north-central Florida and 51.84 in/yr for south-central Florida (National Oceanic and Atmospheric Administration, 2008). These two climatological divisions cover the central Florida study area (Fernald and Purdum, 1998). Most of the rain in central Florida comes from summer storms during June to September that are associated with scattered, short-lived convective thunderstorms and tropical weather systems such as hurricanes. Monthly average rainfall can be above 7 in. during those months, when two-thirds of the annual rainfall typically accumulates, but these convective thunderstorms can be highly localized. Rainfall during November to May affects larger geographic areas, and is associated with frontal systems that originate in the northern latitudes and move south. Monthly average rainfall typically is less than 3 in. during these months. Tropical storms, hurricanes, and El Niño climate conditions can cause the annual rainfall to exceed the average by 10 in. or more (National Oceanic and Atmospheric Administration, 2008). Spatial variability across central Florida can sometimes exceed the temporal variability from year to year (Chen and Gerber, 1990). For example, annual average rainfall is the greatest (above 60 in.) in many areas along the east coast of Florida, but is below 45 in. in many areas near Lake Okeechobee in the center part of the State. Typically, average rainfall is higher near the east coast in the dry season and is higher near the west coast in the wet season (Ali and others, 2000).

Evapotranspiration is an important hydrologic process whereby wetlands lose water to the atmosphere through alternate pathways. Water evaporates into the atmosphere from soil and from the surface of open water in wetlands. Water also is lost to the atmosphere by plants through transpiration as plant roots extract water from the soil and release water vapor into the atmosphere through leaf openings. Evaporation and transpiration losses often are combined and referred to as evapotranspiration. Rates of evapotranspiration vary seasonally and spatially. Seasonal differences occur at a given location because evapotranspiration is much greater in summer than in winter, primarily as a function of solar radiation. Spatially, evapotranspiration increases from north to south across central Florida (Figure 8), again as a function of solar radiation. Moreover, variations in evapotranspiration can be very large depending on the type of ecosystem. For example, the highest evaporation rates occur from the open surfaces of lakes and other water bodies, and can amount to almost 110 percent of annual precipitation (Sumner, 2006). In places where the water table is deep and sandy soil is present, evapotranspiration can be less than 50 percent of annual precipitation. Wetland evapotranspiration is typically within these extremes and depends on the plant type (grasses, shrubs, or trees), density of plant coverage, and availability of water.

Annual variations in rainfall in central Florida (Spechler and Kroening, 2007) occur as a result of multidecadal cycles of warmer and cooler sea-surface temperatures that affect the entire eastern United States (a detailed discussion is provided in Enfield and others, 2001). Annual variations are evident when long- and short-term records are examined. For example, in central Florida annual rainfall was well below average in 2000, close to average in 2001, and 5 to 10 in. above average during 2002–04 (Figure 9). Water levels in isolated, lacustrine, and riverine wetlands fluctuate in response to the annual and seasonal variations in rainfall and evapotranspiration in Florida. However, evapotranspiration losses are more consistent on a monthly and annual basis than rainfall because they are primarily a function of solar radiation and depth to the water table. Therefore, seasonal and annual rainfall patterns are a predominant influence on wetland water levels.

Figure 8. Average annual potential evapotranspiration in Florida (reprinted from Fernald and Purdum, 1998, and published with permission)

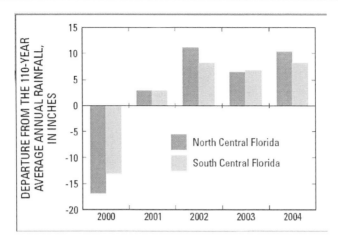

Figure 9. Regional annual rainfall departures from the long-term average for the period 2000–04 (modified from Lee and others, 2009)

A 120-ft tower for the collection of evapotranspiration data in a pine upland. Photograph credit: South Florida Water Management District.

The seasonal patterns of rainfall in central Florida vary spatially across the region. In the southern part of central Florida, convective thunderstorms during the warm summer months contribute more than half of the annual rainfall. Average monthly rainfall rates greatly exceed evapotran- spiration rates from June to September (Figure 10), and wetland water levels typically rise. Groundwater levels also rise as the wet season progresses, such that successive storms generate increasing runoff to wetlands, streams, and rivers. Summer rainfall and the additional effect of runoff typically cause wetland water levels to reach a seasonal maximum between July and September (Figure 11). In some years, large individual rainfall events, such as those associated with tropical storms, hurricanes, or El Niño climate patterns, can shift the seasonal maximum wetland water level to fall or, rarely, early winter.

In the northern part of central Florida, a greater proportion of the annual rainfall occurs in the winter months of January, February, and March. This pattern has been observed in long-term data sets (1961–90) (Fernald and Purdum, 1998) and in more recent data (1982–88) (Southwest Florida Water Management District, 2009a,b). Winter rainfall in this region comes from frontal storms—cold continental air masses that push into northern Florida and collide with warmer, wetter maritime air moving up from the south (Chen and Gerber, 1990). In general, winter storm fronts dissipate as they move south, and contribute less rainfall to wetlands in the southern part of central Florida. Winter months have the lowest evapotranspiration rates of the year (Bidlake and others, 1996; Sumner, 2001). Therefore, although winter rainfall is less than summer rainfall, it can generate proportionately greater runoff. For this reason, wetland water levels often reach a secondary maximum between January and March. For example, when peak wetland water levels were ordered by month at a **cypress wetland** (GS–2) in the Green Swamp, July was the most common summer month and March was the most common spring month for peak water levels to occur (Southwest Florida Water Management District, 2008).

Throughout central Florida, evapotranspiration rates begin to rise in February (early spring) as days warm and increase in length. April and May (late spring) are among the months with the lowest average rainfall of the year (Figure 10). The dry conditions in the late spring occur throughout central Florida in response to a recurring climate pattern called the Bermuda high, a region of high atmospheric pressure that persists off the Atlantic coast of Florida (Chen and Gerber, 1990). With decreasing rainfall and increasing evapotranspiration, wetland water levels typically reach an annual minimum sometime between May and June, and many wetlands often become dry (Figure 11). Wetlands usually experience a smaller secondary water-level minimum toward the end of the calendar year, between the summer and spring peaks (Figure 11). The lack of an early spring peak in water levels can result in prolonged dry conditions in wetlands between two consecutive summer peaks (such as in 1984–85; Figure 11).

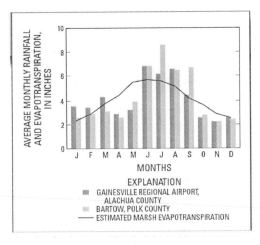

Figure 10. Average monthly rainfall in northern and southern areas of central Florida (data from National Oceanic and Atmospheric Administration, 2008) and estimated marsh evapotranspiration (Lee and others, 2009)

Right: Cardinal flowers (Lobelia cardinalis) add brilliant color to Florida marshes and wet meadows during the wet season from July to October. Photographer credit: Paul Fellers, Lake Region Audubon Society.

PRIMER FACTS

Annually, water levels in many central Florida wetlands have two highs and two lows. Highest water levels typically occur in March and July; lowest in December and May through June.

Water levels in flood-plain wetlands of central Florida have a seasonal response to rainfall and evapotranspiration similar to that of isolated wetlands. The year-to-year variability in water levels in relation to rainfall can be interpreted from long-term monitoring data. Stream discharge and water levels are measured for most of the principal rivers in central Florida by the USGS and by the regional Water Management Districts, and many streams have more than five decades of water-level measurements. These measurements can be used to reconstruct flooding patterns in riverine and flood-plain wetlands if the topography of the river channel and the adjacent flood plain has been mapped (Lewelling, 2003; 2004) (Feature C—Wetland Bathymetry and Flooded Area). The largest rainfall events generate extreme flooding that inundates large expanses of flood-plain wetlands. Rising river levels also cause river water to go into bank storage (water absorbed in the permeable bed and banks of streams). Because flood-plain deposits in bank storage areas tend to be highly permeable, the resulting hydraulic connection with adjacent wetlands raises wetland water levels in flood plains, even without overbank flooding (Winter and Woo, 1990).

Long-term monitoring of water levels in isolated wetlands across central Florida has been far more limited than river monitoring. Several hundred isolated wetlands have been routinely monitored in the northern Tampa Bay area (Hillsborough, Pasco, and Sumter Counties) for about 10 years. This is the largest concentration of monitored wetlands in central Florida (Southwest Florida Water Management District, 1996). However, 10 years of water- level data are typically not sufficient to describe the long-term effects of rainfall on wetland water levels. For this reason, the water-level condition of the tens of thousands of isolated wetlands in central Florida must be inferred from the relatively small number of sites that have been monitored for periods longer than 10 years.

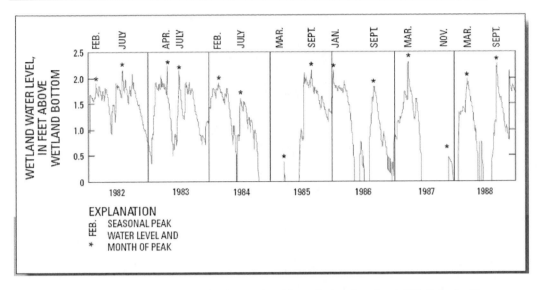

Figure 11. Seasonal variation in the wetland water level in an isolated wetland (GS-2) in the Green Swamp area of Lake County, Florida (data from Southwest Florida Water Management District, 2009b)

Some of the longest wetland water-level records available are for six natural cypress wetlands in the Green Swamp of Sumter and Lake Counties that have been continuously monitored for almost 30 years. The wetlands are located in the middle part of the central Florida region. The Green Swamp wetlands are reliable indicators of climate effects on water levels because they have not been substantially affected by land-use changes or groundwater pumping, Historical water-level data for the six isolated cypress wetlands in the Green Swamp indicate the relation between annual rainfall and the amount of time a wetland is dry. It is useful to compare the timing and duration of dry conditions instead of wet conditions because surface-water levels are unambiguous when a wetland is dry. In contrast, comparing wet conditions in wetlands may be misleading because wet conditions reflect a continuum from a puddle of water in the deepest location of one wetland to widespread flooding in another.

C. WETLAND BATHYMETRY AND FLOODED AREA

Hydrologic conditions have been monitored in isolated wetlands throughout Florida for several decades by local, regional, and State agencies. Typically, hydrologic conditions are monitored by determining the wetland water level at a staff gage located at a fixed point (preferably near the deepest point) in a wetland (Figure C–1A). However, because wetland depths and shapes vary substantially, water levels among individual wetlands are not directly comparable. Moreover, it is difficult to translate periodic and widely distributed water-level measurements into a regional view of wetland hydrologic status. The usefulness of long-term data sets of wetland water levels would greatly increase if the data described not only the depth of water at a point in the wetland, but also the amount of the total wetland area that was flooded at a specified time.

Flooded area, expressed as a percentage of the total wetland area, is a versatile and descriptive measurement that can be compared through time for an individual wetland or compared spatially for numerous wetlands in a region during a particular month or year (Haag and others, 2005; Lee and Haag, 2006). Comparing the flooding patterns of natural wetlands to flooding patterns in wetlands affected by human activities also provides a useful tool for assessing how those activities currently affect wetlands, and for predicting future wetland conditions.

The size of the flooded area can be determined for a given water-surface elevation if a bathymetric map exists for a wetland. Bathymetric maps show contours of bottom depth throughout a body of water, and bathymetric mapping is a well-established tool in lake studies where the depth of a lake bottom is usually determined using sonar instruments towed by boats. Bathymetric maps also can be constructed for isolated wetlands. Because water levels in isolated wetlands fluctuate seasonally and many wetlands dry out, wetlands are usually shallow enough to wade or to walk through during part of the year. For this reason, land-surveying techniques can be used to map the bottom elevation of an isolated wetland. Alternatively, if the wetland is flooded, the bottom elevation can be derived by subtracting measured water depths from the elevation of the water surface. Measurements can be made along lines or transects across the wetland (Figure C–1A), and the location of the measured points can be determined using digital geographic positioning system (GPS) technology or by using set distances along compass lines (Haag and others, 2005). For wetlands that are partially flooded, the approaches can be combined (Haag and others, 2005). The bathymetric data then can be used to define the relations between the wetland water level (stage), size of the flooded area, and volume of water in the wetland at a given stage (C–1A). The density of bathymetric data points affects the accuracy of subsequent estimates of wetland flooded area and stored water volume (Haag and others, 2005).

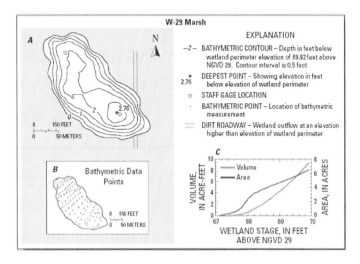

Figure C–1A. *A,* Wetland bathymetric contours, *B,* density of bathymetric data points, and *C,* stage-volume and stage-area curves for W-29 Marsh, Cypress Creek Well Field, Pasco County, Florida (right; modified from Lee and others, 2009)

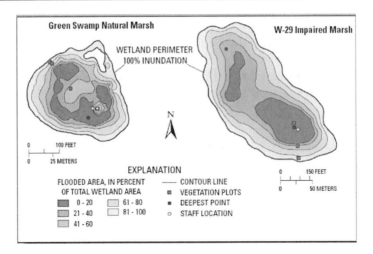

Figure C–1B. Maps generated from bathymetric data that are used to contour the shape of the flooded area as different percentages of the total wetland area become flooded (above, modified from Lee and others, 2009)

Accurate determination of a wetland perimeter is necessary to establish the elevation at which a wetland is said to be 100-percent inundated or flooded (Figure C–1B). Wetland perimeter determinations sometimes rely on hydric soils indicators. The presence of soils with a color and consistency that results from continuous inundation can mark the wetland perimeter. A wetland perimeter also can be determined from vegetation indicators. For example, the position of saw palmetto can be used because these plants cannot tolerate inundation for more than a few weeks. Other vegetation indicators of wetland perimeters have been documented for central Florida (Carr and others, 2006).

The elevation of the wetland bottom, used to draw bathymetric contours, is most easily measured during the dry season when many wetlands have little or no standing water. Photographer credit:Dan Duerr, U.S. Geological Survey.

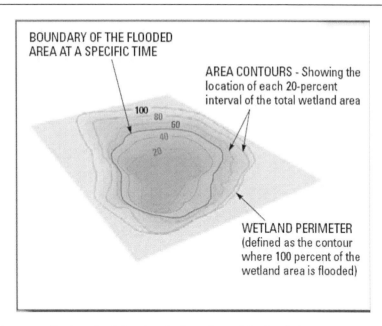

BOUNDARY OF THE FLOODED
AREA AT A SPECIFIC TIME

AREA CONTOURS - Showing the
location of each 20-percent
interval of the total wetland area

WETLAND PERIMETER
(defined as the contour
where 100 percent of the
wetland area is flooded)

Figure C–2. Conceptualized wetland showing the boundary of the flooded area located in different 20-percent intervals of the total wetland area

Bathymetric mapping data can be used to show areas of the wetland bottom that would be flooded as each 20-percent interval of the total wetland area becomes flooded (Figure C–2). Once bathymetric data have been used to generate stage-volume and stage-area curves, then historical wetland water levels can be used along with these curves to reconstruct historical changes in wetland flooded area (Figure C–3). Historical flooding behavior in isolated wetlands then can be summarized using flooded-area duration graphs. These graphs display the percentage of the total historical time that the flooded area of the wetland occupied different intervals of the total wetland area (Figure C–3). The historical time period depends upon the number of years that wetland water levels have been measured.

A similar flooding pattern was observed in isolated wetlands in west-central Florida that were located in similar physical, hydrologic, and climatic settings, even though the wetlands were of different sizes (Lee and others, 2009). However, markedly different flooding patterns can result from human-induced changes to wetlands. For example, the flooded extent will be smaller in a wetland affected by groundwater withdrawals compared to a wetland unaffected by withdrawals (Haag and others, 2005; Lee and others, 2009) (Figure C–4). When flooded areas are compared using this approach, the percentage of the total wetland area that is no longer flooded, and therefore is vulnerable to ecological change, becomes quantifiable. Vegetation is adapted to survive short-term variations in flooding. However, when changes in flooded area become long-standing, the vegetation will change and so will the area of the original wetland that continues to function as a wetland (Haag and others, 2005).

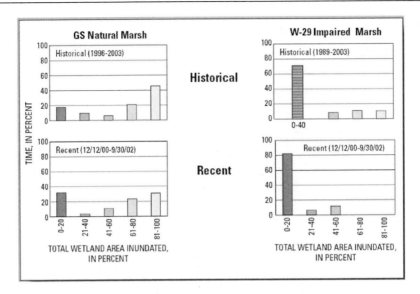

Figure C–3. Comparison of the flooded area of a natural wetland (GS Natural Marsh, Sumter County, Florida) and an impaired wetland (W-29 Impaired Marsh, Pasco County, Florida) during recent and historical time periods to indicate wetland areas that are not routinely flooded (right; modified from Lee and others, 2009)

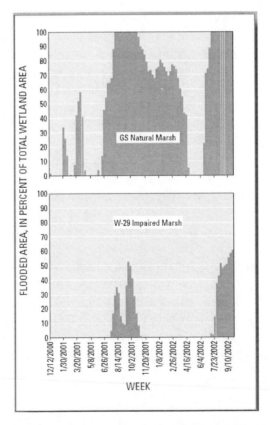

Figure C–4. Percentage of the total wetland area flooded on average each week in a natural and an impaired marsh. (Flooded areas beyond 100 percent of the total wetland area are not shown) (above; modified from Lee and others, 2009)

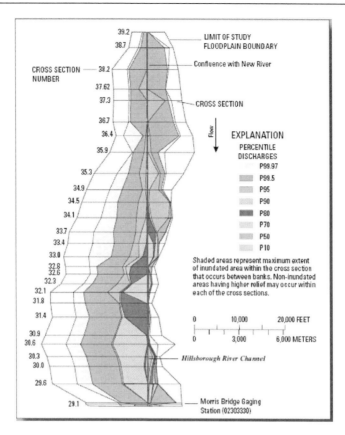

Figure C–5. The Hillsborough River inundates increasing areas of flood-plain wetlands as the river flow increases (right; modified from Lewelling, 2004)

Land-surveying methods similar to those used in isolated wetlands are used to define the elevation profile of riverine and flood-plain wetlands. The areal extent of numerous riverine wetlands has been mapped throughout central Florida, and the extent and frequency of flooding has been determined as part of a regulatory process for recommending the minimum flows and levels for rivers in Florida (Lewelling, 2003; Lewelling, 2004; Munson and Delfino, 2007; Munson and others, 2007; Neubauer and others, 2008). The extent of historical flooding in riverine wetlands is determined by calculating the area of the wetland flooded by streamflows that occur across a range of magnitudes and frequencies. An example of the variation in streamflow is provided for a 10-mi reach of the Hillsborough River, between river miles 29.1 and 39.2. The most infrequent flood peaks, with a recurrence interval less than 10 percent (discharge percentile $\geq$ 90), flood the largest areas of the flood plain (Figure C–5) and the increase in inundated area is greater in a downstream direction.

Selected References about Wetland Bathymetry

Carr, D. W., Leeper, D. A. & Rochow, T. E. (2006). *Comparison of six biologic indicators of hydrology and the landward extent of hydric soils in west-central Florida,* USA: Wetlands, v. *26,* no. 4, p. 1012-1019.

Haag, K. H., Lee, T. M. & Herndon, D. C. (2005). *Bathymetry and vegetation in isolated marsh and cypress wetlands in the Northern Tampa Bay Area,* 2000-2004: U. S. Geological Survey Scientific Investigations Report 2005-5109, 49 p.

Lee, T. M. & Haag, K. H., (2006). *Strength in numbers: Describing the flooded area of isolated wetlands*: U. S. Geological Survey Fact Sheet 2006-3118, 4 p.

Lee, T. M., Haag, K. H., Metz, P. A. & Sacks, L. A., (2009). *The comparative hydrology, water quality & ecology of selected natural and augmented freshwater wetlands in west-central Florida*: U. S. Geological Survey Professional Paper 1758, 152 p.

Lewelling, B. R., (2003). *Extent of areal inundation of riverine wetlands along Cypress Creek and the Peace, Alafia,* North Prong Alafia & South Prong Alafia Rivers, west-central Florida: U. S. Geological Survey Water-Resources Investigations Report 02-4254, 72 p.

Lewelling, B. R., (2004). *Extent of areal inundation of riverine wetlands along five river systems in the Upper Hillsborough River watershed,* west-central Florida: U. S. Geological Survey Scientific Investigations Report 2004-5133, 49p.

Munson, A., Kelly, M., Morales, J. & Leeper, D. (2007). *Proposed minimum flows and levels for the upper segment of the Hillsborough River,* from Crystal Springs to Morris Bridge & Crystal Springs: Brooksville, Southwest Florida Water Management District, Report of the Ecologic Evaluation Section, 205 p.

Munson, A. B. & Delfino, J. J. (2007). Minimum wet-season flows and levels in southwest Florida rivers: *Journal of the American Water Resources Association,* v. *43*, no. 2,p. 522-532.

Neubauer, C. P., Hall, G. B., Lowe, E. F., Robison, C. P., Hupalo, R. B. & Keenan, L. W. (2008). *Minimum flows and levels method of the St. Johns River Water Management District, Florida, USA: Environmental Management,* v. *42*, no. 5, p. 1101-1114.

Wilcox, C. & Huertos, M. L. (2005). A simple, rapid method for mapping bathymetry of small wetland basins: *Journal of Hydrology,* v. *301*, p. 29-36.

Water levels monitored during nearly three decades (1980–2007) in Green Swamp cypress wetlands fluctuated in response to widely varying annual rainfall. Rainfall data collected at the Bartow, Florida, climate station (National Oceanic and Atmospheric Administration, 2008), less than 50 mi from the Green Swamp, varied more than 40 in/yr during this time period—from 35.31 to 79.61 in. Although the six wetlands were located several miles apart, they demonstrated similar flooding patterns during the 28-year period (Figure 12). The correspondence in the duration and timing of dry days among these six wetlands is due to their similar hydrologic response to regional rainfall patterns, and indicates that patterns observed at these six wetlands may occur in numerous other wetlands in the same region. On average, during the 28-year period, each wetland was dry approximately 40 percent of the year (35–41 percent) and wet the remainder of the year (59–65 percent). However, between years wetland hydrologic conditions varied as widely as the annual rainfall, with the average dry period ranging from 5 to 75 percent of the year (Figure 12).

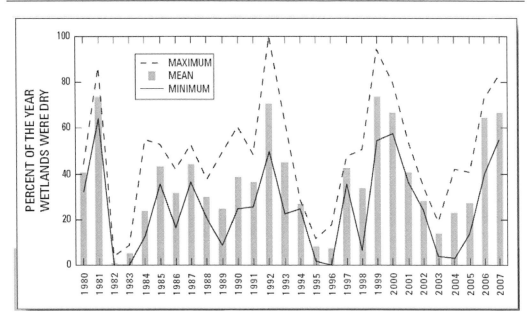

Figure 12. Average percentage of the year when six isolated cypress wetlands in the Green Swamp area of Lake and Sumter Counties, Florida, were dry during 1980–2007 (data from Southwest Florida Water Management District, 2008)

As annual rainfall increases, the amount of time wetlands are dry generally decreases, although the same annual rainfall can generate a different number of dry days depending upon the seasonal distribution of rainfall. However, the decrease in the number of dry days with increasing annual rainfall has a limit, as illustrated by the following example. The isolated cypress wetlands in the Green Swamp were dry about 54 percent of the year, on average, when the annual rainfall was less than 45 in/yr, which occurred in 9 of the 28 years (Figure 13). When annual rainfall was 45 to 55 in/yr, and was closer to average (about 52 in/yr), the wetlands were dry about 38 percent of the year, or close to the long-term average condition (approximately 40 percent of the year). When the climate was wetter than average (rainfall 56–65 in/yr), the wetlands were dry about 22 percent of the year. When the annual rainfall was far above average (more than 65 in/yr), the amount of time the wetlands remained dry stayed about the same (24 percent of the year). Thus, the number of dry days was about the same whether the year was wet or extremely wet (Figure 13). This pattern prevails because isolated wetlands are shallow and lack the capacity to store the excess rainfall. Regardless of the additional rainfall, once the wetlands fill, the excess rainfall spills out and runs off, leaving wetlands to dry out similarly when the wet season ends.

Surface-Water Flow in Wetland Drainage Basins

Surface water is rainfall that has not infiltrated the soil and entered the groundwater system, and has not returned to the atmosphere as evapotranspiration. Surface water flows overland following a gradient from areas of higher elevation to areas of lower elevation, and eventually collects in wetlands lakes, streams, and rivers, before flowing into the oceans. Surface water contributes to wetlands in central Florida as overland flow, channelized streamflow, and outflow from nearby lakes and ponds. Isolated wetlands (by definition) receive inflow from streams only during times of very high rainfall when other nearby surface features overflow. Flood- plain wetlands receive overbank flow from rivers and streams when river stage is high. Usually there is a delay between the onset of rainfall and the peak river flows that cause flood-plain wetland inundation.

Under average rainfall conditions, most isolated wetlands retain direct rainfall within the wetland boundaries and also are able to store runoff from the immediate surrounding land surface. Under the wettest conditions, however, some isolated wetlands overflow. Water spills out through inconspicuous surface channels, and flows into wetlands at successively lower elevations, conveying runoff across an almost imperceptibly sloping land surface to the lowest elevation in the drainage basin—typically a stream or river. It has been suggested that the definition of isolated wetlands be refined to include the recurrence interval of wetland outflows, for instance, in months, years, or decades (Winter and LaBaugh, 2003). Because of the lack of monitoring data, however, this level of understanding is not yet attainable for most central Florida wetlands.

The role of wetlands as headwaters to Florida streams is well recognized, and in fact, most Florida streams originate in swamps (Livingston, 1990). The Green Swamp, which covers about 870 mi^2 of wildlife management area in Hernando, Lake, Pasco, Polk, and Sumter Counties, is a region of high groundwater levels and vast wetland areas, and it is the headwaters to four major rivers originating in central Florida (Brown, 1984). The frequency and magnitude of flows between wetlands in undeveloped basins such as the Green Swamp are likely to be considerably different than those in drainage basins where the land-surface elevations between wetlands have been altered by land development and ditching. In both settings, however, wet-season connections are an important pathway for wetland colonization by plants and animals that otherwise are isolated from one another.

Central Florida encompasses the drainage basins of seven major rivers (Figure 14), and wetlands are present in the headwater areas of each basin. These drainage basins are the Upper St. Johns River, Middle St. Johns River, Kissimmee River, Ocklawaha River, Peace River–Myakka River, Tampa Bay tributaries (the Hillsborough, Alafia, and Manatee Rivers), and Withlacoochee River. Wetlands occupy different percentages of the respective land areas of the seven drainage basins (Figure 14). The Ocklawaha River drainage basin has the smallest percentage of wetland area (7 percent), whereas the Upper St. Johns River drainage basin has the greatest percentage (32 percent).

PRIMER FACTS

Surface water is rainfall that has not infiltrated the soil and entered the groundwater system, and has not returned to the atmosphere as evapotranspiration. Surface-water flows overland following a gradient from areas of higher elevation to areas of lower elevation, and eventually collects in streams, rivers, lakes, and wetlands, before flowing into the oceans

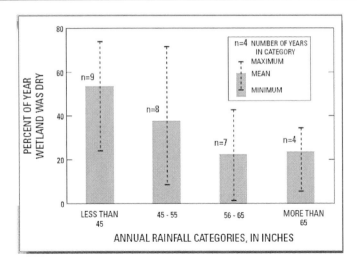

Figure 13. Percentage of the year an isolated cypress wetland (GS-2) in the Green Swamp area of Lake County, Florida, was dry during 1980– 2007, for years with rainfall in a given category at Bartow, Florida (data from Southwest Florida Water Management District, 2008)

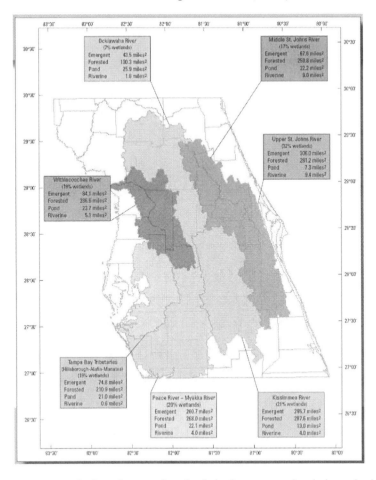

Figure 14. The percentages of selected types of wetlands in the seven major drainage basins in central Florida

Until recently, the shallow and inconspicuous surface- water channels that link wetlands together at high water levels have been difficult to map and therefore are difficult to describe. The relief of most of these features is far less than the 5-ft contour intervals commonly used to define landsurface elevations. In the Green Swamp, for example, the land surface was described as sloping about 3.3 ft in 2.7 mi along one northwest-southeast transect (Brown, 1984). Many forested wetlands in central Florida, in fact, are present in patches across a landscape referred to simply as "flatwoods."

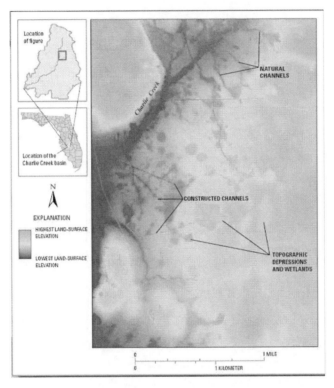

Figure 15. High resolution (LIDAR) digital elevation map showing constructed and natural flow channels connecting topographic depressions and wetlands to a stream in the Charlie Creek drainage basin, Hardee County, Florida (LIDAR data from Al Karlin, Southwest Florida Water Management District, written commun., 2008)

Flood-plain forest along the Withlacoochee River. Photographer credit: Paul Fellers, Lake Region Audubon Society.

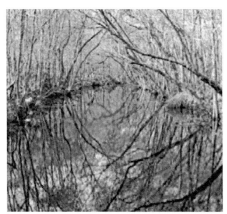

Anclote River.
Photographer credit: Dan Duerr, U.S. Geological Survey.

The channels connecting wetlands to other wetlands or to streams become evident when land-surface elevations are resolved to dimensions of centimeters or inches. In Hardee County, for example, isolated wetlands are evident in a digital elevation map of the northeast part of the Charlie Creek drainage basin (T.M. Lee, U.S. Geological Survey, written commun., 2008) (figure 15). The topographic features shown in figure 15 are derived from remote-sensing, and light detection and ranging (LIDAR) techniques (Al Karlin, Southwest Florida Water Management District, written commun., 2008). The usually isolated wetlands shown can alternatively divert runoff from or deliver runoff to Charlie Creek, a tributary stream to the Peace River-Myakka River drainage basin. Much of the land (up to 30 percent) in the Charlie Creek basin is used for grazing cattle and for other kinds of agriculture. When mapped using high resolution techniques, elevation differences that are less than 1 ft reveal the pleated furrows and mounds of the farmed plots, and also the ditches that were plowed into wetlands to drain them to nearby streams (figure 15). Constructed channels follow the slope of the land toward the stream and connect wetlands across distances of 0.5 mi or more despite the low relief. Natural flow channels also can be seen linking low-elevation wetlands to the stream. The density of isolated wetlands may increase closer to the river because the erosion and flooding associated with the stream can enhance the karst subsidence processes that create topographic depressions (Metz and Lewelling, 2009). The importance of wetlands for water- quality enhancement is greater in upstream reaches of drainage basins than in downstream reaches because they occupy a higher proportion of the land surface in headwaters, relative to the size of the streams, than in downstream areas. Alterations that affect the functioning of wetlands adjacent to small streams in the upstream parts of drainage basins can substantially affect stream hydrology, water quality, and ecology (Brinson, 1993).

The collective importance of wetlands as a water resource in central Florida becomes evident when the volume of water cycling through wetlands in a drainage basin is compared to the streamflow in the same drainage basin. For example, wetlands compose about 23 percent of the comparatively small (88 mi^2) Anclote River drainage basin in Pasco County. About 1,200 cypress wetlands and 400 marshes are present in the drainage basin upstream from the USGS streamflow gage at Elfers, Florida, based on the National Wetland Inventory (Figure 16). This density is approximately equivalent to two cypress wetlands and one marsh wetland for every 100 acres of drainage basin, given that cypress wetlands average about 9 acres in size and marshes average about 3 acres in size in this drainage basin. If these wetlands have mean water depths approximately equal to the average depths for the marsh and cypress wetlands studied by Haag and others (2005) (1.16 and 0.69 ft, respectively), the filled wetlands in the Anclote River drainage basin would store a volume of water equal to about 20 percent of the average annual discharge from the basin. This finding is based on an average annual daily discharge of 62.8 ft^3/s at the USGS Anclote at Elfers gage from 1947 to 2008 (U.S. Geological Survey, 2009a). If wetlands dry and refill more than once in a year (the natural pattern), then this percentage would increase. The importance of wetlands as water bodies in central Florida is revealed by extension when it is considered that the average annual discharge for the seven principal streams in central Florida is in excess of 8,595 ft^3/s (Fernald and Purdum, 1998).

Wetlands function as headwaters to many streams in central Florida; therefore, maintaining the connectivity of wetlands to other surface-water features is fundamental to maintaining streamflows. Just as rivers experience the contrasts of flood peaks and low-flow conditions, isolated wetlands are water bodies that experience hydrologic extremes. Although isolated wetlands are unconnected to other surface-water bodies most of the time, their infrequent, but natural cycles of overflow require that surface-water connections be preserved to maintain their hydrologic status, just as the flood-plain corridors are preserved along rivers. Rivers at low and average streamflows typically stay within a narrowly incised stream channel and infrequently inundate the adjacent flood plain with its forested wetlands. In a far more subtle fashion, isolated wetlands accommodate average and low water-level conditions by flooding only the areas concentric to their deepest points, whereas extreme high water levels get distributed well beyond the wetland perimeters into lower elevation wetlands in the basin.

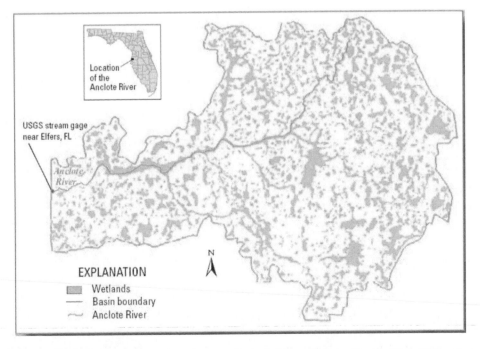

Figure 16. Wetlands in the Anclote River drainage basin in Pasco County, Florida (U.S. Fish and Wildlife Service, 2009a)

Infiltration, Groundwater Movement, and Groundwater/Surface-Water Interactions

Water enters the ground through infiltration, which includes the downward movement of precipitation through soils and rocks in the unsaturated zone (where the pores in the soil and rock are filled with air and water), and seepage from stored surface water in wetlands, lakes, and rivers. In this process, called groundwater recharge, water continues to move downward until it reaches the saturated zone (where all the pores in the soil or rock are filled with water). The top surface of the saturated zone is referred to as the water table, and all water below the water table is groundwater. Groundwater moves vertically and laterally in the saturated zone through the shallow aquifer (sometimes called the surficial aquifer system) and also through the deeper intermediate and regional aquifer systems in response to differences in hydraulic head. Hydraulic head, or potential, is determined by both elevation and pressure. The pressure is maintained by overlying layers of relatively impermeable rock containing clay, silt, and other nonporous material. Differences in hydraulic head can cause groundwater to move upward toward the land surface or into surface-water bodies, including wetlands, in a process called groundwater discharge. This process also occurs through springs, seeps, or even artesian wells.

Many wetlands in central Florida are closely connected to the groundwater system. Wetlands that receive groundwater inflow from the surficial aquifer system or the shallow Upper Floridan aquifer are considered to be in a groundwater discharge setting. If wetlands supply water to the underlying aquifer, they are considered to be in a recharge setting. The timing and magnitude of water movement are determined by the elevation difference between the wetland water level and the underlying aquifer water level. When the wetland water level is higher than the aquifer water level, the wetland recharges the aquifer. Alternatively, when the underlying aquifer water level is higher than the wetland water level, groundwater can discharge into the wetland. These movements of water can occur vertically and/or laterally. The rate of water movement is determined by the permeability of the geologic deposits and the water levels in the aquifers. Flow paths in some isolated wetlands change seasonally, whereby they may become discharge wetlands during the rainy season, and recharge wetlands during the dry season. Other isolated wetlands have flow paths that vary spatially. These "flow through" systems can receive groundwater discharge in one part of the wetland where the surrounding water table is higher than the wetland elevation, and also recharge the aquifer in another part of the wetland where the surrounding water table is lower than the wetland elevation.

Flood-plain wetlands also may have complex flow paths, receiving groundwater inflow from upslope areas and gaining water from or losing water to the adjacent river channel, depending on the river stage. In flood plains that receive groundwater inflow, there is a complex community of tiny invertebrates that live in the subsurface, or hyporheic zone, of the flood-plain bottom and associated wetlands. Many of these organisms spend their entire lives in this underground zone where recharging and discharging waters mix. Other invertebrates use the hyporheic zone as a refuge during dry periods and then recolonize the surface of streambeds and adjacent flood-plain wetlands once surface-water flow resumes (Hancock and others, 2005).

In some regions of the United States, wetlands that appear to be isolated have a subsurface connection to nearby surface water by way of the aquifer, and are an integral part of the groundwater flow system (Winter, 1998; Winter and LaBaugh, 2003). In much of central Florida, however, groundwater in the surficial aquifer system typically travels only very limited horizontal distances before recharging deeper aquifers, making groundwater connections between wetlands and lakes less common. Factors that influence this subsurface connectivity include the aquifer thickness, separation distance, wetland depth, depth of the nearby water body (lake or river), and elevation differences (Lee, 2002).

The exchange of water between wetlands and groundwater is an important hydrologic process throughout Florida. This is especially true in central Florida, where the highly permeable limestone of the Upper Floridan aquifer is closer to land surface than elsewhere in the State, and more thinly covered by a clay confining unit than in other areas (Figure 6). It is the proximity of this soluble limestone to land surface in central Florida, and the relatively thin blanket of the clay confining unit and surficial sand deposits, that create the distinctive karst terrain in the region (White, 1970). Dissolution of the limestone by infiltration of rainfall, which is mildly acidic (Riekerk and Korhnak, 1992), causes a distinctive pattern of land subsidence that promotes formation of the numerous small depressions that become wetlands, lakes, and sinkholes in the region (Figure 5) (Sinclair and others, 1985; Tihansky, 1999). The limestone beds of the Upper Floridan aquifer dip southward and increase in distance below land surface from north to south along the Florida peninsula. South of Lake Okeechobee, the Upper Floridan aquifer is not used for water supply, principally because of the unsuitable water quality.

The majority of wetlands in central Florida interact with groundwater in the surficial aquifer system. A few wetlands (for example, River Styx in Alachua County) are found where groundwater from the Upper Floridan aquifer discharges at the land surface (Feature B—Seepage Wetlands). In general the interaction between groundwater and individual wetlands depends upon the localized pattern of groundwater flow in the surficial aquifer and the rate of groundwater movement (Winter and Woo, 1990). The direction and rates of groundwater movement depend on the geometry and permeability of geologic materials around the wetland (commonly called the hydrogeologic setting), and breaks in land slope near the wetland (Figure 17A-C).

Three general groundwater flow patterns are favorable for wetland formation (Winter and others, 1998). These flow patterns are favorable because the water table in the surficial aquifer intercepts the land surface. Wetlands can form at seepage faces that are present at breaks in the land slope (Figure 1 7*A*), a flow pattern somewhat less common in the low relief landscape of central Florida than it is in the Florida panhandle. When the water table in the surficial aquifer slopes toward a river, groundwater commonly discharges in the wetlands on flood plains near river channels (Figure 17*B*). When rain and runoff accumulate in depression wetlands, the sustained flow of water out of the wetland and into the underlying aquifer creates a recharge mound in the water table (Figure 17*C*). The relation between groundwater flow patterns and wetlands is complicated because flow patterns may change seasonally and may not persist year-round.

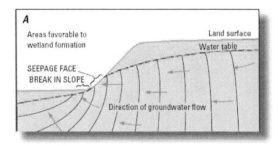

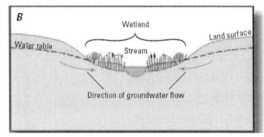
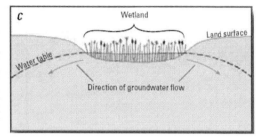

Figure 17. Typical groundwater flow configurations around wetlands (modified from Winter and others, 1998)

Recharge mounds in the water table have been the most persistent groundwater flow features observed around a number of isolated marsh and cypress wetlands in the flatwoods of west-central Florida (Figure 18) (Lee and others, 2009). These mounds embody the valuable storage function provided by wetlands in central Florida. Water slowly moves downward and laterally from the wetland into the surficial aquifer, "mounding up" until it moves downward to the intermediate confining unit. Subsequent vertical movement can ultimately result in recharge to the Upper Floridan aquifer.

PRIMER FACTS

The source of water to wetlands can be *A,* from groundwater discharge at seepage faces and breaks in slope of the water table, *B,* from streams, and *C,* from precipitation in cases where wetlands have no stream inflow and groundwater gradients slope away from the wetland.

Under the wettest conditions, the water table also could rise higher than the wetland water level on one side of the wetland, allowing groundwater to move laterally through the wetland, and eventually recharge the Upper Floridan aquifer. For example, a marsh in Martin County exhibited a pattern of horizontal flow to the adjacent surficial aquifer (Wise and others, 2000). In both settings, however, the surficial aquifer recharges the deeper Upper Floridan aquifer.

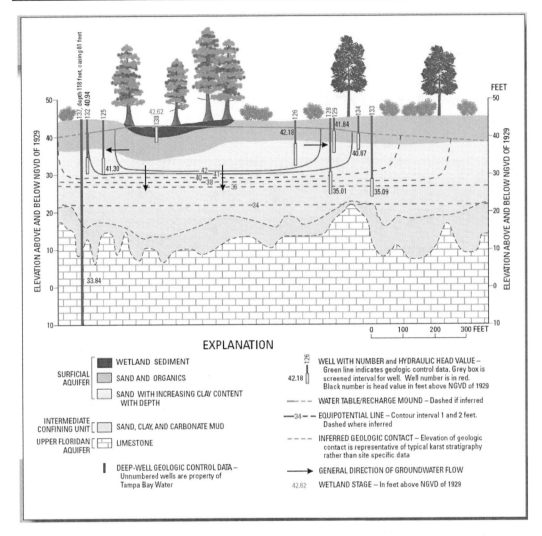

Figure 18. Hydro- geologic section through an isolated wetland (S-68 Cypress) in Pasco County, Florida, showing the water table and the direction of groundwater flow (modified from Lee and others, 2009)

In some central Florida counties, freshwater wetlands are present in groundwater discharge areas where water from the Upper Floridan aquifer discharges upward to the inter-mediate aquifer system and surficial aquifer. An example of such an area is the Charlie Creek drainage basin in Hardee County (Figure 19). An extensive groundwater discharge area is present around headwater wetlands in the northern part of the basin, as well as along stream channels and near sinkholes where the land surface drops abruptly and is often below the potentiometric surface in the Upper Floridan aquifer. Because confining clays commonly separate the Upper Floridan and surficial aquifers, upward flow may be slow. However, when discharge conditions exist they preclude downward losses from the surficial aquifer, allowing more runoff from wetlands into streams. Excessive groundwater withdrawals from the Upper Floridan aquifer can convert discharge areas to recharge areas and reduce streamflow.

In karst areas, groundwater withdrawals can have a substantial effect on groundwater/surface-water interactions.

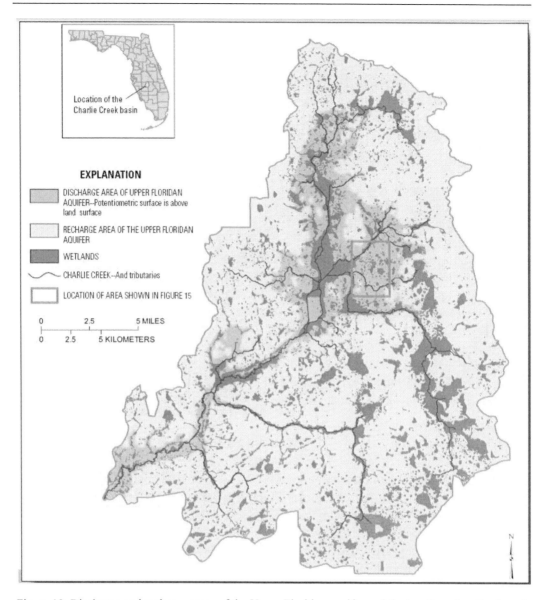

Figure 19. Discharge and recharge areas of the Upper Floridan aquifer and the location of wetlands and stream channels in the Charlie Creek drainage basin of Hardee County, Florida, for September 2006 (Ortiz, 2007; LIDAR data from Al Karlin, Southwest Florida Water Management District, written commun., 2008).

Groundwater withdrawals from the Upper Floridan aquifer are concentrated in central Florida, although 59 of the 67 counties in the State use the aquifer as the primary source of groundwater (Marella, 2004). Of the 20 counties with the largest groundwater withdrawals from the Upper Floridan aquifer, all except Duval are in the central Florida study area (table 1).

Monitoring Hydrologic Characteristics in Wetlands

Some wetland hydrologic characteristics can be measured using relatively simple instruments deployed to record key indicators, such as wetland water level, rainfall, and groundwater levels in the drainage basin surrounding the wetland (Figure 20). Long-term records of hydrologic data in wetlands are an invaluable tool for resource managers because they assist in determining changes in wetland size, flooding patterns, and responses to changes in rainfall and other climatic variables.

Although rainfall can be monitored in or near individual wetlands, evapotranspiration measurements commonly require sophisticated instruments, and evaporation instrumentation is typically mounted on a tower in a location representative of a specified environmental setting. As of 2009, there were at least 20 micrometeorological stations for measurement of evapotranspiration located throughout Florida in various environmental settings, including an Everglades slough, several lakes, slash pine plantations, and agricultural areas with differing types of crop cover. Additional stations are planned or have already been installed in cypress, wet prairie, and marsh settings. Included in the types of data collected at the evapotranspiration stations are rainfall, air temperature, relative humidity, and wind speed. Additional data used in estimates of evapotranspiration are collected through the National Oceanic and Atmospheric Administration Geostationary Operational Environmental Satellite network and include the areal distribution of solar insolation (the amount of sunlight received on the Earth's surface) and albedo (the ratio of the light reflected by the Earth to that received by it) (U.S. Geological Survey, 2008c).

PRIMER FACTS

In karst areas, groundwater withdrawals can have a substantial effect on groundwater/surface-water interactions. Groundwater withdrawals from the Upper Floridan aquifer are concentrated in central Florida, although 59 of the 67 counties in the State use the aquifer as the primary source of groundwater (Marella, 2004). Of the 20 counties with the largest groundwater withdrawals from the Upper Floridan aquifer, all except Duval are in central Florida (table 1).

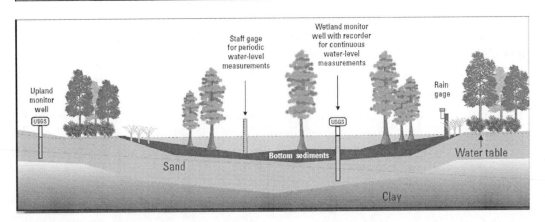

Figure 20. Instrumentation for hydrologic monitoring in Florida wetlands

Table 1. Counties having the greatest groundwater withdrawals from the Upper Floridan aquifer, 2000 (Marella, 2004)

County	Withdrawals, in million gallons per day
Polk	317.73
Orange	280.46
Hillsborough	194.86
Duval[1]	150.00
Pasco	139.24
Highlands	133.77
Brevard	123.55
Manatee	118.25
Osceola	114.65
DeSoto	110.01
Volusia	96.72
Lake	90.41
Seminole	88.20
Hardee	81.73
Indian River	74.01
Marion	66.04
Alachua	59.16
Hernando	49.32
Okeechobee	47.76
St. Lucie	46.98

[1]County not included in the central Florida study area.

WATER QUALITY AND SOILS IN WETLANDS

Wetland water quality is affected by rainfall, groundwater inflow and outflow, surface-water inflow and outflow, and the presence or absence of oxygen (aerobic or anaerobic conditions, respectively), which determines the biological activity of microbial organisms in wetlands. The biological activity of microorganisms involves complex chemical reactions in wetland water and soils that transform nitrogen, sulfur, carbon, phosphorus, and other elements into forms useable by bactera, algae, plants, and other organisms (Richardson and Vepraskas, 2001). Moreover, the residence time or retention time of water in wetlands, which is a hydrologic characteristic, helps determine how much and how fast the various chemical constituents change and what kinds of chemical and biological transformations occur. A sufficient residence time is necessary for the breakdown and mineralization of organic material that would otherwise accumulate in wetlands. This is one reason why it is often detrimental to wetland function to create a channel across a wetland that might increase outflow rates and decrease residence time.

Rainfall is one of the important sources of water in many Florida wetlands, and strongly affects wetland pH, dissolved constituents, specific conductance, and alkalinity. Florida wetlands that derive most of their water from rainfall typically have a low pH (4.0–5.5), because the average pH of rainfall in Florida ranges from 4.3 to 4.7, and is about 4.7 in central Florida (Fernald and Purdum, 1998). These wetlands also have low concentrations of dissolved constituents (Figure 21) and are poorly buffered because concentrations of calcium, magnesium, potassium, sodium, chloride, sulfate, and bicarbonate are very low in rainfall—typically less than 5 mg/L. Specific conductance, a measure of the total amount of dissolved constituents in water, ranges from 35–115 μS/cm in northern Florida cypress wetlands (Ewel, 1990). Studies in west-central Florida indicate that specific conductance ranges from 50 to 275 μS/cm. Alkalinity, a measure of the buffering capacity of the water in the wetlands, also is low in central Florida wetlands (less than1.0–18.0 mg/L as calcium carbonate).

Surface-water inflow is an important source of water to wetlands in central Florida, but it is difficult to assess because the topography is relatively flat in many areas and the catchment area of wetlands may be small or large depending on very slight changes in land surface elevation. Studies of cypress wetlands in Florida pine flatwoods in Alachua County indicate that the rain-catchment area is 2–3 times larger than the vegetated wetland area (Riekerk and Korhnak, 2000). Catchment areas were calculated using a water-budget approach (Feature D—The Use of Water Budgets to Describe Wetlands). Much of the catchment area beyond the palmetto fringe in that study consisted of saturated soils, and under those conditions runoff would be greater than during drier conditions.

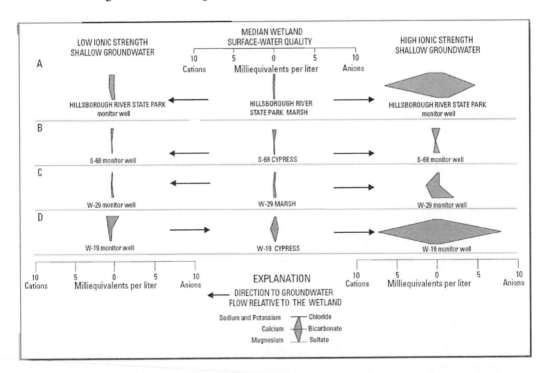

Figure 21. Comparison of water quality in wetland surface water and shallow groundwater at selected wetlands in central Florida illustrated using Stiff diagrams that show the relative amounts of dominant cations and anions (modified from Lee and others, 2009)

Surface-water runoff may carry suspended sediment into wetlands. Surface-water runoff may have higher dissolved oxygen concentrations than water in some receiving isolated wetlands due to simple physical aeration. It also may contain elevated concentrations of nutrients if the area drained has soils enriched with fertilizers or other sources of nitrogen and phosphorus.

Sundew (Drosera capillaris) growing on acidic wetland soils. Photographer credit: Michael Hancock, Southwest Florida Water Management District

D. Use of Water Budgets to Describe Wetlands

A wetland water budget incorporates all identifiable sources of water gain and loss in a particular wetland during a specified time period—a day, week, month, or year. If these sources can be reliably quantified, the water budget then can be used to estimate the change in water storage in the wetland during that same period. The ability to predict those changes, particularly in relation to changes in climate or by human activities, is useful to water managers in local, regional, and State agencies, and refining water-budget approaches to wetlands is of interest throughout central Florida.

There is particular interest in estimating water budgets for the design of mitigation wetlands related to projects that alter or eliminate existing wetlands. Water-budget studies can be used to develop more accurate predictions of the long-term persistence and functioning of these mitigation wetlands, especially under changing climate conditions.

If there is no change in the quantity of water stored in a wetland, then the inputs balance the outputs, and wetland water levels do not change. In central Florida, however, wetlands are dynamic systems and the quantity of water stored does change measurably over short periods, and more sub- stantially over longer periods of time (Lee and others, 2009). For an isolated wetland (one that is not connected by streams to other surface-water bodies) the change in the wetland water volume over an interval of time equals the difference between the inflow and outflow volumes, as expressed in the following equation:

$$\Delta S = P - ET + R + G_i - L \tag{1}$$

where

   ΔS is change in wetland volume,

   P is precipitation,

   ET is evapotranspiration,

   R is runoff into the wetland,

   G_i is groundwater inflow, and

   L is leakage, defined as the wetland water that leaks out to the underlying groundwater.

There is no surface-water outflow component if water budgets are calculated during periods of time when wetland water levels do not rise above the elevation of the wetland perimeter. A surface-water outflow term must be added to the equation, however, if water-budget periods include times when wetland water levels rise above the elevation of their perimeter.

A substantial amount of data is needed to develop a wetland water budget. The relative size of the components of a wetland water budget varies with the size of the flooded area (Figure D–1). One critical element is a detailed topographic survey of the wetland so that the surface-water volume in the wetland can be calculated accurately as the wetland stage changes over time.

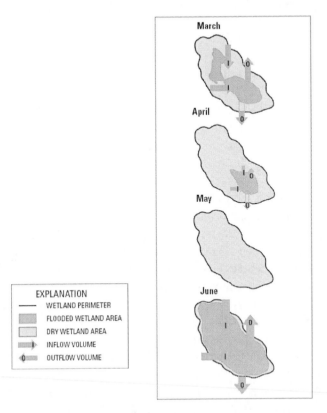

Figure D–1. Conceptualized wetland showing seasonal changes in the magnitude of water-budget components. Relative size of arrows indicates differences in volume. Volumes of the water-budget components change with the size of the flooded area.

Water-budget components also vary spatially across the State. In central Florida, evapotranspiration is less in the northern counties than in southern counties because solar radiation is lower in the north. Wetlands on the central ridge generally have higher leakage compared to those in the coastal plain where the water table is higher.

Some components of a wetland water budget are more easily measured than others, and the more accurate these measurements and estimates are, the more reliable the wetland water budget will be. Precipitation is recorded at weather stations, but these are typically some distance away from the wetland under study. Many factors affect the accuracy of weather station data and their applicability to wetlands in the region. Urbanization, elevation differences, lake effects, and wind conditions can cause substantial variations in precipitation from one place to another in central Florida.

PRIMER FACTS

A substantial amount of data is needed to develop a wetland water budget. The relative size of the components of a wetland water budget varies with the size of the flooded area (Figure D–1). One critical element is a detailed topographic survey of the wetland so that the surface-water volume in the wetland can be calculated accurately as the wetland stage changes over time.

Rain gages located within or at the edge of wetlands can provide highly accurate rainfall data, but the data must be collected at frequent intervals and collection devices must be carefully maintained.

Surface-water runoff into a wetland comes from several sources. There may be indirect runoff to isolated wetlands from the surrounding watershed as sheetflow or shallow channel flow. Streams occasionally overflow their banks and lakes can overtop their shorelines, thereby contributing surface water to wetlands. Inflow to wetlands must be gaged to measure water volume gain accurately. Likewise, surface-water outflow from a wetland during periods of heavy rainfall must be gaged using a weir or other device to accurately measure the water volume lost.

Groundwater can contribute inflow to a wetland if the groundwater level is at or above the wetland stage. The water levels in monitor wells outside the wetland perimeter can indicate whether shallow groundwater is discharging to a wetland as a contributing water source. A network of at least three monitoring wells is needed to determine the hydraulic gradient or general direction of groundwater flow in the vicinity of a wetland. Water-level measurements in the well network should be collected over time, because the direction of groundwater flow can change seasonally with increasing or decreasing rainfall and evapotranspiration. The rate of groundwater flow can be determined using information about the hydraulic conductivity of the geologic material in the wetland basin. Differences in water quality (including pH and specific conductance) between wetland water and the shallow groundwater around a wetland can be used to infer groundwater movement into or out of a wetland.

Leakage occurs when the groundwater level is below the bottom of a wetland and the wetland is not well confined by clay or other relatively impermeable material. The process also occurs around the wetland perimeter when the water level in adjacent groundwater is lower than the wetland water level. Leakage can be in a downward direction, or it can occur laterally into the wetland basin. This leakage recharges the shallow aquifer. Leakage from wetlands can be induced or accelerated when the water table is lowered by activities such as ground-water withdrawal.

The process of evapotranspiration includes water lost as evaporation from open water or soil, and water lost as transpiration through plants. Evapotranspiration varies with the evaporative demand of the atmosphere and the availability of water. Rates of evapotranspiration are highest in wetlands and lakes where water is near or above land surface, and lowest along the ridges where the soil is permeable and the depth to the water table is greater. There are concerted efforts in central Florida to develop improved estimates of evapotranspiration in a range of habitat and land-use types using technologically advanced climate stations. These more refined estimates can yield substantially improved estimates of evapotranspiration for use in wetland water budgets.

Selected References about Wetland Water Budgets

Heimburg, K. F. (1984). *Hydrology of north-central Florida cypress domes,* p. 72-82, *in* Ewel, K. C. & Odum, H. T., eds., Cypress Swamps, University of Florida Press, 472 p.

Healy, R. W., Winter, T. C., Labaugh, J. W. & Franke, O. L. (2007). *Water budgets: Foundations for effective water- resources and environmental management: U. S.* Geological Survey Circular 1308, 90 p.

Lee, T. M., Haag, K. H., Metz, P. A. & Sacks, L. A. (2009). *The comparative hydrology, water quality & ecology of selected natural and augmented freshwater wetlands in west-central Florida*: U. S. Geological Survey Professional Paper 1758, 152 p.

Sumner, D. M. (2001). *Evapotranspiration from a cypress and pine forest subjected to natural fires, Volusia* County, Florida, 1998-99: U. S. Geological Survey Water-Resources Investigations Report 01-4245, 56 p.

Sumner, D. M. (2006). Evapotranspiration measurement and estimation in Florida---State of the art and future directions, *in Proceedings of the University of Central Florida 2nd Annual Stormwater Research Symposium*, May 4-5, 2006, Orlando, Florida, p. 125-138.

Saw palmetto (Seranoa repens) may surround isolated cypress wetlands, and grow up to the perimeter. It will not grow in the wetland basin, where there is frequent or prolonged inundation. Photographer credit: Michael Hancock, Southwest Florida Water Management District.

Many of the vital elements necessary for plant and animal life move through wetland environments in complex cycles that are influenced by microbial communities adapted to life in either aerobic or anaerobic conditions. When soils are saturated with water, conditions in most of the soil substrate are anaerobic, as is the case with much of the substrate in wetlands. However, conditions are often aerobic at the soil/ water interface. When wetland soils dry out during the dry season (October–May in much of central Florida), air enters the pore spaces and creates an aerobic environment. Wetlands naturally oscillate between being flooded and dry over space and time and, therefore, support a greater variety of microbial processes that transform essential elements than is found in upland areas.

Sulfur and carbon are vital elements that have a gaseous phase in their cycling. Organic sulfur from the breakdown of decaying animal and plant material is transformed into hydrogen sulfide under anaerobic conditions (in the absence of oxygen) and released into the atmosphere with the characteristic "rotten egg" smell commonly associated with wetlands. Hydrogen sulfide also can be transformed into sulfate and attached (adsorbed) to clay in the sediment or released into the atmosphere where it is converted to sulfur dioxide. Dissolved organic carbon and particulate organic carbon can form from the breakdown of plant and animal material in wetland water and soils. These organic carbon compounds can be taken up and broken down under anaerobic conditions by bacteria to form methane gas, or swamp gas, which is released to the atmosphere when wetland sediments are disturbed. Respiration of organic carbon compounds under aerobic conditions generates carbon dioxide, which is released to the atmosphere, where it is sometimes referred to as a greenhouse gas.

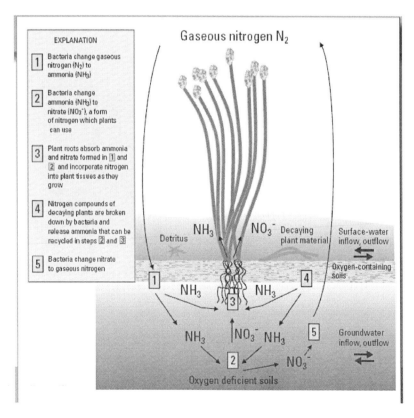

Figure 22. Simplified nitrogen cycle in wetlands (modified from Carter, 1996)

Nitrogen (N) is an element that is abundant in the atmosphere as nitrogen gas (N_2) (Figure 22). Dead and decaying wetland plants and animals release nitrogen as ammonia (NH_3) under anaerobic conditions in a process called ammonification. Once the ammonia is exposed to oxygen, such as in the aerobic layer at the soil-water interface, it is transformed to nitrate (NO_3^-). The nitrate may be taken up by plants as an essential nutrient, or it may become adsorbed to soil particles. If excess nitrate is bound up in anaerobic sediments, it can be converted back to nitrogen gas by microbial processes called denitrification and returned to the atmosphere. Otherwise, it can leach downward and dissolve in the groundwater.

Phosphorus (P) is an element essential for plant and animal life that does not have a gaseous phase, but instead is cycled solely in the sediments and waters of wetlands (Figure 23). Most of the time, the majority of the phosphorus in a wetland is bound to organic litter and peat, and to inorganic sediments. Phosphorus is often a limiting plant nutrient in wetland ecosystems, including marshes and deep-water swamps, because it has to be in an inorganic form and water soluble to be taken up by plants. If those conditions are not met, then the element is not bioavailable for plant growth until it has been chemically transformed. Particulate organic phosphorus (phosphorus bound to organic matter such as peat and to clay particles) as well as dissolved organic phosphorus molecules (such as phosphoproteins and phospholipids) cannot be absorbed by plants because they are large molecules. The main inorganic form of phosphorus is called orthophosphate (PO_4^-) and it is the most bioavailable form to plants. Some inorganic phosphorus binds to metals (such as iron and aluminum), rendering it insoluble and thereby unavailable for plant absorption. These insoluble inorganic phosphates often precipitate from the water column onto the wetland sediment surface. When wetland sediments are resuspended, depending on the pH of the water and the dissolved oxygen concentrations, phosphorus can be transformed and become more bioavailable. Generally, phosphorus is most bioavailable at a slightly acidic to neutral pH.

Carnivorous pitcher plants (Sarracenia purpurea) grow in wetlands with low nutrient availability and they use insects and small invertebrates as a source of nitrogen. Photographer credit: Dan Duerr, U.S. Geological Survey.

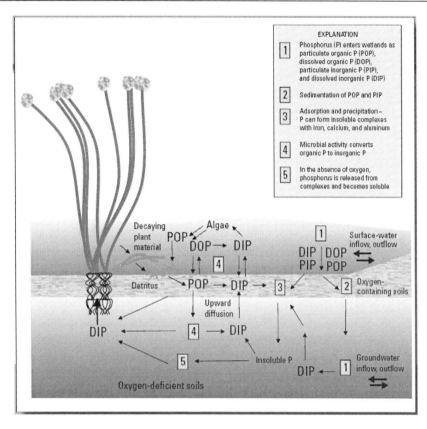

EXPLANATION

1 Phosphorus (P) enters wetlands as particulate organic P (POP), dissolved organic P (DOP), particulate inorganic P (PIP), and dissolved inorganic P (DIP)

2 Sedimentation of POP and PIP

3 Adsorption and precipitation – P can form insoluble complexes with iron, calcium, and aluminum

4 Microbial activity converts organic P to inorganic P

5 In the absence of oxygen, phosphorus is released from complexes and becomes soluble

Figure 23. Simplified phosphorus cycle in wetlands.

Concentrations of plant nutrients (the bioavailable forms of nitrogen and phosphorus) are minimal in rainwater. Therefore, many wetlands have low concentrations of plant nutrients because their primary water source is rainfall. Concentrations typically are less than 100 µg/L for individual forms of nitrogen and phosphorus (Ewel, 1990). Concentrations of nutrients also are generally low in wetlands that have groundwater inflow (unless there is contamination from surface-water sources that contain fertilizers or wastewater). For example, in some wetlands, the breakdown of nitrogen is very slow, and carnivorous plants consume insects and small invertebrates as a source of nitrogen.

Wetland soils are described as hydric because they develop under conditions of saturation or flooding that are prolonged enough to allow anaerobic conditions to develop. Anaerobic conditions develop when soil is saturated because the pore spaces in the soil are filled with water instead of air. Saturated soil can be up to 90-percent water by weight under flooded conditions. The small amount of oxygen present in the water is quickly used up by microorganisms in the saturated soil. Furthermore, oxygen from the atmosphere moves 10,000 times more slowly into saturated soil than into the air- filled pores in drained soil. The breakdown of organic matter in the absence of oxygen is very slow, and explains why organic matter accumulates in thick layers in wetlands flooded during much of the year.

Some wetlands maintain a mineral soil, whereas other wetlands develop organic soils. Mineral (inorganic) soils by definition have less than 20 to 35 percent organic matter. Most Mineral soils in Florida have a neutral to slightly acidic pH, although mineral soils in flood-plain wetlands have a higher pH because of the calcium carbonate content of river water.

Many flood-plain wetlands have mineral soils that are dry during low-flow periods. When the mineral soils are flooded permanently or semi-permanently, they develop a black, blue- gray, or neutral gray color due to the transformation (reduction) of iron in the absence of oxygen. Iron in its reduced form is more soluble and can be easily leached out of wetland soils. When these mineral soils are no longer flooded and dry out, the iron oxidizes and turns a reddish or yellow-brown color. Sometimes wetland plants transfer oxygen down to their root zone as they grow in saturated soils, and iron is oxidized along the thin traces of small plant roots, leaving behind a net-like orange-red pattern.

Organic wetland soils develop over time as partially decayed vegetation accumulates, as it does in many palustrine and lacustrine wetlands. Compared to mineral soils, organic soils typically are darker in color and have a lower pH, higher porosity, higher water-holding capacity, and often lower nutrient availability. The plant decomposition results in fragmented plant fibers that retain compounds like wax that are not water soluble, and lose cellulose and plant pigments that are water soluble. In muck soils (which are black), more than 65 percent of the plant material is decomposed material, whereas in peat soils (which tend to be brown), less than 35 percent of the plant material has decomposed. Peat tends to accumulate in deep marshes with long hydroperiods that prevent oxidation. Many of the organic compounds in the decomposing plant material leach out and are available to stimulate plant growth in these systems. When organic soils dry out, the peat or muck will compact and oxidize upon exposure to air. This compaction can be a problem in chronically dewatered wetlands as the soil surface subsides and trees begin to fall.

Soil subsidence is measured near the base of wetland trees in the Eldridge Wilde Well Field in west-central Florida. Photographer credit: Michael Hancock, Southwest Florida Water Management District.

The cycle of drying and flooding determines the availability (alternating presence and absence) of oxygen in wetland soils. Oxygen affects the rate of breakdown of plant material, and accelerates the decomposition of dead plants that accumulate in wetlands. Oxygen also affects the biochemical reactions in wetlands, and in turn the form, solubility, and mobility of minerals such as iron, manganese, and other elements. The degradation of plant material and the transformation of minerals result in distinctive soil color patterns and banding, which have broad use in wetland delineation, an integral part of the wetland regulatory process. The patterns of color in wetland soils also can be used to infer patterns of wetland hydrology (inundation and drying) over time.

There are seven orders (major types) of hydric soils that are present in central Florida (histosols, alfisols, spodsols, entisols, mollisols, inceptisols, and utilisols), and a complex system of soil taxonomy (naming conventions) has been developed to identify and describe subgroups within those major orders (Carlisle and Hurt, 2007). Wetland ecosystems can be associated with all of the major soil orders. A complete list of soil map units (by county) that have hydric soils as a principle component is in the Hydric Soils of Florida Handbook (Carlisle and Hurt, 2007). Soils are often used to identify the areal extent of wetlands (wetland delineation), and wetland delineation has important ramifications for land use and land management.

The inherent ability of wetlands to transform many water-quality constituents has led to their use as "treatment" wetlands to specifically improve the quality of surface water or other water sources prior to discharge to rivers or lakes, or to recharge to the surficial or Upper Floridan aquifer. For example, wetlands are being constructed near the outflow of Lake Hancock in Polk County to improve the water quality of the lake outflow before it is discharged into the upper Peace River (Southwest Florida Water Management District, 2006). Marsh wetlands have been restored or constructed to improve the quality of water in Lake Apopka (St. Johns River Water Management District, 2004; 2006) (Feature E—Marsh Restoration—A Key to Improving Water Quality in Lake Apopka).

There are numerous examples of wetlands being used for treatment of wastewater effluent in central Florida, and the treatment goals differ among the projects. Gainesville Regional Utilities in Alachua County has proposed an infiltrating wetland to treat wastewater effluent prior to aquifer recharge (Wetland Solutions, Inc., 2007). The treatment wetlands are designed to reduce nitrate nitrogen con- centrations below the drinking water standard of 10 mg/L by optimizing natural microbial processes that eliminate nitrate nitrogen. Constructing the wetlands on soils with high permeability would have the added advantage of facilitating groundwater recharge while also creating wetland habitat. The city of Clermont has proposed adding treated wastewater effluent to a freshwater marsh in Lake County. The marsh is shallow and has a long hydroperiod (8–10 months). Water- budget analyses (Feature D—Use of Water Budgets to Describe Wetlands), soil evaluations, and vegetation studies were used to determine the ability of the wetland to take up, store, and process potentially large quantities of phosphorus (Dolan and others, 1981). In 1985, the city of Orlando began construction of a wetland complex to treat wastewater before it is discharged into the St. Johns River. The treatment wetland was supplied with more than 2 million wetland plants, and once it became established, more than 170 different bird species and numerous other wildlife species were observed in the wetland.

E. Marsh Restoration—A Key to Improving Water Quality in Lake Apopka

Marsh restoration has proven to be a critical component to the improvement of water quality in Lake Apopka, which has been referred to as the most polluted large lake in Florida

(St. Johns River Water Management District, 2006). Lake Apopka is a 31,000-acre natural lake in Orange and Lake Counties that forms the headwaters of the Ocklawaha River. The lake, which is the fourth largest in the State, was an important tourist attraction in the 1940s, and supported a robust recreational fishing industry. Fishing cabins dotted the shoreline, and contributed to the local economy. Birds also were abundant, and more than 335 species have been observed by birdwatchers on the north shore of the lake.

The lake has sustained substantial alterations over a long period of time. The alterations began in 1888 with the construction of the Apopka-Beauclair Canal (Figure E-1), which lowered lake levels by about 30 percent. During the land boom of the 1920s, towns on the lake shore began dumping raw sewage and wastewater from citrus processing plants into Lake Apopka.

In 1941, a levee was built across the north shore of the lake and 20,000 acres of shallow wetlands north of the levee (about one-third of the lake area) were drained for muck farming operations. Muck is dark soil rich in decaying plant material, and it was left behind when the wetlands were drained. The subtropical climate allowed farmers to produce as many as three crops per year in the exposed fertile soils. Farmlands were typically flooded to kill nematode plant parasites, and this sediment-laden water was then drained back into the lake until it was needed for crop irrigation. The accumulated sediments eventually raised the lake bottom by about 5 ft. Hurricane winds in 1947 hastened the demise of the lake by removing vast beds of emergent vegetation (Bachmann and others, 2001), and in 1947 the first algae bloom was documented. Treated wastewater discharges from shoreline communities through the 1 980s also added to the nutrient load, and direct discharges from citrus processing plants until the 1 980s further contributed to nutrient enrichment of the lake. The destruction of the north shore marshes not only reduced the natural cleansing capacity of the lake, but also greatly increased the pollution load as billions of gallons of nutrient-rich and pesticide-laden irrigation water subsequently drained unabated into the lake (St. Johns River Water Management District, 2006).

The large amounts of suspended sediments and nutrients, especially phosphorus, added to the lake during a 50-year period resulted in chronic algae blooms and a reduction in lake water clarity (Bachmann and others, 2005). These water- quality changes eventually killed rooted and submersed aquatic vegetation, and the subsequent loss of vegetated spawning beds ended the recreational fishery in the lake. However, the dead plants and fish were not removed from the system, and their decaying tissues further enriched the lake in nitrogen, phosphorus, and other compounds. As noted earlier, Lake Apopka ultimately became the most polluted large lake in Florida (Lowe and others, 2001). Lake Apopka received further attention in 1998 when hundreds of migratory birds died in and near the north shore following the flooding of 6,000 acres of former farms, which attracted birds and fish (Lightfoot, 2001). High concentrations of organochlorine pesticides, including toxaphene, were subsequently found in the soils.

Efforts to restore the lake to its natural condition and to improve water quality to Class III status (fit for recreation) began in the 1980s. The 1985 Lake Apopka Restoration Act provided for planning, diagnostic studies, and feasibility studies. The 1987 Surface Water Improvement and Management Act included Lake Apopka as a priority water body requiring restoration. Finally, the 1996 Lake Apopka Improvement and Management Act authorized the St. Johns River Water Management District to set criteria that could be used to limit future phosphorus discharges into the lake, and provided funding for a mandatory buyout of the farms on the north shore of the lake. This buyout of about 90 percent of the farms was completed in 1999. The restoration of Lake Apopka is expected to last at least 25 years, and will use a comprehensive approach (St. Johns River Water Management District, 2006).

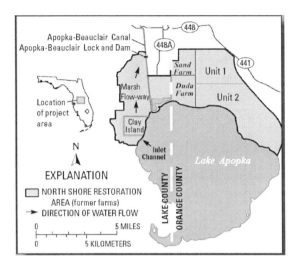

Figure E–1. The Lake Apopka Restoration project area (modified from St. Johns River Water Management District, 2006)

The Lake Apopka Marsh Flow-way Project will help improve water quality in the lake. Photographer credit: St. Johns River Water Management District.

Birds are abundant in the Lake Apopka ecosystem and vulnerable to contaminants. Photographer credit: St. Johns River Water Management District.

Wetlands were an important functional part of the historic Lake Apopka ecosystem, and they play a crucial role in lake restoration efforts (St. Johns River Water Management District, 2006). Native emergent plants established in the lake will stabilize lake sediments and improve shoreline aquatic habitat. The North Shore Muck Farm Restoration Project will include about 13,000 acres of former farm land. Much of the acreage will be flooded to a shallow depth using a variety of water-control structures to promote the growth of wetland vegetation and thereby provide habitat for ducks, wading birds, and other wildlife.

The Lake Apopka Marsh Flow-way Project, which will restore about 3,400 acres of farmland, is designed to filter up to 98 percent of the lake waters twice yearly as they circulate through a series of wetland cells managed as emergent marshes. The flow-way, in reality a type of "treatment" wetland, is on the northwest shore of the lake and is designed to reduce phosphorus concentrations by 30 to 50 percent and suspended particulates by up to 90 percent. A portion of the treated water is returned to the lake and the remainder is sent downstream through the Apopka-Beauclair Canal (St. Johns River Water Management District, 2009).

Selected References about Lake Apopka Restoration

Bachmann, R. W., Hoyer, M. V. & Canfield, D. E. (2001). *Evaluation of recent limnological changes in Lake Apopka: Hydrobiologia, v. 448*, p. 19-26.

Bachmann, R. W., Hoyer, M. V., Vinzon, S. A. & Canfield, D. E. (2005). *The origin of the fluid mud layer in Lake Apopka, Florida: Limnology and Oceanography, v. 50*, no. 2, p. 629-63 5.

Lightfoot, T. L. (2001). *Organochlorine disaster in Florida—2 years later: Journal of Avian Medicine and Surgery, v. 15*, no. 2, p. 138-140.

Lowe, E. F., Battoe, L. E., Coveney, M. F., Schelske, C. L., Havens, K. E., Marzolf, E. R. & Reddy, K. R. (2001). *The restoration of Lake Apopka in relation to alternative stable states: Hydrobiologia, v. 448*, p. 11-18.

St. Johns River Water Management District, (2006). *Lake Apopka— A decade of improvement now accelerating,* accessed on January 2, 2008, at http://www. sjrwmd. com/ publications. html.

St. Johns River Water Management District, (2009). The Lake Apopka Marsh Flow-way—Using nature to filter pollutants from lake water, accessed on September 23, 2009, at http:// www. sjrwmd. com/publications. html.

ECOLOGY OF FRESHWATER WETLANDS IN CENTRAL FLORIDA

Wetland ecology is dependent on the complex and dynamic interactions between the hydrologic, physical, chemical, and biological components of wetland ecosystems. The water source and hydrologic regime directly influence water-quality characteristics, such as pH, dissolved oxygen concentration, and nutrient availability. These characteristics then determine the biological community response, which may in turn alter the physical environment and the water quality of the wetland. Wetlands vary over time in the composition of their plant and animal communities as the wetlands experience wetter or drier conditions. Those conditions are influenced by hydrologic processes, human activities, and other disturbances such as fire. The latter, when coupled with fluctuating water levels, can maintain the ecological integrity of Florida wetlands, especially marshes (Kushlan, 1990). The distribution of plant species, and the observed cycles of plant colonization and replacement in wetlands, result in a continuum of over- lapping sets of species that respond to both subtle and conspicuous environmental cues. The aquatic animal populations in Florida wetlands, with the exception of birds, are not as diverse as those in the northern temperate wetlands (Kushlan, 1990). The population of wetland birds, however, is very diverse, and is expanded seasonally in winter by birds migrating from northern latitudes, and in summer by birds migrating from the Caribbean and South America (Sunquist and others, 2002).

Wetlands are a part of the larger landscape units in which they are distributed, and the terrestrial area or upland surrounding a wetland is an integral part of the wildlife habitat that wetlands provide. Many animals are dependent for essential parts of their life cycles on the terrestrial habitats that connect and surround wetlands, and wildlife activities such as nesting, hibernation, aestivation (resting during dry periods), foraging/feeding, and dispersal all require adjacent terrestrial habitat and protected corridors.

Bacteria and Algae

Bacteria are probably the most abundant organisms in wetlands, but their small size makes them difficult to sample and their contribution to wetland characteristics and processes are complex. These single-celled organisms mediate and control the rates of many vital transformations of important compounds in wetlands, such as carbon, nitrogen, phosphorus, and sulfur. Bacteria are critical for the breakdown of plant leaves, stems, and roots as plants die and fall to the bottom of wetlands. They also break down woody debris that would otherwise accumulate and quickly fill forested wetland basins. Finally, bacteria decompose and remineralize the many dead invertebrates and other animal remains that are deposited in wetlands. Perhaps most importantly, they have evolved into forms that can thrive under both the aerobic (oxygen-rich) and anaerobic (oxygen-depleted) conditions found throughout wetlands, so that the transforming functions are continuous and uninterrupted regardless of wetland state. Most bacteria get their energy from the breakdown of other organic materials and are described as heterotrophic. The Cyanobacteria (also known as blue-green bacteria or blue-green algae) is a unique group of autotrophic bacteria that converts light into energy through photosynthesis. Cyanobacteria can fix atmospheric nitrogen and when they die, nitrogen is added to the wetland ecosystem. Some Cyanobacteria, such as *Lyngbya, Nostoc, Oscillatoria,* and *Schizothrix,* produce mucilaginous sheaths along their filaments and form dense mats in wetlands.

Algae are a diverse group of simple single-celled plants that convert light into energy through photosynthesis using pigments such as chlorophyll. These plants contribute substantially to the high productivity of wetlands, and have a vital role in absorbing atmospheric carbon dioxide and dissolved nutrients such as phosphorus. Algae in freshwater wetlands include filamentous, unicellular, and colonial green algae, diatoms with glass-like silicaceous outer skeletons, eulgenoids, desmids, dinoflagellates, and numerous other groups (Stevenson and others, 1996).

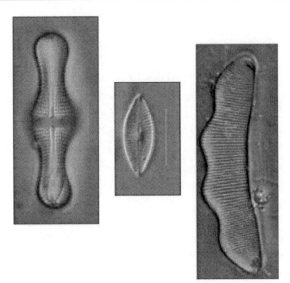

Diatoms in freshwater wetlands vary in shape and size. Photographer credit: Jan Stevenson, Michigan State University.

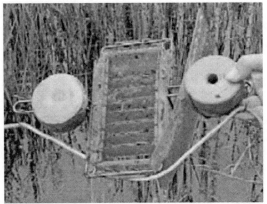

Filamentous green algae growing on an algae sampler from a marsh in Pasco County. Photographer credit: Kim Haag.

Algae grow on many different surfaces in virtually all classes of wetlands (Figure 24). The algae that grow on the surface of soft organic and inorganic bottom sediments are called epipelon, and algae that grow on sand are termed epipsammon. Small amorphous masses of bottom-dwelling (benthic) algae can sometimes float to the wetland water surface, buoyed by accumulated gas bubbles. Epiphyton are algae that grow on plant surfaces, such as the stems and leaves of submersed, emergent, and floating plants, as well as on the bases of tree trunks and cypress knees. Periphyton is a term that refers to communities of benthic algae, associated organisms including cyanobacteria and fungi, and calcium carbonate. These communities can form thick tangled mats that have structure and coat the wetland bottom and the surfaces of higher plants. Periphyton often has a distinct appearance that varies from one wetland to another depending on water-quality conditions.

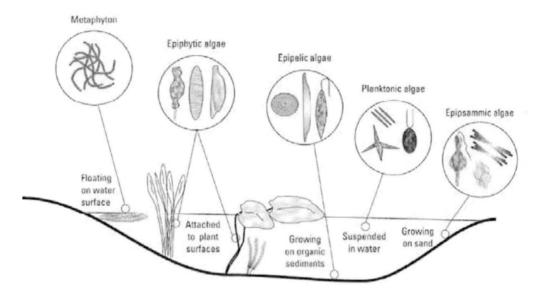

Figure 24. Algae habitats in wetlands

Cypress trees on the riverine flood plain adjacent to the Suwannee River. Photographer credit: Scott Orr, U.S. Geological Survey.

Some types of filamentous algae that grow submersed in open water, such as the stoneworts *Chara* spp. and *Nitella* spp., have a growth structure resembling that of higher plants. Other algae form clouds of loosely aggregated filaments that float at the surface of wetlands (the metaphyton), and take advantage of available sunlight. The mostly single-celled algae that grow in the open water are called phytoplankton. Some phytoplankton species grow attached to one another in balls or filaments (colonial algae) with a small number of single cells of the same species grouped together. Phytoplankton sometimes have become dislodged or detached from algal masses growing on the soft bottom sediments and live for a time in the open water. Alternatively, phytoplankton in the water column can eventually settle to the bottom and begin growing there. This kind of internal cycling of algae from one habitat to another is characteristic of the overall internal cycling found throughout isolated wetlands.

Algae are a vital biological component of wetlands and play an essential role in the chemical and biological processes that characterize these systems. As important primary producers in wetlands, algae convert solar energy and dissolved nutrients into plant cells. In that process, they generate oxygen, raise the pH of the water, and decrease the concentration of carbon dioxide. During the night, algae consume oxygen when they undergo respiration, and they can cause oxygen depletion (anoxia) in parts of a wetland if the algal mats are large. Algae are a food source for many invertebrates, in particular zooplankton, crayfish, snails, and larval flies. Some fish also feed on algae, especially in the summer months when aquatic insects may be less abundant.

Algae are a source of dissolved organic material (dissolved organic carbon, for example) in wetlands. If they are growing on the wetland bottom, algae may be a sink for phosphorus because the algae tend to absorb substantial amounts of phosphorus directly from the sediments before it can be released to the overlying wetland water column. In alkaline systems with a pH greater than 7.4, such as those found in wetlands augmented with groundwater, algae contribute to sediment formation as they precipitate calcium from the augmentation water into encrusting deposits of calcium carbonate. Algae growing on plant stems and leaf surfaces may accelerate the breakdown of those plants as they die and decay, and speed up the return of dissolved nutrients and organic materials to the wetland ecosystem.

Communities of Aquatic Plants

The communities of aquatic plants that populate wetlands give them much of their distinctive character and appearance, although the various wetland communities described in this section can be present in one or several different wetland systems. For example, forested wetland communities are present in Palustrine, Lacustrine, and Riverine System wetlands. Likewise, emergent wetland communities are present in both Palustrine and Lacustrine System wetlands.

Aquatic plants are a relatively small group of vascular plants adapted to survive and flourish under conditions that characterize wetlands: intermittent flooding of variable duration, a range of water depths, and saturated, oxygen- depleted soils. The following are some of the most obvious adaptations of aquatic plants:

- Buttressed tree trunks of cypress, water tupelo, and swamp black gum provide additional support in the water.
- Modified root systems (such as cypress knees) extend above ground to increase the opportunity for oxygen uptake.
- Floating leaves have a thickened cuticle to prevent water absorption and maximize exposure to sunlight.
- Floating stems filled with air spaces allow plants to root in shallow water and float at the surface.
- Prolonged seed viability allows germination to be postponed until favorable hydrologic conditions occur.
- Spongy tissue in leaves, roots, and stems provides buoyancy and an oxygen reservoir.

Ferns and colorful lichens growing in forested wetlands. Photographer credit:Michael Hancock, Southwest Florida Water Management District.

Bromeliads such as the quill-leaf airplant (Tillandsia fasciculata) add color to forested wetlands in spring and early summer. Photographer credit: Paul Fellers, Lake Region Audubon Society.

Aquatic plants, especially submersed and emergent species, provide food and habitat for invertebrate populations, which in turn support fish, birds, and other predators in the food web. The decay and accumulation of aquatic vegetation contribute to the internal cycling of nutrients in wetlands, and the buildup of organic material on the wetland bottom.

Forested Wetlands

Trees are the dominant plants in forested wetlands. Common tree species include cypress and several hardwoods such as sweet bay, sweet gum, elm, oak, and red maple. Community composition in forested wetlands is dependent on patterns of seasonal flooding and small differences in the surface elevation of the wetland bottom.

Cypress strands in riverine flood plains that have some water flow support bald cypress (*Taxodium distichum*), whereas isolated still-water cypress domes are most often dominated by pond cypress (*Taxodium ascendens*). The largest bald cypress tree in the United States can be found in western Seminole County, and is estimated to be 3,500 years old. The pond cypress trees that grow in isolated wetlands are often shorter at the wetland edge than in the middle, giving the wetlands a "dome-like" profile. This pattern occurs because the conditions for growth, primarily the long hydroperiod, are much better in the center of the dome as opposed to the edges. Cypress trees are called deciduous conifers, because they lose their needles each winter and regrow them in the spring. In addition to cypress, some of the most common trees in forested wetlands in central Florida are cabbage palm (*Sabal palmetto*), dwarf palmetto (*Sabal minor*), red maple (*Acer rubrum*), sweet gum (*Liquidambar styraciflua*), sweet bay magnolia (*Magnolia virginiana*), swamp bay (*Persea palustris*), and loblolly bay (*Gordonia lasianthus*). Swamp laurel oak (*Quercus laurifolia*) is one of the most flood tolerant of the oaks, and grows in areas that are flooded for as much as half of the growing season. Like cypress, trees in the genus *Nyssa* require periodic drought for germination. The most common species are swamp tupelo (*Nyssa sylvatica* var. *biflora*) and water tupelo (*Nyssa aquatica*). Slash pine (*Pinus elliottii*) is found in some Florida cypress domes and swamps. Pond pine (*Pinus serotina*) is found at the edges of bay swamps that burn every 15 to 20 years, because the cones require fire to open and germinate.

Other plants are commonly found in the forested wetlands of central Florida because of the vertical structure and basal hummocks provided by the trees themselves. Epiphytes (or "air plants") grow on the trees in wetlands, but are not parasitic because they use the trees only as a surface for attachment. They also take advantage of the condensation and rainfall that collects on the trees. Examples of epiphytes in swamps are orchids, bromeliads, lichens, mosses, and some species of ferns. Some of the richest communities of lichens are in cypress wetlands, where they can add bright color, and some species are particular to only one species of tree. Bromeliads such as *Tillandsia* also add bright points of color on trees and shrubs when the flowers are present. More than 20 species of vines often can be found growing on trees and other woody plants in swamps and wet woodlands, as well as along the perimeters of freshwater marshes and at the edges of lakes. Native vines include climbing hempweed (*Mikania scandens*), bamboo vine (*Smilax laurifolia*), saw greenbrier (*Smilax bono-nox*), grapevine (*Vitis* spp.), poison ivy (*Toxicodendron radicans*), and rattan vine (*Berchemia scandens*). Skunk vine (*Paederia foetida*) is an invasive plant from Asia that is now found throughout the southeastern United States, including Florida, where it appears to prefer sunny flood plains and bottom lands.

Ground-cover plants are often sparse in forested wetlands, due to prolonged inundation and because the canopy prevents light penetration. Common ground-cover species include swamp fern (*Blechnum serrulatum*), cinnamon fern (*Osmunda cinnamomea*), royal fern (*Osmunda regalis*), and chainfern (*Woodwardia* spp.). In wetlands, aquatic mosses are far less abundant than vascular plants. Aquatic mosses are present primarily in wetlands of the Riverine System and in permanently flooded and intermittently exposed parts of some wetlands in the Lacustrine System. The most common genera include *Sphagnum, Fissidens, Drepanocladus,* and *Fontinalis*.

Scrub-Shrub Wetlands

The dense, low-growing woody vegetation in scrub-shrub wetlands is, by definition, less than about 20 ft tall. This vegetation includes both true shrubs that never attain a greater height, and young trees of other species that never attain their maximum height (120 ft for some species) due to the harsh conditions. A variety of herbaceous plants also are present in scrub-shrub wetlands, and are generally indicative of a wetland area that is undergoing environmental change due to some type of disturbance, such as increased or decreased water flow, recent fire, or increased silt deposits from surrounding areas that have been clear cut. Some scrub-shrub wetlands are a successional stage that will ultimately become a forested wetland, whereas other scrub- shrub wetlands are stable communities. Common scrub-shrub plants include swamp honeysuckle (*Rhododendron vicosum*), elderberry (*Sanbucus nigra canadensis*), willow (*Salix* sp.), primrose willow (*Ludwigia peruviana*)**,** buttonbush (*Cephalanthus occidentalis*), dahoon holly (*Ilex cassine*), gallberry (*Ilex glabra*), Virginia willow (*Itea virginica*), and wax myrtle (*Myrica cerifera*). Walter's viburnum (*Viburnum obovatum*) is a colonial shrub with a much-branched trunk that forms a dense tangle of arching trunks and branches along seasonally inundated shallow stream banks, sloughs, hydric hammocks, and river flood plains. Many shrub species also are present in forested wetlands; for example, fetterbush (*Lyonia lucida*) is very common in Florida swamps. An invasive plant of concern that crowds out native species in scrub-shrub wetlands is Brazilian pepper (*Schinus terebinthefolius*).

Emergent Wetlands

Emergent wetlands such as marshes and wet prairies have erect, rooted, herbaceous (non-woody) vegetation during most of the growing season in most years. These wetlands support a wide variety of grassy and broad-leaved herbaceous plants that typically extend above the wetland water surface. A variety of emergent marshes and wet prairies are present in central Florida, and they often derive their names from the dominant plants or plant associations found in them. For example, a "maidencane marsh" is named after the dominant maiden- cane grass (*Panicum hemitomon),* whereas a "flag marsh" is populated by fire flag (*Thalia geniculata*) and other plants with flag-shaped leaves. Although marshes may have one or two dominant plants, other plant species commonly are present, adding to the characteristic diversity of many marsh communities. Marshes in central Florida also can be grouped into systems that tend to be distributed most frequently in particular geographic areas (Kushlan, 1990). They include flat- woods marshes, highlands marshes, St. Johns River marshes, and Kissimmee River marshes. These marsh systems may vary somewhat in their predominant plant associations. Paynes Prairie is a large highlands marsh in Alachua County that includes a mosaic of saw grass, water lily, and maidencane marshes (Feature F—Paynes Prairie—A Dynamic Highlands Marsh Ecosystem).

Freshwater emergent marshes typically have zones of vegetation that are distributed across a gradient of water depths. Floating and submersed species (see Pond and Aquatic Bed Wetlands) grow in the wetland center where water is deepest and the hydroperiod may be 9 months or more. Common floating plants include duckweed (*Lemna minor*) and salvinia (*Salvinia rotundifolia*), whereas common submersed plants include bladderworts (*Utricularia* spp.) and pondweeds (*Potomogeton* spp.). Moving away from the wetland center, the water typically becomes shallower and the hydroperiod becomes shorter. Some of the most commonly found emergent plants at shallower depths are maidencane (*Panicum hemitomon*), pickerelweed (*Pontederia cordata*), lemon bacopa (*Bacopa caroliniana*), arrowheads (*Sagittaria* spp.), beakrushes (*Rhynchospora* spp.), sedges (*Carex* spp.) and spikerushes (*Eleocharis* spp.). Along the wetland edges, in the zone transitional to uplands, the ground may be flooded rarely and in many wetlands the ground is moist, but never inundated.

Species commonly found along the wetland edge include blue maidencane (*Amphicarpum muhlenbergianum*), spadeleaf (*Centella asiatica*), Baldwin's spikerush (*Elocharis baldwinii*), dog fennel (*Eupatorium* spp.) and St. Johns wort (*Hypericum* spp.).

Marsh beggar-tick (Bidens mitis) in bloom in a wet prairie in Alachua County. Photographer credit: Michael Hancock, Southwest Florida Water Management District.

Marshes with short hydroperiods, such as flatwoods marshes, have patterns of seasonal plant dominance in addition to spatial dominance. For example, maidencane and floating hearts are dominant in spring, and beakrush and bald rush become more abundant later in the year (Kushlan, 1990). Other seasonal vegetation patterns directly related to hydrology include flowering phenology (flower blooming and other regularly recurring biological phenomena that are influenced by climate), whereby shorter emergent species bloom in early spring when the water is shallow, and taller emergent species flower in summer and fall when water is deeper.

Wet prairies are a special type of emergent wetland that are flooded less frequently than any other type of Florida marsh, with a typical hydroperiod of only 50–100 days per year (Duever, 1997). The soils in wet prairies are sandy, and peat formation is curtailed by their short period of inundation. In wet prairies, the need for adaptation to widely fluctuating hydrologic conditions is especially pronounced, and the plant species that populate these prairies must have ample tolerance for both flooding and drying. For example, species with shallow root systems, such as St. Johns wort, die when the prairies dry out but readily reseed once water returns (Kushlan, 1990). Wet prairies have a short hydroperiod, and because they support both aquatic and upland species at different times of the year, and wet prairies can be extremely diverse communities. Dominant grasses include bluestems (*Andropogon* spp.), blue maidencane (*Amphicarpum muhlenbergianum*), carpetgrass (*Axonopus* spp.), maidencane (*Panicum hemitomon*), whitetop sedge (*Dichromena colorata*), and wiregrass (*Aristida stricta*). Other common (and colorful) plants include blue-eyed grass (*Sisyrinchium nashii*), hatpins (*Eriocaulon compressum*), meadow beauty (*Rhexia* spp.), and yellow-eyed grass (*Xyris* spp.). Wet prairies are maintained as grasslands without trees or even large shrubs by periodic fires, usually at 1- to 5-year intervals. The invasive species melaleuca (*Melaleuca quinquenervia*) is a tree that can thrive in wet prairies in spite of their characteristic hydroperiod, and melaleuca control is required for effective wetland management. More than half of the parks and preserves in central Florida have patches of wet prairie, and prime examples are in the Kissimmee Prairie Preserve State Park and Myakka River State Park (Duever, 1997).

Brazilian pepper (Schinus terebinthefoious). Photographer credit: Kim Haag, U.S. Geological Survey.

Yellow-eyed grass (Xyris caroliniana). Photographer credit: Kim Haag, U.S. Geological Survey.

F. PAYNES PRAIRIE—A DYNAMIC HIGHLANDS MARSH ECOSYSTEM

Paynes Prairie is a unique highlands marsh ecosystem that covers about 21,000 acres and presently includes the largest freshwater marsh and wet prairie in north-central Florida (Florida Department of Environmental Protection, 2002). This part of central Florida is characterized by karst topography with associated uplands, shallow lakes, prairies, and numerous large sinkholes.

Many marshes and lakes in the area are hydrologically unstable because, over time, solution features form and wetlands can be drained, or previously functional drainages become blocked and surface depressions can reflood (Kushlan, 1990). The dynamic drainage patterns characteristic of the region have had substantial consequences for the Paynes Prairie ecosystem, most notably an extraordinarily wide range of water levels in historical times.

History and Hydrology

Paynes Prairie is perched above a 6-ft layer of sandy clay. This relatively impermeable surficial layer was deposited by an ancient surface-water body flowing over the more permeable sands and limestone characteristic of most of the Florida peninsula (Myers and Ewel, 1990). Today, Paynes Prairie is a large highland marsh in Alachua County, but in the 1600s, the largest cattle ranch in Spanish Florida, named La Chua, was based at the prairie. When William Bartram visited the area in 1774, he described the basin as dry grassland called the Alachua Savannah (Myers and Ewel, 1990). The area was occupied by the Seminole Indians in the early 1 800s, and the modern name is thought to be derived from a Seminole Chief named King Payne. The major drainage feature within the prairie, Alachua Sink, became plugged in the early 1870s. The basin filled with water and developed into Alachua Lake, which supported steamboat operations. By 1891, the lake water level began to decline, and within 2 years a large marsh was formed (Myers and Ewel, 1990). In the 1900s, cattle operations began on the prairie, but the State ultimately determined that the habitat was worthy of preservation, and in 1971, Paynes Prairie became the first State preserve in Florida.

Similar highland marshes of substantial size are found throughout central Florida, lthough many have been drained for agricultural purposes (Kushlan, 1990). The existence of these marshes is attributable to the alternating effects of compaction of surface sediments that retard water loss and the formation of solution features that drain surface water into the aquifer.

Vegetation and Wildlife

There are at least 20 distinct biological communities in Paynes Prairie. Four hundred and twenty-two plant species in 108 families have been identified from the deep water marshes, shallow wet prairies, and pasture lands (Easterday, 1982; Patton and Judd, 1986). Fluctuations in rainfall have caused variations in the aquatic and upland vegetation present. For example, studies by Jacobs and others (2002) indicated that maidencane (*Panicum hemitomon*) and swamp smartweed (*Polygonum hydropiperoides*) were common in wet prairies when rainfall was near average, but during dry periods mock bishop's weed (*Ptilimnium capillaceum*), dog fennel (*Eupatorium capillifolium*), and other plants tolerant of dry conditions became widespread. The ecosystem is vulnerable to invasion by non-native plants. The variety of habitat types provides a rich matrix for wildlife, including alligators, bison, wild horses, and over 270 species of birds. The proximity of a busy State highway, and the associated wildlife mortality, has yielded a wealth of data on resident wildlife as chronicled by observations of wildlife killed in collisions with motor vehicles (Smith and Dodd, 2003).

Protection and Management

Many small highland marshes in central Florida have been drained for farming or grazing, whereas others have been mined for peat (Kushlan, 1990). Paynes Prairie is one of the few large highland marshes that is protected. In addition to being the first State preserve, Paynes Prairie was designated as a National Natural Landmark by the U.S. Department of the Interior in 1974, and all waters within the preservation area are designated as Outstanding Florida Waters.

Above: Paynes Prairie. Photographer credit: Margaret Glenn, Institute of Food and Agricultural Sciences, University of Florida.

Wild horses graze on wet pastures at Paynes Prairie. Photographer credit: Michael Hancock, Southwest Florida Water Management District

An Outstanding Florida Water is a water body designated as being worthy of special protection because of its natural attributes. This special designation is intended to protect existing good water quality. Surface waters are susceptible to contamination by excess nutrients associated with development (Dugger, 1976). Paynes Prairie Preserve State Park is designated as a multiple-use feature designed to protect the water quality of the area, preserve the flood storage capacity of the Prairie Creek system, and provide natural resource-based public outdoor recreation and other related uses (Florida Department of Environmental Protection, 2002). Management goals include controlling water depth and flooding frequency so that they imitate the conditions that existed in the late 1700s when William Bartram first visited the site. An alternate management strategy has been suggested that would incorporate manipulation of water levels over a wider range in 30- to 50-year cycles (White, 1974).

Selected References about Paynes Prairie

Dugger, K. R. (1976). A management model for Paynes Prairie: Gainesville, University of Florida, *M.S. thesis,* 158 p.

Easterday, J. C. (1982). A flora of Paynes Prairie Basin and Alachua Sink Hammock: Gainesville, University of Florida, *M.S. thesis,* 139 p.

Florida Department of Environmental Protection. (2002). Paynes Prairie Preserve State Park Unit Management Plan: Tallahassee, Fla., 8 p.

Gottgens, J. F. & Montague, C. L. (1988). Categorized bibliography of the Paynes Prairie Basin, Florida: Palatka, Fla., St. Johns River Water Management District, Special Publication SJ 88-SP3, 30 p.

Jacobs, J. J., Mergelsberg, S. L., Lopera, A. F. & Myers, D. A. (2002). *Evapotranspiration from a wet prairie wetland under drought conditions: Paynes Prairie Preserve,* Florida, USA: Wetlands, v. *22,* no. 2, p. 374-385.

Kushlan, J. A. (1990). Freshwater marshes, *in* Myers, R. L. & Ewel, J. J., eds., *The ecosystems of Florida: Gainesville,* University Presses of Florida, p. 324-363.

Myers, R. L. & Ewel, J. J., eds., (1990). *The ecosystems of Florida: Gainesville,* University Presses of Florida, 765 p.

Patton, J. C. & Judd, W. S. (1986). Vascular flora of Paynes Prairie State Preserve: Gainesville, University of Florida, *M.S. thesis,* 160 p.

Paynes Prairie Preserve, accessed January 12, (2007). at http:// www. floridastateparks. org/paynesprairie.

St. Johns River Water Management District (2003). Orange Creek Basin, accessed January 12, 2007, at http://www. sjrwmd. com.

Smith, L. L. & Dodd, C. K. (2003). Wildlife mortality on U. S. Highway 441 across Paynes Prairie, Alachua County, Florida: Florida Scientist, v. *66,* no. 2, p. 128-140.

White, L. D. (1974). *Ecosystem analysis of Paynes Prairie: Gainesville,* University of Florida, School of Forest Resources and Conservation Research Report No. 24, 500 p.

Pond and Aquatic Bed Wetlands

Pond and aquatic bed wetlands are dominated by plants that grow on or below the water surface during much of the growing season in most years and, therefore, require regularly and semi-permanently flooded wetland habitat. The plants may be attached to the wetland bottom, or they may be unattached and float on the surface. Common submersed species include coontail (Ceratophyllum demersum), milfoil (*Myriophyl lum* spp.), bladderworts (*Utricularia* spp.), and naiad (*Najas* spp.). Rooted species that have floating leaves include water lilies (*Nymphaea* spp.), floating-leaf pondweed (*Potamogeton natans*), and water shield (*Brasenia schreberi*). Common species that float freely on the wetland water surface and are not rooted include duckweed (*Lemna* spp.), giant duckweed (*Spirodela* spp.), mosquito fern (*Azolla* spp.), and water-meal (*Wolffia* spp.). Invasive floating aquatic plants of particular concern include water hyacinth (*Eicchornia crassipes*) and water lettuce (*Pistia stratiotes*), because they tend to crowd out native vegetation in wetlands where they become established. Hydrilla (*Hydrilla verticillata*) is a submersed invasive species of concern.

Aquatic Insects and other Invertebrates

The aquatic insects and other invertebrates inhabiting submersed and emergent aquatic plant beds can be abundant, and they serve as an important food source for many other organisms in the food web of central Florida wetlands. Small side swimmers (Amphipoda) feed on fragments of partially decayed plant material (detritus), which collects in a thin film on submersed plant leaves and stems. Seed shrimp (Ostracoda) are tiny benthic invertebrates that swim among the submersed aquatic plants in wetlands and eat detritus and plant material such as algae. Amphipods and ostracods are primary consumers (eating plant material) that provide food for the numerous larger insects and invertebrate predators found in wetlands. Crayfish (*Procambarus* sp.) and glass shrimp (*Palaemonetes* sp.) are widespread and feed on decaying plants materials, many of which support a rich microbial layer that has high nutritional value.

Floating and emergent wetland plants.
Photographer credit: Kim Haag, U.S. Geological Survey.

Crayfish (Procambarus sp.) are omnivorous consumers in wetlands where they feed on a variety of insects, worms, tadpoles, dead organisms, and vegetation. Photographer credit: Laura Line, Water & Air Research, Inc.

Snails and mollusks are found in wetlands with some groundwater or surface-water inflow, because the pH and the calcium carbonate concentration are high enough in those wetlands to allow for shell formation. Common wetland snails include the pouch snail (*Physella* sp.), ash gyro (*Gyraulus parvus*), marsh rams-horn (*Planorbella trivolvis*), banded mystery snail (*Viviparous georgianus*), and the Florida apple snail (*Pomacea paludosa*). The native apple snail is the largest snail in North America, and clusters of its large white eggs can be seen above the water line on emergent vegetation in April and May (U.S. Geological Survey, 2009b). Small mollusks (which have a pair of shells) commonly found in wetlands include the Asiatic clam (*Corbicula fluminea*) and fingernail clams (*Musculium* spp., *Sphaerium* spp.). Freshwater limpets (Ancylidae), which have a single thin shell, are found in some wetlands with a relatively low pH.

Many mayflies (Ephemeroptera) are filter feeders or collectors who remove organic material from plant surfaces and from the water column. Beetles (Coleoptera) are mostly predators or omnivores whose adults live on the water surface and on plant surfaces, and whose larval stages are submerged during their development. Adults in this abundant group are well adapted to the low-oxygen concentrations characteristic of most central Florida isolated wetlands because they use atmospheric sources of oxygen. True bugs (Hemiptera) are not as numerous in many wetlands as the beetles, but are often represented by many different species, including water scorpions, water striders, water boatmen, and the giant water bug. Dragonflies and damselflies (Odonata) are predators both as aquatic nymphs and as flying adults in and around wetlands. Odonates are especially common in wetlands with submersed aquatic vegetation such as bladderworts (*Utricularia* spp.), because the nymphs can prey on other invertebrates that cling to the feathery leaflets. Larval flies (Diptera), especially midges (Chironomidae) and mosquitoes (Culicidae), are well adapted to living in the low dissolved-oxygen environments in Florida wetlands. For example, midge larvae use red hemo-globin-like pigments to increase their ability to absorb oxygen.

Wetland hydrology affects wetland insects and other invertebrates in numerous direct and indirect ways (Figure 25).

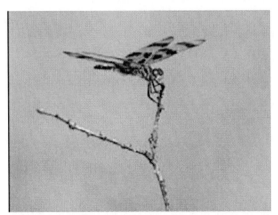

The dragonfly Celithemis eponia, commonly known as the Halloween pennant for the bright orange and yellow coloring on its wings, is a frequent visitor to central Florida wetlands. Photographer credit: Michael Hancock, Southwest Florida Water Management District.

These effects differ in magnitude and relative importance in isolated wetlands compared to riverine wetlands or fringing wetlands. For example, a flood pulse causes rapid and sudden input of sediment and nutrients to flood-plain wetlands when a river overflows its channel and the wetlands are inundated. However, rainfall and associated runoff to isolated wetlands may result in a more gradual influx of nutrients, and flooding following rainfall (which is typically low in nutrients) may actually dilute nutrient concentrations in isolated wetlands. Aquatic invertebrate populations tend to be larger in wetlands without fish, or in wetlands with submersed and emergent vegetation, such as marshes, where fish cannot easily find them. Moreover, wetlands that have some surface-water connection to other nearby wetlands may have more diverse amphibian and fish populations because of the increased opportunity for recolonization after a dry period. However, fish predation can reduce invertebrate populations substantially, and may reduce wetland bird populations through its impact on their invertebrate food supply (Kushlan, 1990).

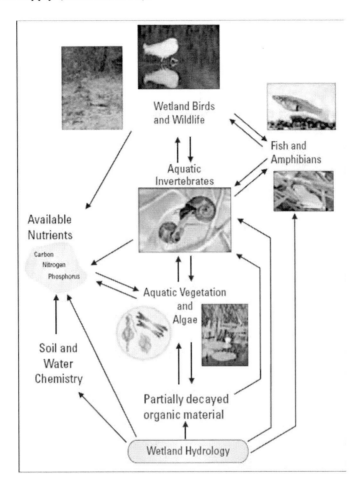

Figure 25. Effects of hydrology on wetland invertebrates and other biota (right)

Mosquito fish (Gambusia affinis) may be abundant in isolated wetlands, where they feed on mosquito larvae and other small invertebrates. Photographer credit: Robert McDowall.

Fish, Amphibians, and Reptiles

Fish are typically small in isolated depression wetlands because these wetlands are generally shallow systems. Nearly all fish in isolated wetlands in central Florida are less than 6 in. long, and if no deep holes are present to act as a refuge where standing water remains even during seasonal drought conditions the majority of fish are less than 3 in. long (Main and others, 2007). Fish in isolated wetlands are adapted to a range of conditions that include low pH, low specific conductance (20–460 µS/cm), and low dissolved oxygen concentrations (0.5–4.5 mg/L). Many live near the water surface, where they can take advantage of the thin film of oxygen-rich water. The eastern mosquitofish (*Gambusia affinis*) is one of the most abundant fish species in isolated Florida wetlands. Other common species include the redfaced topminnow (*Fundulus cingulatus*), least killifish (*Heterandria formosa*), pygmy killifish (*Leptolucania ommata*), Everglades pygmy sunfish (*Elassoma evergladei*), and the blue spotted sunfish (*Enneacanthus gloriosus*). When a connection develops between isolated freshwater wetlands and other surface-water bodies, there is an opportunity for fish to repopulate wetlands that have experienced seasonal drying and lost their fish populations.

Flood-plain wetlands provide habitat for larger fish, which may use wetlands during some or all of their life cycles. Fish habitats are more diverse in flood-plain wetlands than in isolated depression wetlands because the deposition and erosion of sediments cause meandering of shallow channels on the flood plain that create temporary wetlands. Connections with the main river channel open and close periodically and fish have opportunities to return to the main channel when flood-plain wetlands dry up seasonally. Some fish use flood-plain wetlands to complete their lifecycle, primarily for spawning and as nursery areas for juvenile fish. Fish spawning requires slow moving or still water, which is characteristic of flood-plain wetlands. Other fish move into flood-plain wetlands, whenever they are flooded, to exploit rich-feeding areas. Invertebrates tend to be abundant in flood-plain wetlands because of the presence of decaying plant material, algae, and other food sources. Common groups of fish in flood-plain wetlands include many species that live in the rivers themselves such as sunfish (*Lepomis* spp.), bass (*Micropterus* spp.), and minnows (*Notropis* spp.)

Redear sunfish (Lepomis microlophus) live in shallow vegetated areas of flood-plain wetlands and feed on invertebrates. Photographer credit: Noel Burkhead ©, U.S. Geological Survey. Published with permission.

Wetlands along lake margins are commonly used by large fish for spawning and nesting. These wetlands contain aquatic plants that conceal newly hatched juvenile fish, and the shallow water limits the size of aquatic predators. Small fish species inhabit lake-margin wetlands for the same reasons. The abundant invertebrates that live in these wetlands provide a rich food supply for fish regardless of their life history stage. Common fish species in lake-margin wetlands include crappie (*Pomoxis nigromaculatus*), bluegill (*Lepomis macrochirus*),red ear sunfish (Lepomis microlophus), and largemouth bass (*Micropterus salmoides*).

Most of the fish in central Florida wetlands are omnivorous and live off a diet of algae, plant material, insects, and other invertebrates; mosquito larvae are a common source of food. Because of size constraints, very few fish species consume other fish. The small size of most wetland fish make them ideal prey for numerous animals, including large aquatic insects such as giant water bugs (Belostomatidae), larger fishes like the largemouth bass, amphibians such as the bullfrog (*Rana catesbeiana*), reptiles like the American alligator (*Alligator mississippiensis*), birds such as the snowy egret (*Egretta thula*), and mammals like the racoon (*Procyon lotor*).

Central Florida wetlands contain many amphibians and reptiles, primarily frogs, salamanders, alligators, turtles, and water snakes. Amphibians are most numerous in isolated wetlands that dry out seasonally and do not have large fish, which would otherwise prey on them. Frogs and salamanders live entirely in the water during their egg and larval stages, whereas adult amphibians spend part of the time in nearby upland habitats (Feature G—Amphibians as Bioindicators in Wetlands). This life-history aspect is one important reason to protect upland areas around wetlands (wetland buffer zones), which enable the free movement of amphibians between habitats.

G. AMPHIBIANS AS BIOINDICATORS IN WETLANDS

Large and diverse communities of amphibians (frogs and toads) are commonly found in and around central Florida wetlands, and recent interest has developed in using amphibians as bioindicators of wetland condition. Bioindicators are living organisms that are sensitive to changes within ecosystems such as wetlands.

Approaches using amphibian bioindicators may involve individual indicator species, entire species assemblages, or comprehensive indicator communities whose presence, numbers, and conditions are indicative of a particular set of environmental conditions (Adamus, 1996). Several factors have led to the recent interest in using amphibians as bio-indicators of wetland condition. They include the sensitivity of amphibians to changes in water quality and habitat modification in wetlands, and the documented worldwide decline in amphibian populations associated with wetlands (Stuart and others, 2004). A number of studies indicate that amphibians may be ideal bioindicators of wetland condition because factors that negatively affect amphibian populations also affect overall wetland condition.

Why Are Amphibians Useful Bioindicators?

Amphibians are widespread in central Florida and are found in many different types of wetlands. They have a two- stage life cycle, whereby they breed and spend their larval stages in aquatic habitats and then move to nearby upland habitats as adults. Therefore, they are potential indicators of environmental disturbance in wetlands and associated uplands (Delis and others, 1996; Mushinsky and others, 2004). Because amphibians have relatively short life cycles, and can respond to stress within a short time, scientists can quickly acquire and analyze monitoring data and determine the occurrence of ecosystem stressors (Rapport, 1992).

Amphibian skin is highly permeable, and this permeability allows them to absorb moisture through their skin. Therefore, water-borne substances can move relatively freely into their bodies, making them sensitive to contaminants in water, soil, and air (Lehitinen and others, 1999). After absorption, many toxic compounds are accumulated and stored in amphibian fatty tissue, so they can be efficiently sampled.

Amphibians are adapted to survive normal fluctuations in wetland hydroperiods. Because many central Florida wetlands are seasonally dry, amphibians can serve as year- round (instead of seasonal) indicators to help estimate the average length of the wetland inundation period. For example, the average hydroperiod of a wet prairie wetland in central Florida is 150 to 200 days per year (CH$_2$M Hill, 1996). If the hydroperiod length is decreased or increased, then amphibian populations may fluctuate in size (Guzy and others, 2006). By estimating the average population size over several years at a particular wetland, it is possible to determine when disturbance has caused changes in bioindicator species populations. This is possible by categorizing wetlands based on amphibian reproductive success variables (Mushinsky and others, 2004), and using them in a "reference conditioning approach" (Snodgrass and others, 2000). Reference conditioning is an assessment technique that compares a site with substantial human disturbance to a similar site with minimal disturbance.

A further advantage of using amphibians as bioindicators is that many frogs and toads can be identified without physically capturing them. Many frogs and toads have their own distinctive and characteristic call or chorus. By using amphibian chorus calls, species can be identified reliably in an area (Southwest Florida Amphibian Monitoring Network, 2009). Therefore, a wetland can be characterized without sacrificing any animals.

What Factors Contribute to Amphibian Declines?

There are several factors that may contribute to a decline in amphibian populations. The most prominent factor is loss and fragmentation of habitat (Dodd and Smith, 2003). Studies have directly related amphibian declines to land-use disturbances that range from wetland modification to wetland elimination (Lehitinen and others, 1999). Amphibian colonization of created (mitigation) wetlands is often slow because amphibians often preferentially return to their original breeding ground, even if newly excavated or impounded wetlands are nearby (Pechmann and others, 2001).

PRIMER FACTS

A further advantage of using amphibians as bioindicators is that many frogs and toads can be identified without physically capturing them. Many frogs and toads have their own distinctive and characteristic call or chorus. By using amphibian chorus calls, species can be identified reliably in an area (Southwest Florida Amphibian Monitoring Network, 2009). Therefore, a wetland can be characterized without sacrificing any animals.

The squirrel tree frog (Hyla squirella) is found in marshes, mixed hardwood swamps, and cypress swamps. Photographer credit: Michael Hancock, Southwest Florida Water Management District.

Changes in hydrology and hydroperiod can affect the reproductive success rate in amphibians (Snodgrass and others, 2000; Means and Means, 2008). If the inundation period is decreased or eliminated due to drainage, then larval amphibians will not metamorphose into adults, reducing the reproductive success rate substantially. Alternatively, if the wetland hydroperiod is increased due to prolonged flooding or wetland augmentation and fish colonize the wetlands, then the reproductive success rate also can decrease because of fish predation (Snodgrass and others, 2000).

Amphibians can act as sentinel species that are affected early or quickly by various types of chemical contamination in wetlands. Industrial and agricultural chemicals, including pesticides, may cause amphibian deformities (Power and others, 1989). Increases in the incidence of pathogens and parasites may be symptomatic of amphibians weakened or stressed by factors affecting wetlands. Disease reduces reproductive success, and infected amphibians often develop deformities (Blaustein and Johnson, 2003a). However, when using amphibians as bioindicators, it is necessary to discriminate between factors directly related to wetland condition and other factors that have a negative effect on amphibian populations but are not directly related to wetland condition. For example, predation and competition by introduced species, such as the Cuban tree frog (*Osteopilus septentrionalis),* can reduce amphibian populations (Gamradt and Kats, 1996), but they are not indicative of wetland condition. Ultraviolet exposure (UV–B), which has increased in intensity worldwide because of the thinning ozone layer, can cause deformities in tadpoles (Blaustein and Johnson, 2003b), lowering reproductive success and increasing predation.

Assessing wetlands using bioindicators such as amphibians is a useful technique because it allows researchers to determine the condition of the entire system using a single method. Common amphibian characteristics, such as their small size, two-stage life cycle, susceptibility to contaminants, and ease of detection without being collected, make amphibians a potentially useful indicator species assemblage for central Florida wetlands (Mushinsky and others, 2004).

The barking tree frog (Hyla gratiosa) breeds in wetlands and shallow ponds from March to August. Photographer credit: Henry R. Mushinsky, University of South Florida.

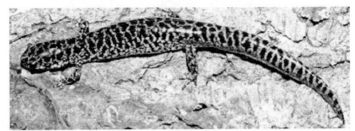

Ambystoma cingulatum, the flatwoods salamander, is a Federally Threatened amphibian species. It is found in seasonally wet pine flatwoods that support long leaf pine, slash pine, and wiregrass, and it breeds in marshy ponds, borrow pits, and swamps. Photographer credit: Jamie Barichivich, U.S. Geological Survey.

Selected References about Amphibians in Wetland

Adamus, P. R. (1996). *Bio-indicators for assessing ecological integrity of prairie wetlands: Corvallis, Ore., U. S. Environmental Protection Agency,* National Health and Environmental Effects Research Laboratory.

Blaustein, A. R. & Johnson, P. T. J. (2003a). *Explaining frog deformities: Scientific American,* v. *288*, p. 60-65.

Blaustein, A. R. & Johnson, P. T. J. (2003b). *The complexity of deformed amphibians: Frontiers in Ecology and the Environment,* v. *1*, p. 87-94.

CH$_2$M Hill, (1996). Wetland impact mitigation and planning— Level cost estimating procedures: Gainesville, Fla., *Technical Memorandum* E. 1 . F, 196 p.

Delis, P. R., Mushinsky, H. R. & McCoy, E. D. (1996). *Decline of some west-central Florida anuran populations in response to habitat degradation: Biodiversity and Conservation,* v. *5*, p. 1579-1595.

Dodd, C. K. & Smith, L. L. (2003). Habitat destruction and alteration: Historical trends and future prospects for amphibians, *in* Semlitsch, R., ed., Amphibian Conservation: Washington, D. C., Smithsonian Books, p. 94-112.

Freda, J. & Dunson, W. A. (1986). *Effects of low pH and other chemical variables on the local distribution of amphibians: Copeia,* v. *1986*, p. 1155-1162.

Gamradt, S. C. & Kats, L. B. (1996). *Effects of introduced mosquito fish and crayfish on California newts: Conservation Biology,* v. *10*, p. 1155-1162.

Guzy, J. C., Campbell, T. S. & Campbell, K. R. (2006). *Effects of hydrological alterations on frog and toad populations at Morris Bridge Well Field, Hillsborough County*, Florida: Biological Science, v. *69*, no. 4, p. 276-287.

Lehitinen, R. M., Galatowitsch, S. S. & Tester, J. R. (1999). *Consequences of habitat loss and fragmentation for wetland amphibian species: Wetlands*, v. *19*, p. 1-12.

Means, R. C. & Means, R. P. M. (2008). *Assessment of amphibian response to wetland augmentation—Final Report: Palatka, Fla.*, Technical report prepared for the St. Johns River Water Management District, 40 p.

Mushinsky, H. R., McCoy, E. D. & Gonzalez, S. M. (2004). *Measuring wetland health comparing vegetation and anurans as indicators: Brooksville*, Fla., Technical report prepared for the Southwest Florida Water Management District, 66 p.

Pechmann, J. H. K., Estes, R. A., Scott, D. E. & Gibbons, J. W. (2001). *Amphibian colonization and the use of ponds created for trial mitigation of wetland loss: Wetlands*, v. *21*, no. 1, p. 93-111.

Power, T., Clark, K. L., Harfenist, A. & Peakall, D. B. (1989). *A review and evaluation of the amphibian toxicological literature: Ottawa*, Canadian Wildlife Service Technical Report no. 61.

Rapport, D. J. (1992*). Evaluating ecosystem health: Journal of Aquatic Ecosystem Health*, v. *1*, p. 15-24.

Snodgrass, J. W., Bryan, A. L. & Burger, J. (2000). *Development of expectations of larval amphibian assemblage structure in southeastern depression wetlands: Ecological Applications*, v. *10*, p. 1219-1229.

Southwest Florida Amphibian Monitoring Network (2009). Frog Watch, accessed March 10, 2009, at http://www. frogwatch. net.

Stuart, S. N., Young, B. E., Chanson, J. S., Cox, N. A. & Boucher, T. M. (2004). *Status and trends of amphibian declines and extinctions worldwide: Science*, v. *306*, p. 1783-1786.

The harmless yellow rat snake (Elaphe obsolete quadrivittata) is often found near hardwood hammocks, swamps, marshes, and wet prairies. Photographer credit: Dan Duerr, U.S. Geological Survey.

Numerous reptiles, including snakes, turtles, and alligators, spend much of their lives in wetlands. The black swamp snake (*Seminatrix pygaea*) is found in and around wetlands, primarily cypress swamps, marshes, and lake edges, and feeds on tadpoles, worms, small fish, frogs, and salamanders. The eastern mud snake (*Farancia abacura*) is found in swamps and other wetlands around lakes and rivers, where it feeds primarily on aquatic salamanders. The Florida banded water snake (*Nerodia fasciata pictiventris*) prefers the shallow waters of swamps, marshes, ponds, lakes, streams, and rivers where it feeds on live or dead fish, frogs, and aquatic invertebrates. The Florida cottonmouth, or water moccasin (*Agkistrodon piscivorus conanti*), lives in marshes, swamps, sloughs, rivers, lakes, ponds, reservoirs, retention pools, canals, and roadside ditches. Cottonmouths, which are venomous, feed on fish, frogs, mice, rats, and other small mammals.

The brown water snake (Nerodia taxispilota), which is not poisonous, is commonly found in rivers, cypress strands, swamps, lakes, and ponds. Photographer credit: Dan Duerr, U.S. Geological Survey.

The American alligator (Alligator mississippiensis) feeds on fish, birds, and small mammals. Photographer credit: Michael Hancock, Southwest Florida Water Management District.

Many turtles eat aquatic plants, and sleep and hide among them as well. The markings on their shells help camouflage their presence, and the shells of some turtles even mimic aquatic plants. The common cooter (*Pseudemys floridana*) is a basking turtle that spends much of the day lying in the sun on logs or floating mats of vegetation in marshes, and along rivers, streams, lakes, ponds, ditches, and sloughs. Cooters, which feed on aquatic plants, will slide into the water at any sign of danger. Florida redbelly turtles (*Pseudemys nelsoni*) also feed on aquatic plants in marshes, ponds, and lakes. The common snapping turtle (*Chelydra serpentine*) typically inhabits marshes, ponds, and lakes where it spends most of its time underwater and feeds on fish and other small animals.

The American alligator (*Alligator mississippiensis*) has an important function in wetlands, because it can create localized depressions or wallows that can retain water during dry periods. These "holes" are often connected by one or a series of channels that they excavate. The channels are used by turtles, fish, and many organisms as refuges or hiding places. Moreover, the soil and bottom material that alligators move aside as they thrash about to create their wallows form raised areas that harbor shrub species adapted to growing on these mounds. Alligator movements maintain small areas of open water that are colonized by many invertebrates, which provide food for wading birds and mammals such as raccoons. Alligators are top predators in marshes and swamps and control the numbers and distribution of prey organisms.

Birds and Other Wildlife

The aquatic vegetation in wetlands supplies birds and other wildlife with food and foraging grounds, nest-building materials, nursery areas, and shelter from weather and predation. Wetlands provide the principal habitat for almost all waterfowl, and about 75 percent of all waterfowl breed only in wetlands. The variety of vegetation types and the gradient of water depths in wetlands create a large number of micro- habitats for birds. Many groups of birds have become adapted to exploit the variety of wetland microhabitats. Among the wading birds, obvious adaptations include leg length and bill shape. Some of the most common wading birds are the herons, egrets, bitterns, rails, ibis, limpkins (*Aramus guarauna*), and the roseate spoonbill (*Platalea ajaja*). Seasonal variations in water level, temperature, and dissolved oxygen (which affects the supply of prey species) can result in changing species composition throughout the year at an individual wetland. The wood stork (*Mycteria americana*), snail kite (*Rostrhamus sociabilis*), and the Florida sandhill crane (*Grus canadensis pratensis*) are protected species found in Florida marshes.

Numerous paddling birds frequent wetlands year-round or seasonally. Their webbed feet, rear leg placement, and water-resistant feathers are important adaptations for wetland environments. The American coot (*Fulica americana*) has lobed feet that enable it to run across the water surface before taking flight. Coots and purple gallinules (*Porphyrula martinica*) feed among the floating and emergent vegetation, especially on surface-dwelling insects such as beetles and true bugs. A number of ducks migrate to Florida in the winter, or stop on their way to more southern latitudes, including the blue-winged teal (*Anas discors*), green-winged teal *(Anas crecca),* northern pintail *(Anas acuta),* American widgeon (*Anas americana*), lesser scaup (*Aythya affinis*), and greater scaup (*Aythya marila*). The ring-necked duck (*Athya collaris*) is an especially common overwintering duck species along the St. Johns River.

Wetland birds are more abundant in emergent wetlands, compared to other wetland types. At least 16 species of wading birds are found in Florida emergent wetlands (Collopy and Jelks, 1989). Some wading birds nest in swamp forests and forage in the nearby marshes. Others, such as the Florida sandhill crane and the whooping crane (*Grus americana*) graze and forage on surrounding uplands but use aquatic plants to build their nests and typically build those nests in wet prairies, small marshes, and well-vegetated small ponds. A large study of sandhill cranes in DeSoto, Hardee, Highlands, Manatee, Okeechobee, Polk, and Sarasota Counties indicated that successful breeding is positively related to annual rainfall, because preferred nesting areas only hold water when there is adequate rainfall (Layne, 1983). Reduced hydroperiods in wetlands used for nesting by sandhill cranes, either from below-average rainfall or drainage projects, would likely have a negative effect on their populations.

The diet of the white ibis (Eudocimus albus), which feeds by probing with its long beak, includes small fish and reptiles, frogs, and aquatic insects. Photographer credit: Michael Hancock, Southwest Florida Water Management District.

PRIMER FACTS

Woodstorks (*Mycteria americana*) are a protected species found in Florida marshes and cypress wetlands. They feed by holding their bill open in the water until a fish or other prey is detected. Photographer credit: Michael Hancock, Southwest Florida Water Management District.

Birds can serve as indicators of wetland ecosystem integrity because they are often closely associated with a particular ecosystem or habitat type, and any changes in the ecosystem will be reflected in bird population changes (Batzer and others, 2006). For example, aquatic vegetation is vitally important to bird populations using wetlands; in particular, submersed vegetation provides a substrate for prey species. Shoreline vegetation, such as pickerelweed, maidencane, and other low grasses, allows wading and paddling birds to forage and move about in a sheltered microhabitat rich in invertebrates and hidden from many predators. The spread of cattails along the shores of wetlands may result in declines of wading and paddling birds because its dense growth makes bird movement difficult. Wetlands with disturbed edges or that receive excess nutrients are most susceptible to cattail invasion and spread. Water birds also can serve as indicators of wetland pollution by heavy metals, radionuclides, pesticides, and pharmaceuticals/personal care products present at levels that might otherwise go undetected (Feature E—Marsh Restoration—A Key to Improving Water Quality in Lake Apopka). This is because birds feed at higher levels of the food web, and the levels of contaminants present in wetlands are magnified as they move up through the food chain.

Mammals are not as abundant in Florida wetlands as they are in wetlands in other parts of the country (Kushlan, 1990). Many mammals that live in or near central Florida forage for food in wetlands where they find abundant prey. They generally spend the rest of their time in surrounding uplands, although wetland vegetation also provides protective cover. Some mammals commonly found in central Florida wetlands include the cotton mouse (*Peromyscus gossylinus*), marsh rice rat (*Oryzomys palustris*), golden mouse (*Ochrotomys nuttali*), meadow jumping mouse (*Zapus hudsonius*), marsh rabbit (*Sylvilagus palustris*), nutria (*Myocastor coypus*), and river otter (*Lutra canadensis*). The Florida water rat (*Neofiber alleni*) feeds on the roots and shoots of plants such as the cattail, and is a species that inhabits an ecological niche filled by the muskrat in marshes farther north. Other larger mammals that use wetlands occasionally include the white-tailed deer (*Odocoileus virginianus*) and raccoon (*Procyon lotor*).

Marsh rabbits (Sylvilagus palustris) are good swimmers that move about primarily at night and feed on marsh plants. Photographer credit: Michael Hancock, Southwest Florida Water Management District.

Two mammals in particular have the capacity to do harm to wetlands. The feral hog (*Sus scrofa*) is an invasive species that was brought to Florida from Spain in 1539. Foraging by these large mammals damages the community structure of wetlands by changing the vegetation species composition. For example, in the wet prairies of the Savannas Preserve State Park in St. Lucie County, an assessment of overturned ground from rooting activity by feral hogs indicated that almost 20 percent of the marsh periphery was damaged (Engeman and others, 2003). Because the park is home to a number of threatened and endangered plant species, damage of this magnitude is a substantial concern to park managers. The nutria is another invasive mammal species. Thirteen nutria were brought to the United States in 1937 to produce fur for the fashion industry. A hurricane in 1940 destroyed the nutria cages, releasing the rodents into the wild. They subsequently began to thrive in swamps and wetlands, where they live in shallow burrows and feed voraciously on aquatic plants. Their foraging and feeding are destructive to central Florida wetlands.

White-tailed deer (Odocoileus virginianus) browse on emergent and woody plants in wetlands. Photographer credit: Michael Hancock, Southwest Florida Water Management District.

Feral hogs (Sus scrofa) are widely found in flatwoods with freshwater marshes, ponds, sloughs, and cabbage palm (Sabal palmetto) hammocks. Their rooting, wallowing, and foraging are ecologically destructive, and they compete for food with native wildlife species. Photographer credit: Dan Duerr, U.S. Geological Survey.

Effects of Fire on Wetland Ecology

Fire, principally caused by lightning, is a natural occurrence in Florida wetlands, and examples of charcoal embedded in peat deposits demonstrate the historical frequency. Fire limits the invasion of woody vegetation, thereby affecting the plant composition in wetlands. It is critical in reducing the volume of accumulated litter, which would eventually fill a wetland and accelerate the natural progression to a drier community type. Fire also transforms organic carbon into inorganic carbon and aids in releasing nutrients back into the wetland ecosystem when burned material is inundated during the rainy season. Fire is relatively rare (once in 50 to 100 years) in bottom-land forests, more frequent in wet flatwoods such as pond pine (once in 15–50 years), and relatively common (once in 1–3 years) in shallow Florida marshes (Kushlan, 1990).

A cypress wetland in Volusia County showing evidence of recent fire, and regrowth of ferns, palmetto, and other ground cover. Photographer credit: Steve Miller, St. Johns River Water Management District.

Fire can kill many trees in flood-plain forests, and may foster decay and rot in surviving damaged trees. The thin bark of water tupelo, black tupelo, laurel oak, and water oak provide little protection from fire. The thicker bark of cypress, sweetbay, and red maple make them more resistant to damage by fire. Most of the tree species with thicker bark will reproduce following fire if the roots have not been damaged or killed. Trees growing in thick accumulations of peat are more likely to be severely damaged by the high heat of peat fires than trees growing in more mineral soils, where fire temperatures tend to be lower. However, if the peat is in direct contact with the water table (and therefore saturated), fire frequency and severity are low. Some wetland plant species adapted to withstand fire have seeds and other structures that only disperse following exposure to fire.

Although lightning continues to cause natural fires, roads, agriculture, and urban development now limit the spread of fires that help maintain wetlands. Prescribed burns are used to mimic the pattern of natural fires to maintain ecosystems in wetland forests as well as upland forests. Prescribed fires can reduce the accumulation of plant material periodically, and limit the possibility of rare but catastrophic fires fueled by excessive vegetation.

HUMAN ACTIVITIES THAT AFFECT WETLANDS IN CENTRAL FLORIDA

Humans affect wetlands in central Florida through wetland protection, mitigation, alteration, and destruction. Wetland protection is a relatively recent human activity. In Florida, the State and the U.S. Army Corps of Engineers protect wetlands by regulating development in areas near wetlands, by acquiring wetlands and areas adjacent to wetlands, and by requiring local governments to produce long-term plans to ensure wetland protection. Wetland mitigation also is a recent phenomenon, and includes wetland enhancement, restoration, creation, and preservation. Wetland alteration has a long history, usually a result of hydrologic modifications such as dredging, filling, drainage, and water contamination. Alterations typically produced wetlands of smaller size, shorter hydroperiod, and impaired function. However, downgradient drainage impediments such as roads, dikes, or berms can result in increased wetland acreage. Wetland destruction sometimes causes wetland loss over a large area, but more often wetland loss is cumulative and involves the elimination of increasing numbers of small wetlands over time. This incremental and cumulative wetland loss can greatly change the ecological landscape.

Wetland Protection

Wetlands are protected at the Federal, State, and County level in Florida by a network of laws and regulations that often intersect and sometimes overlap in complex ways. Nongovernmental organizations such as the Audubon Society, Sierra Club, Nature Conservancy and others are interested and involved in the protection of wetland functions and values.

Wetlands are the only ecosystem specifically protected by law in the United States, and several Federal agencies provide wetland protection. The U.S. Army Corps of Engineers addresses wetland issues related to watercraft navigation and water supply. The U.S. Army Corps of Engineers also developed the Wetland Delineation Manual (U.S. Army Corps of Engineers, 1987), which is used by all Federal agencies (and many others) for legally determining wetland boundaries. The U.S. Environmental Protection Agency, in partnership with State and local governments, is responsible for restoring and maintaining the chemical, physical, and biological integrity of the Nation's waters and thus, has authority to protect wetland resources as an integral part of those waters. The U.S. Fish and Wildlife Service manages fish and wildlife game species and protects threatened and endangered species within wetlands. The Natural Resources Conservation Service regulates agricultural activity that may affect wetland ecosystems.

Figure 26. Florida Water Management Districts

Regulatory agencies in central Florida use their permitting programs as tools to guard against harm to wetlands, which are considered by law to be "waters of the State" and are protected as such. The Florida Legislature created a wetland regulation program called the Environ- mental Resource Permit (ERP) program, which was fully implemented by the Florida Department of Environmental Protection and the Water Management Districts (Figure 26) beginning in 1995. The Florida Department of Environmental Protection has two regulatory district offices in central Florida to ensure compliance with departmental rules, including those relating to wetlands. The ERP program requires that any person or organization that proposes the construction of new facilities (including those that are residential, commercial, governmental, or highway related) and/or proposes to fill a wetland must have an approved ERP. The ERP also addresses stormwater runoff quality and quantity. An ERP is approved for a specific purpose, and typically contains a number of conditions that must be met by permittees. It is the intent of the State ERP Program that there be "no net loss" in wetlands and other surface-water functions. The permit not only requires that "primary impacts" will not be harmful, but also mandates that "secondary impacts" due to construction will not cause harm to wetlands and their wildlife. Finally, although a project may not cause harm in and of itself, permit applicants must demonstrate that their activities will not contribute to unacceptable cumulative adverse effects on wetlands in a given drainage basin when combined with existing, permitted, or pending projects.

The Water Management Districts require permittees to complete Environmental Monitoring Reports as part of the ERP Program. For example, the Southwest Florida Water Management District has standardized guidelines for their Environmental Monitoring Report, which allows the District to determine compliance status and overall success of mitigation projects. Included in the report is a detailed wetland site map, one or more monitoring areas with permanent "photo points," and a transect from the perimeter to the deepest point in the wetland with plots that are monitored for changes in vegetation, wildlife, and hydrologic condition (Feature H— Wetland Assessment in Central Florida —Approaches and Strategies).

H. WETLAND ASSESSMENT AND MONITORING IN CENTRAL FLORIDA—APPROACHES AND STRATEGIES

The periodic assessment and monitoring of wetlands typically focuses on tracking changes in the hydrologic and biological components of these systems at intervals ranging from months to years. Any assessment and monitoring program must be preceded by efforts to accurately delineate, map, and classify the subject wetlands. Accurate and reliable wetland delineation and classification is largely based on three factors—water, soils, and vegetation.

Florida has adopted a wetland delineation methodology that is binding on all State, regional, and local governments throughout Florida (Section 373.421, Florida Statutes). This methodology, adopted as Chapter 62–340 of the Florida Administrative Code, is a unified statewide approach to wetland and other surface-water delineation and is specific to Florida, in recognition of the vegetative, hydrologic, and soil features that are unique to Florida. The Florida Department of Environmental Protection Wetland Evaluation and Delineation Section performs formal wetland delineations, provides training in wetland delineation and classification, provides technical assistance to other sections of the Department, and ensures the consistent statewide use of the Florida Unified Wetland Delineation Methodology. Wetlands are delineated and mapped on an "as requested" basis related to permitting of individual projects.

The U.S. Fish and Wildlife Service National Wetlands Inventory has produced maps of wetlands in Florida (Feature A—Wetland Mapping and the National Wetlands Inventory), although these maps typically are not at a level of resolution adequate for State permitting purposes. The U.S. Fish and Wildlife Service also has produced periodic reports for Florida summarizing the "status and trends" of wetland gains and losses over time (Frayer and Hefner, 1991; Dahl, 2005). This determination of wetland status and trends is based on a random sample of about 600 4-mi^2 plots selected throughout the State. In addition, the Florida Department of Environmental Protection and the Water Management Districts provide a status of wetlands and the functions they provide as part of their permit application review process.

Successful biological monitoring and assessment of Florida freshwater wetlands requires a robust classification scheme that consistently groups ecosystems with similar biological characteristics and similar responses to disturbance. In addition to the U.S. Fish and Wildlife Service wetland classification system developed by Cowardin and others (1979), several other schemes are used to classify Florida freshwater wetlands. The Florida Land Use and Cover Classifications System (FLUCCS) was developed by the Department of Transportation and is used by a number of other State agencies. The Florida Natural Areas Inventory (FNAI), published by Florida State University (1990) in cooperation with several other State agencies, includes numerous wetland communities. The Florida Department of Environmental Protection, in conjunction with the University of Florida Center for Wetlands, has published a classification scheme with wetland classes that apply to central Florida wetlands (Doherty and others, 2000). This scheme uses a combination of hydrologic, geomorphologic, and biological characteristics (including dominant plant type) to group wetlands together for the purposes of detecting biological condition. There may be considerable overlap between these different classification schemes, but each has specific goals depending on the mission of the agency that developed it.

Monitoring and bioassessment can rely on several target communities—algae, wetland vegetation, macroinvertebrates, amphibians, and others. Algae are useful for wetland assessment because their species identification is well established and the ecological requirements of many algal species are published in the scientific literature. For example, the diatoms *Eunotia naegelii, Eunotia rhomboidea, and Frustulia rhomboides* have a preferred range of specific conductance of 65 to 90 µS/cm (Potopova and Charles, 2003). Therefore, these species would be expected to inhabit wetlands that do not receive groundwater, but would not be expected in wetlands that receive groundwater flow and therefore have a higher specific conductance. Wetland vegetation can be used to compare the presence of taxa in reference sites (undisturbed sites) and sites with known disturbance. Individual plant species can be scored to determine which are unique to reference sites (often called sensitive, ubiquitous, or intolerant), or unique to disturbed sites (tolerant). The macroinvertebrate community can be used to develop measurements, called metrics, that identify dominant groups of aquatic invertebrate organisms, and to compare the relative abundance of those groups at reference sites and sites with known disturbance to compile a numerical score. Some of the available metrics include percent Diptera, percent Odonata, relative abundance of Ephemeroptera and

Trichoptera, and others. Metrics that use macroinvertebrate abundance must have a seasonal component that adjusts for natural variation based on wet and dry conditions. The reproductive success of amphibians, and their abundance at reference and disturbed sites, is also used to assess and compare central Florida wetlands (Feature G— Amphibians as Bioindicators in Wetlands).

PRIMER FACTS

Monitoring and bioassessment can rely on several target communities —algae, wetland vegetation, macroinvertebrates, amphibians, and others. Algae are useful for wetland assessment because their species identification is well established and the ecological requirements of many algal species are published in the scientific literature.

Hydrologic wetland assessments rely on periodic wetland water-level measurements at staff gages and continuous groundwater level measurements in monitoring wells. Photographer credit: Dan Duerr, U.S. Geological Survey.

Algae growing on glass slides that are placed in a floating frame can be identified and used to characterize wetlands. Photographer credit: Kim Haag, U.S. Geological Survey.

Systematic vegetation monitoring by the Southwest Florida Water Management District in isolated wetlands affected by groundwater withdrawals in the northern Tampa Bay area indicated that hydrologic changes in the wetlands affected wetland vegetation (Rochow,

1985; 1998). As a consequence, a standardized Wetland Assessment Procedure was developed by Tampa Bay Water; the procedure is part of their Environmental Management Plan used to manage the 11 Central System well fields (Tampa Bay Water, 2000). These well fields are part of the Tampa Bay Water's Consolidated Water Use Permit for the northern Tampa Bay area (Feature K—Aquifer Recovery in the Northern Tampa Bay Area and Effects on Wetlands). The Wetland Assessment Procedure was revised by the Southwest Florida Water Management District in 2005 (Southwest Florida Water Management District and Tampa Bay Water, 2005; Southwest Florida Water Management District, 2005), and is now used for other water-use permits in addition to Tampa Bay Water's Consolidated Permit. The objective of the Wetland Assessment Procedure is to collect information on vegetation, hydrology, soils, and other indicators of hydrologic changes in monitored wetlands caused by regional groundwater withdrawals. As of 2007, about 400 wetlands were being monitored annually using the procedure to provide a time series of assessment results. The results of this procedure include a record of dominant plant species in each wetland in three zones (transition, outer deep, and deep) along a transect that extends from the wetland edge to the deepest part of the wetland (figure H–1). The assessment also derives numerical scores for different parts of the plant community (ground cover, shrubs and small trees, and medium to large size trees) for the entire wetland and additional information regarding indications of "stress" in the plant communities.

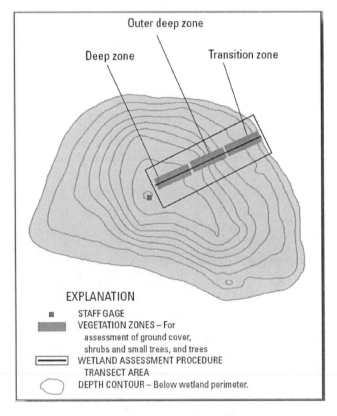

Figure H-1. Conceptual drawing of a Wetland Assessment Procedure transect for monitoring and periodic evaluation of wetlands included in Tampa Bay Water's Consolidated Water Use Permit.

Biological wetland assessment often includes vegetation sampling. Photographer credit: Kim Haag, U.S. Geological Survey.

Selected References about Wetland Assessment and Monitoring

Cowardin, L. M., Carter, V., Golet, F. C. & LaRoe, E. T. (1979). *Classification of wetlands and deepwater habitats of the United States*: Washington D. C., U. S. Fish and Wildlife Service report FWS/OBS-79/31.

Dahl, T. E. (2005). *Status and trends of wetlands in the conterminous United States, 1998 to 2004*: Washington D. C., U. S. Fish and Wildlife Service report, 80 p.

Doherty, S. J., Lane, C. R. & Brown, M. T. (2000). *Proposed classification for biological assessment of Florida inland freshwater wetlands: Tallahassee*, Fla., Technical report prepared for the Florida Department of Environmental Protection, variously paged.

Florida State University (1990). *Florida Natural Areas Inventory, Natural Community Guide:* Tallahassee, accessed June 18, 2008, at http://www. fnai. org/natural communguide. cfm.

Frayer, W. E. & Hefner, J. M. (1991). *Florida wetlands, status and trends*, 1970s to 1980s: Washington D. C., U. S. Fish and Wildlife Service report, 31 p.

Potopova, M. & Charles, D. F. (2003). *Distribution of benthic diatoms in U. S. rivers in relation to conductivity and ionic composition: Freshwater Biology*, v. *48*, p. 1311-1328.

Rochow, T. F. (1985). *Hydrologic and vegetational changes resulting from underground pumping at the Cypress Creek Well Field, Pasco County, Florida: Florida Scientist*, v. *48*, p. 65-80.

Rochow, T. F. (1998). *The effects of water table level changes on freshwater marsh and cypress wetlands in the northern Tampa Bay region—A review: Brooksville*, Southwest Florida Water Management District technical report 1998-1, 64 p.

Southwest Florida Water Management District . (2005). *Test results of a proposed revision to the Wetland Assessment Procedure (WAP)*, October 2004 & development of the final WAP methodology adopted in April 2005: Brooksville, Fla., 147 p.

Southwest Florida Water Management District and Tampa Bay Water. (2005). *Wetland Assessment Procedure (WAP) instruction manual for isolated wetlands: Brooksville*, Fla., 46 p.

Tampa Bay Water. (2000). *Environmental Management Plan for the Tampa Bay Water Central System well fields: Clearwater*, Fla., 58 p.

Although some details of permitting requirements differ among the Water Management Districts in central Florida, there are several examples of collaboration and coordination. One example is the 2006 Central Florida Coordination Area (Figure 26), which pertains to the geographic area where the boundaries of the St. Johns River, South Florida, and Southwest Florida Water Management Districts come together. The Central Florida Coordination Area ensures that consistent and streamlined permitting criteria are used by these three Water Management Districts as they develop and implement alternative water-supply projects to meet projected long-term needs for water supply. These alternative water-supply projects can have important implications for wetland stewardship.

State wetlands protection efforts are broadly based in Florida. According to Florida law, water is a public resource that is for the benefit of the entire State, and is not owned by individuals. The Water Management Districts are authorized to issue permits for the use of water, while also protecting the State's water resources. For example, the St. Johns River Water Management District and the Southwest Florida Water Management District require a Consumptive Use Permit for any well greater than 6 in. in diameter, or any water use that will exceed 100,000 gal/d. Permits are denied if the water withdrawal would cause unmitigated adverse effects on adjacent land use, including damage to wetlands. A systematic field inspection of wetlands in the area of proposed withdrawals and groundwater flow modeling are important tools in the environmental assessment of permit applications. Harm to wetlands from consumptive use can be avoided by altering the timing of withdrawals, plugging drainage ditches, or direct augmentation to raise water levels. Often, efforts to avoid harm to wetlands are sufficient and mitigation rarely has to be used in the permitting process.

Another way in which the Water Management Districts protect wetland resources in central Florida is through the Minimum Flows and Levels program. Minimum Flows and Levels are established to avoid substantial harm from permitted water withdrawals to water resources or ecology of rivers, lakes, springs, and wetlands (minimum levels only). Establishing minimum flows and levels is a requirement of the Florida State legislature for each of the Water Management Districts in the State, but the methods to establish Minimum Flows and Levels are developed and implemented by each Water Management District independently (Neubauer and others, 2008). However, efforts are made by Water Management Districts to make minimum flows and levels consistent throughout the State.

A unified statewide methodology for the delineation of the landward extent of wetlands (and surface waters) is included in the Florida Administrative Code (Chapter 62–340). The methodology is designed to be applied by the Florida Department of Environmental Protection in conjunction with the Water Management Districts in the State, and has been summarized in the Florida Wetlands Delineation Manual (Florida Department of Environmental Protection, 2009). The delineation method depends on a number of criteria, including the dominance of plant species, soils, and other hydrologic evidence. The manual provides reference site examples of wetland identification and delineation, and also includes a list of wetlands types found in Florida and community types not intended to be identified as wetlands. For example, Florida freshwater wetlands generally include swamps, marshes, bay heads, bogs, cypress domes and strands, sloughs, wet prairies, flood-plain swamps and marshes, and hydric seepage slopes, but do not include longleaf or slash pine flatwoods with under-stories dominated by saw palmetto.

Florida has a large and active land acquisition program, which has proven to be a substantial benefit to wetlands. The 1980 Conservation and Recreational Lands Program was the first major program to protect wetlands in the State. Since its inception, the program has acquired well over 1 million acres at a cost of nearly $2 billion. Increased efforts were mandated, and more stable funding was instituted in 1990 with the Preservation 2000 program. In 1998, a $3 billion wetlands programming and funding effort called Florida Forever was developed to enhance land acquisition. The program is overseen by the Florida Department of Environmental Protection and is administered by the Water Management Districts.

Almost 5,000 acres of cypress swamps, bay swamps, marshes, and other pristine lands in Highlands County were acquired in 1931 to protect them from agricultural development. The area became part of Highlands Hammock State Park, one of Florida's first four State parks. Photographer credit: Michael Hancock, Southwest Florida Water Management District.

In some cases, State and Federal programs work in tandem to protect wetlands because the wetlands are located in areas where there are overlying jurisdictions, multiple land uses, or competing interests that complicate protection efforts. For example, the area of central Florida known as the Ocala National Forest lies between the Ocklawaha and St. Johns River in parts of Marion, Lake, Putnam, and Seminole Counties. The forest contains more than 600 wetlands, lakes, and ponds that provide recharge for the Floridan aquifer system. The Forest was dedicated by President Theodore Roosevelt more than 100 years ago, and is the oldest national forest east of the Mississippi. This multiuse area, where many types of aquatic and terrestrial recreation occur, provides habitat for many types of wildlife, and even contains a U.S. Navy bombing range where live impact training is held. Successful wetland protection and preservation in an area as dynamic as this exemplifies the potential for wetland protection available to all regions of the State. Maintaining a balance between conservation and development is an ongoing challenge to resource managers in the Green Swamp area of central Florida (Feature I—The Green Swamp and Use of Wetland Conservation Partnerships). Many Florida counties maintain a policy of "no net loss" of wetland functions due to development or other activities. Counties strive to avoid adverse effects to wetlands, to minimize unavoidable adverse effects where they will occur, and to compensate for adverse effects on wetlands through various types of mitigation.

Marsh grass and wax myrtle (Myrica cerifera) in Conner Preserve marsh, Pasco County.
Photographer credit: Michael Hancock, Southwest Florida Water Management District.

I. THE GREEN SWAMP AND USE OF WETLAND CONSERVATION PARTNERSHIPS

The Green Swamp ecosystem occupies about 870 mi^2 in portions of Hernando, Lake, Pasco, Polk, and Sumter Counties, and is the second largest wetland system in the State, after the Everglades. The area is a complex mosaic of uplands, hydric hammocks, poorly drained pine flatwoods, bay swamps, shrub bogs, cypress swamps, and pastures (Ewel, 1990). About 60 percent of the area is in a natural and undisturbed condition; about half of the natural areas are wetlands (figure I–1), 80 percent of which are forested. About 35 percent of the Green Swamp is used as agricultural land, and much of that is improved pasture. Less than 2 percent of the area is urban land (Brown, 1984).

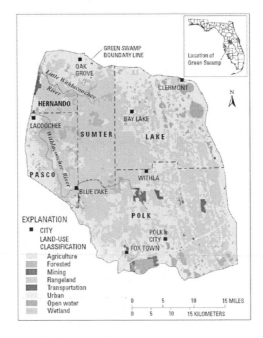

Figure I–1. Generalized land use in the Green Swamp

Hydrology and Geology

Underlying the Green Swamp are three hydrogeologic units (Pride and others, 1966). The surficial aquifer system is directly below the land surface and is composed of sands and sandy clays. The surficial aquifer system is about 90 ft thick in the eastern part of the area and very thin or entirely absent in the western part. Beneath the surficial aquifer system is a clay layer that varies in thickness in the eastern part of the area, and is thin to absent in the western part of the area. Beneath the clay layer is the Floridan aquifer system, which has an average thickness greater than 900 ft and consists of the Suwannee Limestone, Ocala Limestone, and Avon Park Formation.

The Green Swamp is the headwaters of both the surface-water and the groundwater flow systems in central Florida. The drainage basin that includes the Green Swamp contains the highest potentiometric-surface elevation (groundwater elevation) of the Floridan aquifer system in central Florida (Spechler and Kroening, 2007). For example, the potentiometric surface elevation was measured at 133 ft NGVD 29 in September, 1979 (U.S. Geological Survey, 2009. The high potentiometric surface in the Green Swamp provides recharge for the Floridan aquifer system and maintains a potable groundwater supply in the region. Rainfall is the primary source of water to the Green Swamp, and water losses occur through evapotranspiration, groundwater seepage, and streamflow. Drainage from the Green Swamp forms the headwaters of four major Florida rivers (figure I–2): the Ocklawaha River (the largest tributary to the St. Johns River), which flows north; the Hillsborough River and the Withlacoochee River, which flow west; and the Peace River, which flows south.

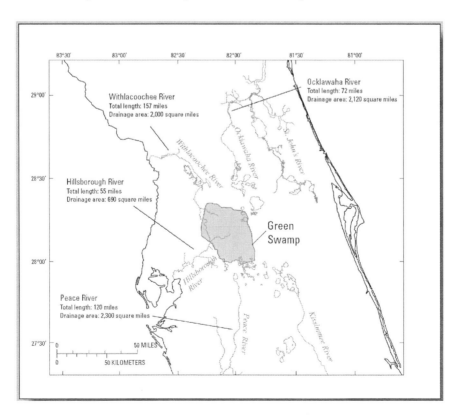

Figure I–2. The Green Swamp is the headwaters for the Hillsborough, Ocklawaha, Peace, and Withlacoochee Rivers

Throughout the Green Swamp, there is a gradual transition between shallow still-water depressions (cypress ponds) and depression channels that carry surface-water flow (cypress strands). The topography is typically so flat that surface flow is seldom observed (Ewel, 1990). Many other cypress ponds are isolated and are not sources of surface-water flow. The flat terrain allows much of the precipitation to be retained, and the numerous wetlands provide substantial water storage. The wetlands not only recharge the aquifer as water eventually percolates downward, but they also reduce flood peaks in rivers, and release water slowly into surface tributaries once rainfall diminishes after the wet season (Brown, 1984). The water that flows from the Green Swamp into rivers is generally of high quality because the long detention times within the basin eliminate much of the decaying plant material that creates oxygen demand in receiving rivers.

The red-tailed hawk (Buteojamaicensis) searches for prey in the Green Swamp. Photographer credit: Paul Fellers, Lake Region Audubon Society.

PRIMER FACTS

The water that flows from the Green Swamp into rivers is generally of high quality because the long detention times within the basin eliminate much of the decaying plant material that creates oxygen demand in receiving rivers.

Plant and Animal Communities

The cypress domes in the Green Swamp share numerous plant species. The domes are shallow, forested, roughly circular depressions that have dome-shaped cross sections as a result of the concentration of tallest and oldest trees in the center. The boundaries of cypress domes are maintained by periodic fires that prevent the invasion of wetland tree species into the surrounding pine flatwoods (Florida Department of Environmental Protection, 2006). The Green Swamp ecosystem is one of the last contiguous wilderness areas in Florida, with diverse plant communities and wildlife habitats that host more than 330 species of animals, including 30 threatened or endangered species. This latter group includes the Florida scrub jay (*Aphelocoma coerulescens*), the wood stork (*Mycteria americana*), and the Florida black bear (*Ursus americanus floridanus*).

Protection and Preservation

The Green Swamp has attracted attention in the water- resources community for decades. In the early 1960s, above- average seasonal rainfall and the effects of Hurricane Donna caused severe flooding in the area. Consequently, the U.S. Army Corps of Engineers developed a plan to use the Green Swamp as part of a structural flood-control system for central Florida (Southwest Florida Water Management District, 2009). A series of proposed levees and water control structures, called the Four Rivers Basins—Florida Project, would have inundated the area and effectively converted the Green Swamp into a flood-water detention basin. The Southwest Florida Water Management District made substantial land purchases in the Green Swamp in preparation for the project. However, concerns about disrupting a unique natural system, and further examination of the habitat and water-supply benefits of the area, led the Southwest Florida Water Management District to choose a non-structural approach to flood protection by leaving the Green Swamp in its natural state.

In 1974, as Walt Disney World opened to the east, a proposal was made to develop 2,000 acres of the Green Swamp (Southwest Florida Water Management District, 2009). By that time, however, there was an understanding of the critical hydrologic role that the Green Swamp plays in recharging the Floridan aquifer system, and the area was not developed. The State of Florida designated approximately 322,000 acres in Polk and Lake Counties, including the Green Swamp, as an Area of Critical State Concern under Chapter 380 of the Florida Statutes. This classification protects a resource of statewide importance that is threatened by unregulated development, and is intended to be a temporary designation that fosters action at the local level to sustain natural resources. The State land planning agency, the Florida Department of Community Affairs, eventually provided oversight for all new development activities in the Green Swamp. Local land development plan regulations must be consistent with this legislation. The 1985 Local Comprehensive Planning Act (Chapter 163, Florida Statutes) ensures that within the jurisdiction of Lake, Polk, Citrus, Sumter, and Hernando Counties, all natural land development limitations and suitabilities pertaining to the Green Swamp are identified as required by the Act.

In the early 1990s, the Green Swamp was added to a land acquisition program—Preservation 2000—that later became known as Florida Forever. The primary goals of the Green Swamp Florida Forever project (Florida Department of Environmental Protection, 2008) are to:

- Conserve and protect lands within areas of critical state concern;
- Conserve and protect significant habitat for native species or endangered and threatened species;
- Conserve, protect, manage, or restore important ecosystems, landscapes, and forests, in order to enhance or protect significant surface-water, coastal, recreational, timber, fish, or wildlife resources that local or State regulatory programs cannot adequately protect; and
- Provide areas, including recreational trails, for naturalresource-based recreation.

The Southwest Florida Water Management District has increased its holdings within the Green Swamp to more than 110,000 acres, and designated these holdings as the Green Swamp Wilderness Preserve. Other agencies, including the St. Johns River Water Management District, have purchased an additional 64,000 acres for use as State parks and wildlife management areas.

The Southwest Florida Water Management District also has purchased conservation easements in more than 6,000 acres of private lands for preservation, protection, recreation, and hunting. Conservation easements allow property owners to continue to own and use the land while protecting it from development. Altogether, the Green Swamp Land Authority and the Florida Department of Environmental Protection have established protection agreements or conservation easements for more than 40,000 acres of privately owned land (Ryan, 2006).

Private conservation organizations also have an active interest in the preservation and protection of the Green Swamp because of its hydrologic importance and importance as a wildlife habitat. The Sierra Club continues to work with the Southwest Florida Water Management District and St. Johns River Water Management District to encourage land acquisition in the Green Swamp through the Florida Forever Program and the Save Our Rivers Program. The Audubon Society works with allied organizations to accelerate acquisition programs and increase funding for public land management in the Green Swamp. Of particular interest to the Audubon Society are efforts to protect the bald eagle (*Haliaeetus leucocephalus*) through habitat conservation and preservation.

Pine-hyacinth (Clematis baldwinii) grows along the margins of swamps and wet pine woods of the Green Swamp. Photographer credit: Paul Fellers, Lake Region Audubon Society.

Selected References about the Green Swamp

Brown, S. L. (1984). *The role of wetlands in the Green Swamp,* in Ewel, K. C. & Odum, H. T., eds., Cypress Swamps: Gainesville, University Presses of Florida, 472 p.

Ewel, K. C. (1990). Swamps, in Myers, R. L. & Ewel, J. J., eds., *Ecosystems of Florida:* Orlando, Fla., University of Central Florida Press, 765 p.

Florida Department of Environmental Protection. (2006). *Green Swamp Wilderness Preserve,* accessed June 29, 2006, at http://www. dep. state. fl. us/WATER/wetlands delineation/grnswamp. pdf.

Florida Department of Environmental Protection. (2008). Green Swamp, Lake and Polk Counties, accessed September 26, 2008, at http://www. dep. state. fl. us/lands/FFAnnual/B_ GreenSwamp. pdf.

Pride, R. W., Myer, R. W. & Cherry, R. N. (1966). *Hydrology of the Green Swamp area in central Florida: Tallahassee,* Fla., Florida Geological Survey Report of Investigations no. 42, 137 p.

Rochow, T. F. & Lopez, M. (1984). *Hydrobiological monitoring of cypress domes in the Green Swamp area of Lake and Sumter Counties*, Florida, 1979-1982: Brooksville, Fla., Southwest Florida Water Management District Technical Report 1984-1, 79 p.

Ryan, M. (2006). *The Green Swamp—Florida's liquid heart,* accessed September 4, 2006, at http://metropolitan. research. ucf. edu/assetts/docs/Naturally_Central_Florida. pdf.

Sierra Club, (2006). *Green Swamp,* accessed February 6, 2006, at http://florida. sierraclub. org/greenswamp. asp.

Southwest Florida Water Management District, (1981). *Green Swamp Flood Detention Area environmental assessment: Brooksville*, Fla., 107 p.

Southwest Florida Water Management District, (2009). *Green Swamp Interactive,* accessed March 3, 2009, at http://www/ swfwmd. state. fl. us/education/interactive/greenswamp/ textonly. html.

Spechler, R. M. & Kroening, S. E. (2007). *Hydrology of Polk County*: U. S. Geological Survey Scientific Investigations Report 2006-5320, 114 p.

Tibbals, C. H. & Grubb, H. F. (1982). *Aquifer test results, Green Swamp area,* Florida: U. S. Geological Survey Water- Resources Investigations Report 82-35, 29 p.

U. S. Geological Survey, (2009). National Water Information System, accessed June 26, 2009 at http://nwis. waterdata. usgs. gov/fl/nwis/gwlevels.

A deep marsh in Pasco County. Photographer credit: Michael Hancock, Southwest Florida Water Management District.

PRIMER FACTS

Wetland mitigation refers to any wetland enhancement, restoration, creation, or preservation project that serves to offset adverse effects on wetlands.

Wetland Mitigation

The term "wetland mitigation" refers to any wetland enhancement, restoration, creation, or preservation project that serves to offset adverse effects on wetlands (Florida Department of Environmental Protection, 2008b). Wetland mitigation is designed to compensate for the intentional destruction of wetlands by land development by requiring the creation of wetlands in an alternate area so as to maintain "no net loss" in wetland function. Wetland mitigation was set forth in Section 404 of the Federal Clean Water Act, which legally allows for the destruction of wetlands provided that their loss is compensated for by the restoration or creation of new wetland areas. Mitigation may be onsite, or it may be offsite if onsite mitigation does not have long-term viability or if offsite mitigation would provide greater ecological value (Florida Department of Environmental Protection, 2008b). Mitigation typically is located within the same drainage basin as the adverse effect to avoid potential unacceptable cumulative adverse effects within the basin.

The addition of groundwater (augmentation) is a form of mitigation that maintains wildlife habitat at Duck Pond marsh in Pasco County. Photographer credit: Michael Hancock, Southwest Florida Water Management District.

Wetland enhancement and restoration ideally return a wetland ecosystem to a close approximation of its condition before disturbance (National Research Council, 1992). Wetland restoration has been defined as any manipulation of a site that contains or has contained a wetland to increase the wetland area or enhance natural qualities of the wetland (Kentula and others, 1993). The Kissimmee River Restoration, overseen by the South Florida Water Management District, is an example of a large wetlands restoration project in central Florida (Feature J—Restoration of Flood-Plain Wetlands in the Kissimmee River Basin).

Regardless of size, success-ful restoration reestablishes critical ecological processes and functions related to chemical, physical, and biological wetland characteristics.

The National Research Council (2001) developed a list of guidelines for restoration of self-sustaining wetlands that relate to many of the major topics presented herein. They include: consideration of the landscape and climate; use of a landscape perspective; restoration of naturally variable hydrologic conditions; a preference for wetland restoration over creation; avoidance of overengineered structures; use of appropriate planting elevations, depth, soil type, and seasonal timing; provision of heterogeneous topography; attention to soil and sediment geochemistry, and groundwater quantity and quality; special consideration for seriously disturbed sites; and use of monitoring.

J. RESTORATION OF FLOOD-PLAIN WETLANDS IN THE KISSIMMEE RIVER BASIN

The restoration of flood-plain wetlands in the Kissimmee River basin is part of the largest ecosystem restoration project ever attempted anywhere in the world (Dahm and others, 1995; South Florida Water Management District, 2009b). Efforts to return the hydrology of the Kissimmee River to pre-channelization conditions were initiated even before the channelization process was completed, because as flood-plain wetlands were incrementally lost during channelization, their ecological value became increasingly clear.

The Kissimmee River flows out of Lake Kissimmee in central Florida and historically flowed into Lake Okeechobee as a meandering river with a braided channel flanked by numerous wetlands (Figure J–1). These wetlands were home to an abundance of aquatic vegetation, wetland birds, fish, and invertebrates that inhabited the sloughs and backwaters surrounding the river on its 1- to 3-mi-wide flood plain. Prior to channelization, almost 95 percent of the flood plain was inundated more than 50 percent of the time, and about 75 percent of the flood plain was inundated almost 70 percent of the time (Toth and others, 1998). Flood-plain wetlands occupied about 45,000 acres and water depths averaged 1 to 2 ft (Toth, 1990).

A series of hurricanes in the 1940s prompted residents and land developers to call for flood-control measures that would avoid future flooding, and in response to these requests, the river was channelized by the U.S. Army Corps of Engineers from 1962 to 1971. As a result, the river was transformed into the C–38 canal, which is about 30-ft deep and about 300-ft wide. The canal was sectioned into a series of five pools each with a water-control structure. The pools were more similar ecologically to lakes than to a riverine habitat because the flow rate was so low. Approximately 30,000 acres of flood-plain wetlands were either converted into canal or drained and covered with canal spoil. The remaining flood- plain wetlands were mostly lost because they were cut off hydrologically from their water source (Koebel, 1995).

The ecological effects of the channelization were substantial. The mosaic of wetland habitats was greatly reduced, and in most areas eliminated. These included backwater sloughs and ponds that supported shrub communities of willow and buttonbush, as well as broad- leaf marshes of pickerelweed, arrowhead, cutgrass, and maidencane. Also affected were cypress swamps, and red maple/popash forests. There was a decline of more than 90 percent in the use of the flood plain by overwintering water fowl (Weller, 1999). Among those species affected was the endangered wood stork. The largemouth bass fishery in the river declined substantially along with populations of other sport fish. These declines were caused by the loss of forage fish (including small-bodied wetland species such as the mosquitofish, least killifish, swamp darter, and sailfin molly), and also to the loss of shallow-water breeding and nesting habitat for sport fish. Moreover, the wetlands were no longer available to filter and retain nutrients, resulting in increased nutrient loads to Lake Okeechobee and exacerbated eutrophication in this historically nutrient-rich lake.

Efforts to return the hydrology of the Kissimmee River to pre-channelization conditions began during the latter stages of the channelization process. These efforts gained additional public support as evidence of the detrimental ecological effects increased. A number of plans were proposed to restore the flood-plain wetlands, complicated by the need to maintain navigation in the river and flood control in the basin during and after restoration. Excessive erosion of any backfilled canal sections was a concern. In addition, many people had moved onto the flood plain and could not be relocated easily.

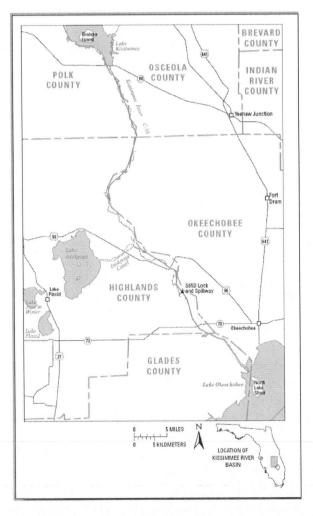

Figure J–1. The Kissimmee River showing channelized reaches and remnant meanders

Large-scale modeling efforts were used to predict flow and sediment movement in the restored river. A pilot project backfilled a 1,000-ft section of C-38 canal in 1994 and removed spoil (dredged material left behind from the channelization) from about 12 acres of the adjacent flood plain. Evidence from this pilot project indicated increased use of the restored flood-plain area by spawning game fish, and increased use by waterfowl as well. The abundance and diversity of both fish and birds increased measurably. Subsequent projects backfilled additional sections of C–38 canal, each several miles long. Water flow was reestablished in the meandering Kissimmee River and periodic flood-plain inundation was restored. Ultimately, about 40 percent of the C–38 canal will be backfilled, restoring about 26,000 acres of flood-plain wetlands and 43 mi of meandering river channel. Following each backfill project, comprehensive monitoring has documented ecological improvements to the Kissimmee River system and associated flood-plain wetlands (South Florida Water Management District, 2009b). Of particular interest are increases in the number of shorebirds, wading birds, and duck species; the reduction of organic deposits on the river bottom and the redistribution of sand bars; an increase in the relative proportion of largemouth bass and sunfish in the fish community of the river; and an increase in the dissolved oxygen concentration in the river (South Florida Water Management District, 2009a).

C-38 and remnant Kissimmee River post-
channelization, circa 1980.

Restored Kissimmee River section Phase 1,
February 2001 (Photographed in January 2003).

The remnant and restored sections of the Kissimmee River and adjacent wetlands. Photograph credit: South Florida Water Management District.

The continued restoration of the Kissimmee River will depend on scientifically based planning, implementation, and monitoring of restoration efforts. Allowing water to flow slowly through the flood-plain wetlands on its way downstream should increase nutrient uptake and retention, and thereby improve water quality in Lake Okeechobee. Adaptive management of the restoration process will allow for adjustments to the implementation process to provide a sound and evolving basis for sequential phases of the flood-plain resto-ration and long-term sustainability of the Kissimmee River ecosystem.

Seasonal drying of wetlands may strand floating and submersed aquatic plants on the exposed wetland bottom. Such vegetation typically regrows when wetlands are subsequently reflooded. Photographer credit: Michael Hancock, Southwest Florida Water Management District.

Selected References about the Kissimmee River Restoration

Dahm, C. N., Cummins, K. W., Valett, H. M. & Coleman, R. L. (1995). *An ecosystem view of the restoration of the Kissimmee River: Restoration Ecology, v. 3*, no. 3, p. 225-238.

Florida Department of Environmental Protection. (2005). *Kissimmee River Restoration continues,* accessed March 4, 2009, at http://www. dep. state. fl. us/secretary. news/2005/06/061 7_03. htm.

Florida Department of Environmental Protection. (2006). *Florida completes 100,000 acre land acquisition for Kissimmee River Restoration*, accessed March 4, 2009, at http://www. dep. state. fl. us/secretary. news/2006/04/0412_01. htm.

Koebel, J. & W., Jr., (1995)*. A historical perspective on the Kissimmee River restoration: Restoration Ecology, v. 3*, no. 3, p. 160-180.

Koebel, J. W., Jones, B. L. & Arrington, D. A. (1999). *Restoration of the Kissimmee River, Florida: Water quality impacts from canal backfilling: Environmental Monitoring and Assessment, v. 57*, p. 85-107.

Merritt, R. W., Higgins, M. J., Cummins, K. W. & Vandeneeden, B. (1999). The Kissimmee River-riparian marsh ecosystem, Florida, in Batzer, D. P., Rader, R. B. & Wissinger, S. A., eds., *Invertebrates in freshwater wetlands of North America: Ecology and Management: New York*, John Wiley and Sons, Inc., 1100 p.

Milleson, J. F., Goodrick, R. L. & VanArman, J. A., (1980). *Plant communities of the Kissimmee River valley: West Palm Beach,* South Florida Water Management District report, 42 p.

Perrin, L. S., Allen, M. J., Rowse, L. A., Montalbano, F., Foote, K. J. & Olinde, M. W., 1982, A report on fish and wildlife studies in the Kissimmee River basin and recommendations for restoration: Tallahassee, Florida Game and Freshwater Fish Commission, 260 p.

South Florida Water Management District, (2009a). Kissimmee River Restoration Fact Sheet, accessed February 6, 2009, at http://my. sfwmd. gov/pls/portal/docs/PAGE/ COMMON/ NEWSR/JTF/JTF_KRR_PROGRESSpdf.

South Florida Water Management District, (2009b). South Florida environmental report executive summary: *West Palm Beach*, Fla., 48 p.

Toth, L. A., (1990). Impacts of channelization on the Kissimmee River ecosystem, in Loftin, M. K., Toth, L. A. & Obeysekera, J. T. B., eds., Proceedings of the Kissimmee River restoration symposium: Orlando, Florida, South Florida Water Management District.

Toth, L. A., (1993). *The ecological basis of the Kissimmee River restoration plan: Florida Scientist,* v. *56,* p. 25-51.

Toth, L. A., Melvin, S. L., Arrington, D. A. & Chamberlin, J., (1998). *Hydrologic manipulations of the channelized Kissimmee River—Implications for restoration: Bioscience,* v. *48.,* no. 9, p. 757-764.

Weller, M. W. (1999). *Use of two water bird guilds as evaluation tools for the Kissimmee River Restoration: Restoration Ecology,* v. *3,* no. 3, p. 211-224.

In some situations, a number of wetland restoration alternatives may bring about the desired goals, and these alternatives typically have different costs associated with them. Water budget analyses (Feature D—Use of Water Budgets to Describe Wetlands) can be used as a tool to evaluate restoration alternatives and make the optimal choice at a particular site. For example, Levy Prairie in Alachua County was chosen for restoration and enhancement of waterfowl habitat. Several alternatives were identified for creating a permanently inundated wetland area of a specified depth in one part of Levy Prairie. Bathymetric mapping (Feature C— Wetland Bathymetry and Flooded Area) was used in conjunction with water-budget analyses to determine the best restoration alternative at the lowest cost (Kirk and others, 2004).

The Natural Resources Conservation Service administers the Federal Wetlands Reserve Program, which offers technical and financial support to provide landowners with the opportunity to protect, restore, and enhance wetlands on their property on a voluntary basis. The goal of the Natural Resources Conservation Service is to achieve the greatest wetland functions and values, along with optimum wildlife habitat, on every acre enrolled in the program and to establish long-term conservation and wildlife practices and protection. There are a number of Wetlands Reserve Program projects underway in central Florida, and several are planned at the Archbold Biological Station in Highlands County (Archbold Biological Station, 2005).

Wetland creation is the construction of a wetland in an area that was not previously a wetland and is isolated from existing wetlands. Wetland creation is often more difficult to achieve than wetland restoration and requires careful hydrologic analyses, detailed soils surveys, an understanding of drainage patterns, and the selection of plants to populate the wetland. One of the most critical factors in wetland creation is the selection of an appropriate site that is compatible with surrounding land uses and will allow a wetland to function naturally and sustainably. Long-term management and oversight is often needed, which can add to the cost of a project. Created wetlands need not be identical to a given natural wetland, but should resemble natural wetlands in function and composition (van der Valk, 2006).

The Florida Department of Transportation has a large and active program of regional multi-project mitigation to offset the adverse effects to wetlands by transportation projects. The Florida Department of Transportation works in conjunction with the Water Management Districts, who ultimately approve the proposed mitigation plans and assist in their implementation using Florida Department of Transportation funds.

Mitigation banking, a particular category of mitigation, refers to wetland acres that have been restored, enhanced, created, or preserved and set aside to compensate for future conversion of wetland habitats. The Florida Administrative Code contains a mitigation banking rule that specifies the guidelines for mitigation banking. Each applicant, public or private, must obtain an environmental resource/mitigation bank permit from the Florida Department of Environmental Protection or one of the Water Management Districts. A long-term management plan must be established to maintain the mitigation bank successfully. In essence, mitigation banking allows land developers and others to trade off planned wetland destruction by establishing in advance a "bank" of wetlands that protects existing habitats elsewhere. Although mitigation banking encourages restoration and can promote interconnected tracts of wetlands, it also allows for the destruction of smaller isolated wetlands that can provide important habitat for wildlife.

Ditches alongside roads can provide habitat for perennial wildflowers such as Bartram's sabatia (Sabatia bartramii). Photographer credit: Paul Fellers, Lake Region Audubon Society.

Wetland Alteration and Destruction

Wetlands are altered and ultimately may be destroyed as a result of human activities that cause physical, chemical, and biological alterations. Those activities include residential and commercial construction projects; flood-control activities involving dikes and levees along rivers; agricultural activities including diking, draining, and cultivation; road construction and the creation and maintenance of rights-of-way; livestock grazing; silvaculture and logging; mining; invasion by nonnative plants and animals; and pollution from household and hazardous waste.

Physical alterations often attempt to convert wetland to dry land so it can be used for other purposes. Physical alterations that change wetland hydrology include filling to raise the bottom level of a wetland; draining the water by ditching, tiling, or pumping; excavating a wetland by dredging and removing soil and vegetation; diversion to prevent the flow of surface water into a wetland; and lowering the groundwater table to prevent groundwater inflow. Clearing vegetation by digging it up, applying herbicides, mowing, or scraping it away also changes wetland function, as does die-off of aquatic vegetation from shading of bridges or other platforms.

Groundwater withdrawal from aquifers is a relatively recent but important source of physical wetland alteration in parts of central Florida. Groundwater withdrawal from the Upper Floridan aquifer in west-central Florida has lowered the potentiometric surface in the aquifer. A lower potentiometric surface in the Upper Floridan aquifer can reduce the water levels in the surficial aquifer system and lower the stage (surface-water elevation) of wetlands in nearby areas (Haag and others, 2005). Lower water levels can cause subsidence and tree fall in cypress wetlands. The effects on wetland hydrologic condition may be reversible if groundwater withdrawals are reduced in volume (Feature K—Aquifer Recovery in the Northern Tampa Bay Area and Effects on Wetlands). Other physical alterations, such as flooding behind dams or diverting surface-water flow into a wetland can cause excessive inundation of wetlands, resulting in their conversion to permanently flooded systems such as ponds or small lakes.

Tree fall in a forested wetland can open the canopy, allowing more light and providing habitat for emergent vegetation such as the southern swamp lily (Crinum americanum). Photographer credit: Dan Duerr, U.S. Geological Survey.

K. AQUIFER RECOVERY IN THE NORTHERN TAMPA BAY AREA AND EFFECTS ON WETLANDS

The Upper Floridan aquifer is the primary source of drinking water for residents in west-central Florida. Reliance on the Floridan aquifer system to meet water demands statewide has increased substantially since 1950 (Marella, 2004), and groundwater withdrawals totaled about 2,453.21 Mgal/d in the 27 counties of central Florida in 2000. The cumulative effects of increasing groundwater withdrawals have lowered the potentiometric surface in the Upper Floridan aquifer, inducing downward leakage from the overlying surficial aquifer system and lowering the water table. This leakage of water to the Upper Floridan aquifer has lowered the water levels in numerous wetlands (and lakes) in the central Florida region.

Tampa Bay Water is the regional utility that provides drinking water for Tampa, St. Petersburg, New Port Richey, and 15 other municipalities (Tampa Bay Water, 1998). The utility provided an estimated 180 Mgal/d to more than 2.5 million customers in Hillsborough, Pinellas, and Pasco Counties in 2007. In fact, Tampa Bay Water is the second largest water supplier in Florida, following Miami-Dade Water and Sewer Department (Marella, 2004). Tampa Bay Water is regulated by the Southwest Florida Water Management District, which issues permits for water use within the district boundaries, including pumping of groundwater and diversions of surface water. Southwest Florida Water Management District has established minimum flows and water levels for rivers, streams, and aquifers (and minimum levels for wetlands and lakes), which act as guidelines that can be used to minimize adverse effects on these systems.

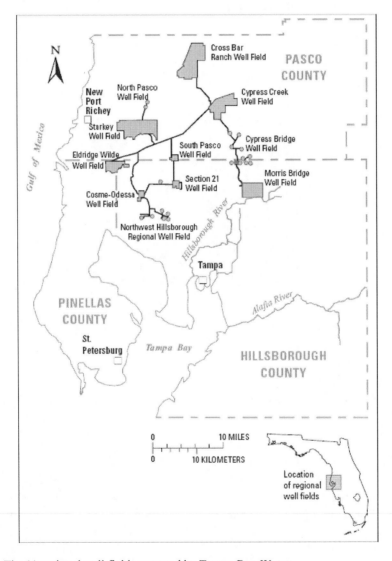

Figure K–1. The 11 regional well fields operated by Tampa Bay Water

In order to protect wetland and lake resources, and meet established minimum flows and levels, Tampa Bay Water committed to reduce groundwater withdrawals and optimize the distribution of those groundwater withdrawals from their regional well fields (Tampa Bay Water, 1998). To accomplish the goal of reducing groundwater withdrawals, the withdrawal permit for the 11 groundwater well fields in the northern Tampa Bay area (Figure K–1) was reduced from 158 to 90 Mgal/d on a 12-month moving average basis by 2008. To compensate for decreased groundwater withdrawals, a mix of alternate sources was used including groundwater, direct surface-water withdrawals, offsite reservoir storage, and desalinated seawater.

To optimize groundwater withdrawals from the regional well fields, the well fields were interconnected and an Optimized Regional Operations Plan was designed (Tampa Bay Water, 2008). This plan uses computer modeling tools and field data to examine current water levels in the surficial aquifer system on a weekly basis and to rotate groundwater pumpage away from areas with the lowest surficial aquifer water levels. By rotating groundwater pumpage based on surficial aquifer system water levels, the detrimental effects of groundwater withdrawals on any one well field are minimized, and water levels in the surficial aquifer system, lakes, and wetlands are kept as high as possible under the prevailing rainfall conditions and current water demands.

Most of the wetlands and lakes in the northern Tampa Bay area are replenished by rainfall and overland flows, and can receive groundwater discharge if aquifer levels are sufficiently high. Under predevelopment conditions, the potentiometric surface was much higher in west-central Florida than it is presently (Marella, 2004), and therefore, many wetlands probably received considerable ground-water discharge. The reductions in groundwater withdrawals have elevated the potentiometric surface in the Upper Floridan aquifer in the vicinity of the 11 well fields (Tampa Bay Water, 2008). Therefore, wetland water levels are expected to return to levels more like those prior to development, especially during periods of average to above-average rainfall (Figure K–2). Even with the recovery in the Upper Floridan aquifer, however, reservoir levels will be lower during periods of below-average rainfall, and Tampa Bay Water may require higher than permitted groundwater withdrawal rates from the well fields to meet regional drinking-water demands (Tampa Bay Water, 2008). Daily water levels in wetlands and lakes on and in the vicinity of the well fields may periodically fall below their minimum levels, but the median water levels in wetlands should not fall below their minimum levels (Southwest Florida Water Management District, 1997). Other management tools, including groundwater augmentation of wetland water levels, may be needed to avoid harm to some wetlands.

PRIMER FACTS

Tampa Bay Water is the regional utility that provides drinking water for Tampa, St. Petersburg, New Port Richey, and 15 other municipalities (Tampa Bay Water, 1998). The utility provided an estimated 180 Mgal/d to more than 2.5 million customers in Hillsborough, Pinellas, and Pasco Counties in 2007. In fact, Tampa Bay Water is the second largest water supplier in Florida, following Miami- Dade Water and Sewer Department (Marella, 2004).

Measuring the groundwater level in a wetland monitor well. Photographer credit: Patricia Metz, U.S. Geological Survey.

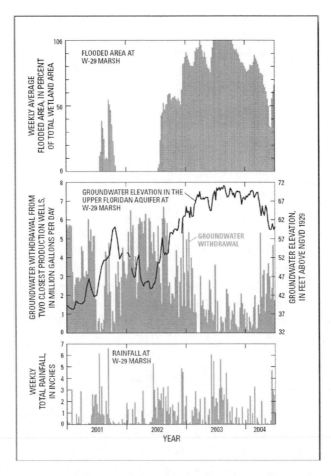

Figure K-2. Reductions in well-field groundwater withdrawals beginning in 2003, and above average rainfall in 2002 and 2003, allowed the recovery of groundwater levels in the Upper Floridan aquifer. W-29 Marsh on Cypress Creek Well Field responded with steadily increasing wetland flooded area (right)

Water level indicators such as the lower extent of the moss collar on cypress trees can indicate the extent of recent water levels in forested wetlands. Photographer credit: Michael Hancock, Southwest Florida Water Management District.

The deepest part of W-29 Marsh was dry in 2001 (left), when the potentiometric surface in the Upper Floridan aquifer was low.

The deepest part of W-29 Marsh was flooded in 2003 (right) when aquifer water levels were higher. Photographer credits: Terrie M. Lee, U.S. Geological Survey.

Selected References about Aquifer Recovery in the Northern Tampa Bay Area

Barnett, C. (2007). Mirage: *Florida and the vanishing water of the eastern U. S. : Ann Arbor*, University of Michigan Press, 239 p.

Glennon, R. (2002). *Water follies: Groundwater pumping and the fate of America's fresh waters*: Washington D. C., Island Press, 313 p.

Marella, R. L. (2004). *Water withdrawals, use, discharge & trends in Florida*, 2000: U. S. Geological Survey Scientific Investigations Report 2004-5 151, 136 p.

Pittman, C. & Waite, M. (2009). *Paving paradise—Florida's vanishing wetlands and the failure of no net loss: Gainesville,* University Press of Florida, 351 p.

Southwest Florida Water Management District. (1996). *Northern Tampa Bay Water Resources Assessment Project*, v. *1 and 2*: Brooksville, Fla., variously paged.

Southwest Florida Water Management District. (1997). Rules of the Southwest Florida Water Management District— Chapter 40D-80, *Recovery and prevention strategies for minimum flows and levels,* accessed March 20, 2009, at http://www. swfwmd. state. fl. us/rules/files/40d-80. pdf.

Southwest Florida Water Management District. (1999). *Establishment of Floridan aquifer recovery levels in the northern Tampa Bay area: Brooksville*, Fla., 240 p.

Tampa Bay Water, (1998). *Northern Tampa Bay new water supply and groundwater withdrawal reduction agreement between West Coast Regional Water Supply Authority,* Hillsborough County, Pasco County, Pinellas County, City of Tampa, City of St. Petersburg, City of New Port Ritchey & Southwest Florida Water Management District: Clearwater, Fla.

Tampa Bay Water, (2008). *Optimized Regional Operations Plan WY 2007: annual report prepared for the Southwest Florida Water Management District,* variously paged.

Physical alterations on property adjacent to wetlands (within about 750–1,200 ft) have been shown to affect wetland plant diversity, including the total number of plant species and the number of individuals in each species. This is because activities that disturb the soil alter the distribution and abundance of seeds available to sprout and grow in wetlands (Houlahan and others, 2006). In addition, nutrient inputs promote plant growth, and plant seeds from garden species in urban areas disrupt native plant communities.

Chemical alterations to wetlands include pollution that raises nutrient levels or introduces toxic compounds. Agricultural and urban runoff to wetlands often results in the addition of excess nutrients, particularly nitrogen and phosphorus. Wetlands have the ability to remove limited quantities of excess nutrients from the water column because they are taken up by algae and wetland vegetation. Elevated nutrient concentrations that cause excessive algal growth can result in the depletion of the already naturally low dissolved oxygen concentrations found in many wetlands. Runoff or leachate from improperly capped or lined landfills has the potential to contaminate wetlands. Stormwater runoff also may contaminate wetlands with oils, greases, and heavy metals from roads and parking lots. Some of those substances, especially heavy metals, may be toxic, whereas others contribute to oxygen depletion as they break down. Wetland bacteria may have the ability to break down or bioaccumulate some toxic substances.

Runoff also may contribute pesticides used on residential and commercial property and roadway easements to nearby wetlands. Pesticides (insecticides, herbicides, fungicides), especially those that are persistent in the environment, can cause mortality of birds, amphibians, and other wetland wildlife. Mosquito control compounds also may eliminate aquatic insects that are important to the wetland food web. Herbicides used to control invasive aquatic plants in public canals and lakes may end up in runoff and damage native wetland plants as well as the target plants.

An important biological alteration that disrupts natural communities and degrades wetlands is the introduction of exotic and invasive species. An exotic species is any species distributed outside of its natural range and dispersal potential, and includes its seeds, eggs, spores, or other biological material capable of propagating that species; exotic species are also known as introduced, alien, or nonindigenous species (National Invasive Species Council, 2006). An invasive species is an exotic species that becomes established in natural or semi-natural ecosystems or habitats, is an agent of change, threatens native biodiversity (of species, populations and/or ecosystems), and whose introduction does or is likely to cause economic or environmental harm or harm to human health (National Invasive Species Council, 2006). Exotic species that can cause alteration and destruction of wetlands include plants, fish, mammals, and other organisms.

PRIMER FACTS

An invasive species is an exotic species that becomes established in natural or semi-natural ecosystems or habitats, is an agent of change, threatens native biodiversity (of species, populations and/or ecosystems), and whose introduction does or is likely to cause economic or environmental harm or harm to human health (National Invasive Species Council, 2006).

Egg mass of the invasive apple snail (Pomacea insularum) on a tree in the flood plain of the Hillsborough River. Photographer credit: Dan Duerr, U.S. Geological Survey.

Two important examples of invasive trees that can degrade and damage wetlands in central Florida are the Australian melaleuca (*Melaleuca quinquenervia*) and Brazilian pepper (*Schinus terebinthefolius*). Melaleuca was introduced to help dry and dewater wetland areas and facilitate development. It has since spread widely and has replaced native vegetation in many wetlands. Control and eradication of melaleuca is an expensive undertaking because the tree produces very large numbers of seeds, and there are no animal species in Florida that consume these seeds. Mature melaleuca trees commonly form dense stands that virtually crowd out all native plant and animal species, especially in disturbed areas. Their growth pattern also allows wildfires to spread more quickly and at a higher temperature. A combination of chemical and biological methods are now showing some success for melaleuca control. Brazilian pepper also has disrupted wetlands throughout central Florida. Imported from South America as an ornamental plant, its seeds are spread widely by birds and mammals, and also by flowing water. Brazilian pepper trees produce a dense canopy that shades out all other plants and provides a poor habitat for wildlife, greatly reducing the quality of biotic communities in the State.

There are numerous examples of invasive submersed, floating, and emergent aquatic plants that have caused alteration and degradation of wetlands in central Florida, including water-hyacinth (*Eichhornia crassipes*), hydrilla (*Hydrilla verticillata*), water lettuce (*Pistia stratiotes*), East Indian hygrophila (*Hygrophila polsperma*), West Indian marsh grass (*Hymenachne amplexicaulis*), torpedo grass (*Panicum repens*), parrot's-feather (*Myriophyllum aquaticum*), and wetland nightshade (*Solanum tampicense*) (University of Florida, 2009). The University of Florida Institute of Food and Agricultural Sciences Center for Aquatic and Invasive Plants in Gainesville is a multidisciplinary research, teaching, and extension unit directed to develop environmentally sound techniques for the management of aquatic and natural area weed species and to coordinate aquatic plant research activities within the State. Aquatic plant management efforts using a combination of biological, mechanical, and chemical methods have shown success in maintenance control of several invasive species, and efforts are ongoing to improve success with species that degrade wetlands, lakes, and rivers.

Some invasive animal species that have the potential to degrade wetlands in central Florida include the Asian swamp eel (or rice eel) (*Monopterus albus*), round goby (*Neogobius melanostomus*), Asian clam (*Corbicula fluminea*), island applesnail (*Pomacea insularum*), greenhouse frog (*Eleutherodactylus planirostris*), and Cuban treefrog (*Osteopilus septentrionalis*). These species damage and degrade wetlands primarily by outcompeting native species. More information about the distribution and biology of invasive aquatic species can be found at the Nonindigenous Aquatic Species information resource of the USGS (*http://nas. er.usgs.gov*). Located at the USGS Southeast Ecological Science Center, Gainesville, this site has been established as a central repository for spatially referenced reports of nonindigenous aquatic species.

The invasive species parrot's-feather (Myriophyllumaquaticum). Photographer credit: Dan Duerr, U.S. Geological Survey.

Potential Effects of Global Climate Change on Wetlands

Wetlands are strongly affected by climate variation, in particular temperature and rainfall (Mullholland and others, 1997). Changes in climate are predicted to occur in the 21st century and beyond; the most commonly accepted general circulation models for the United States simulate increases in temperature and atmospheric carbon dioxide (CO_2), and alterations in precipitation patterns, with change unevenly distributed across the country (Burkett and Kusler, 2000).

Temperature is an important factor in controlling plant species distributions, and the warmer temperatures predicted as part of climate change in Florida likely mean higher winter minimum temperatures (Box and others, 1993). The higher winter minimum temperatures and reduced frequency of freezing conditions could facilitate a northward shift in the distribution of many invasive plants, most of which originated in the tropics. Invasive plant species from the tropics to which wetlands are particularly vulnerable include hydrilla (Ficke, 2005), melaleuca (*Melaleuca quinquenervia*) and Brazilian pepper (*Schinus terebinthefolius*) (Box and others, 1993). Many invasive fish and other vertebrates that are tropical in origin, like the Asian swamp eel (*Monopterus albus*), could also move northward under warmer conditions (Mulholland and others, 1997).

Wetlands are vulnerable to changes in water balance driven by global climate change, including an increase or a decrease in the volume of various water sources, and changes in the rate of evapotranspiration (Brinson, 2006). Water balance is more difficult to predict than temperature change, because it also depends on precipitation, which in turn influences evapotranspiration. Wetlands that depend primarily on precipitation as a water source may be more vulnerable to climate change than those that receive a greater proportion of water from groundwater discharge (Winter, 2000).

A warmer and drier climate in the southeastern United States would probably affect populations of bald cypress (Middleton, 2006). Leaf litter production is lowest and tree regeneration is poorest in areas near the edge of the bald cypress geographic range. Stresses exhibited now in these areas are expected to manifest themselves in lower regeneration rates as climate changes across the southern part of the range. Changing climate also may reduce the seed bank density of associated herbaceous swamp species, because germination of many species depends on moisture conditions in the soil and seed density in the seed bank. If the climate becomes warmer and drier, a number of plant species may not be able to move northward fast enough to avoid local elimination, in particular because aquatic seeds disperse southward on most rivers (Middleton, 2003). The St. Johns River is an exception to this pattern, however, because it flows north.

Wetlands in Citrus County provide flood control, aquifer recharge, and opportunities for recreation. Photographer credit: Dan Duerr, U.S. Geological Survey.

Changes in water balance will likely affect wetland communities more than upland ecosystems for several reasons (Burkett and Kusler, 2000). Wetland plants are sensitive to small changes in the level of the water table and the degree of soil saturation. Development and the associated changes that accompany it (construction of roadways, ditching, diking, and drainage) have altered surface drainage patterns, fragmented existing wetlands, and often obstructed the ability of wetland plants to migrate to preferred habitat as water levels change. Other changes to water quality, including pollution and nutrient enrichment, have already stressed many wetlands, impairing their ability to accommodate further changes in water balance.

Riverine and lacustrine wetlands are not isolated, and their hydroperiods are substantially influenced by adjacent surface waters. Under wetter climate conditions, riverine and lacustrine wetlands could increase in size and vegetation biomass if surface slopes are gradual. If the shorelines are steep, rising water levels during a wetter period could reduce the amount of fringing wetlands around lakes, and increased velocity of runoff along rivers could erode wetland areas. A drier period with lower lake levels would result in establishment of aquatic plants farther toward the lake from the shoreline, displacing natural habitat for water fowl and wildlife. Under prolonged dry conditions, lakes in central Florida would be at risk. As the groundwater level drops, crevices and cavities in the limestone aquifer are emptied and sinkholes can form (Tihansky, 1999). A recent sinkhole occurred under Lake Scott in Polk County in 2006, and drained the entire lake in only a few days. Riverine wetlands, which can be spring fed, would likely become smaller if climate conditions become drier, and some rivers may be transformed from gaining to losing streams. The Peace River, in the southern part of central Florida, illustrates an extreme example of this situation whereby drier conditions are coupled with long-term groundwater withdrawal to support agriculture, urban water supply, and phosphate mining (PBS&J Science and Engineering, 2007). The potentiometric surface of the Upper Floridan aquifer has declined to such an extent that springs, which had previously discharged to the Peace River and provided base flow, now divert water from the river into underlying aquifers (Metz and Lewelling, 2009).

Increased concentrations of atmospheric carbon dioxide from the burning of fossil fuels could stimulate wetland plant growth and biomass accumulation (Mendelson and Rosenberg, 1994). Wetlands provide more long-term storage of carbon than upland systems (Burkett and Kusler, 2000). Increased wetland plant growth is a potential enhanced "sink" for atmospheric carbon dioxide, as are wetland restoration and creation projects (Burkett and Kusler, 2000). However, a drier climate could accelerate the release of sequestered carbon dioxide in wetland sediments through decomposition, oxidation, or more frequent fires (Intergovernmental Panel on Climate Change, 2006).

PRIMER FACTS

Changes in climate are predicted to occur in the 21st century and beyond; the most commonly accepted general circulation models for the United States simulate increases in temperature and atmospheric carbon dioxide (CO_2), and alterations in precipitation patterns, with change unevenly distributed across the country (Burkett and Kusler, 2000).

WETLANDS IN CENTRAL FLORIDA—A SUMMARY OF OUR UNDERSTANDING

Wetlands are among the most dynamic ecosystems in central Florida. They are distributed across a variety of landscape types and are present within isolated depressions, around the fringes of lakes, and along the flood plains of rivers. They undergo continuous changes in water depth, the extent of the flooded area, and the frequency of flooding. Wetland water quality changes continually, depending on the predominant water source and biological activities that take place in the water and soils. Wetlands are inhabited by a large number of plants uniquely adapted to changing water levels, and they are colonized by a variety of animals that can take advantage of the available food and shelter that wetlands offer. Finally, wetlands are vulnerable to changes in land use and the many human activities that occur within their drainage basins and often close to their boundaries.

Wetlands as a landscape feature are often admired from afar for their beauty and their value to society, but in proximity they are often misunderstood and unappreciated. In a natural or undeveloped setting, wetlands store water and alleviate flooding following heavy rainfall, provide for water-quality enhancement during the intervals when they hold water, contribute to the recharge of the aquifer, prevent shoreline erosion especially along rivers, and function as valuable plant and wildlife habitat. Wetlands also provide recreational opportunities and aesthetic value to many residents. However, in a developed or agricultural setting, wetlands can be viewed as an impediment to residential and commercial construction, transportation infrastructure, agricultural activities, and water-resource development. Managing wetlands to maintain their ecosystem functions on a sustainable basis is a goal of many water-resource agencies. This goal has become even more challenging under the prevailing conditions of global climate change. Viewing wetlands in the context of their drainage basins, with respect to both hydrology and ecology, is a promising approach to wetland protection, conservation, and sustainability.

Grand Swamp, Disney Wilderness Preserve, Florida. Photographer credit: Clyde Butcher ©1998. Published with permission.

REFERENCES CITED

Ali, A. I., Abtew, W., Van Horn, S. & Khanal, N. (2000). Temporal and spatial analyses for rainfall in central and south Florida: *Journal of the American Water Resources Association*, v. *36*, no. 4, p. 833-848.

Archbold Biological Station (2005). *Ecological research— The focus, accessed December 10,* 2008, at http://www. archbold-station. org.

Batzer, D. P., Cooper, R. & Wissinger, S. A. (2006). Wetland animal ecology in Batzer, D. P. & Sharitz, R. R., eds., *Ecology of freshwater and estuarine wetlands*: Berkeley, University of California Press. p. 242-284.

Bidlake, W. R., Woodham, W. M. & Lopez, M. A. (1996). *Evapotranspiration from areas of native vegetation in west-central Florida: U. S. Geological Survey Water-Supply Paper* 2430, 35 p.

Box, E. O., Crumpacker, D. W. and Hardin, E. D. (1993). A climatic model for location of plant species in Florida, U. S. A. : *Journal of Biogeography*, v. *20*, no. 6, p. 629-644.

Brinson, M. M. (1993). *Changes in the functioning of wetlands along environmental gradients: Wetlands,* v. *13*, no. 2, p. 65-74.

Brinson, M. M. (2006). Consequences for wetlands of a changing global environment, in Batzer, D. P. & Sharitz, R. R., eds., *Ecology of freshwater and estuarine wetlands: Berkeley,* University of California Press, p. 436-461.

Brown, S. L. (1984). *The role of wetlands in the Green Swamp in Ewel,* K. C. and Odum, H. T. eds., Cypress Swamps: Gainesville, University Presses of Florida, 472 p.

Burkett, V. & Kusler, J. (2000). Climate change: Potential impacts and interactions in wetlands of the United States: *Journal of the American Water Resources Association*, v. *36*, no. 2, p. 3 13-320.

Carlisle, V. W. & Hurt, G. W., eds. (2007). *Hydric soils of Florida handbook* (4th ed.): Gainesville, Fla., Florida Association of Environmental Soil Scientists, 28 p.

Carter, V. (1996). Wetland hydrology, water quality & associated functions, in Fretwell, J. D., Williams, J. S. & Redman, P. J., eds., *The national water summary on wetland resources*: U. S. Geological Survey Water Supply Paper 2425, p. 35-48.

Chen, E. & Gerber, J. F. (1990). Climate, in Meyers, R. L. & Ewel, J. J., eds., *Ecosystems of Florida: Orlando,* University of Central Florida Press, p. 11-34.

Collopy, M. W. & Jelks, H. L. (1989). *Distribution and foraging: Wading birds in relation to the physical and biological characteristics of freshwater wetlands: Tallahassee,* Florida Game and Freshwater Fish Commission, Nongame Program, Final Report no. GFC-85-003.

Cowardin, L. M., Carter, V., Golet, F. C. & LaRoe, E. T. (1979). *Classification of wetlands and deepwater habitats of the United States:* Washington D. C., U. S. Fish and Wildlife Service report FWS/OBS-79/3 1.

Dahl, T. E. (1990). Wetland losses in the United States 1780s to 1980s: Washington, D. C., U. S. Fish and Wildlife Service report, 21 p.

Dahl, T. E. (2000). Status and trends of wetlands in the conterminous United States 1986 to 1997: Washington D. C., U. S. Fish and Wildlife Service report, 82 p.

Dahl, T. E. (2005). Florida's wetlands: An update on status and trends 1985 to 1996: Washington D. C., U. S. Fish and Wildlife Service report, 80 p.

Dahl, T. E. (2006). Status and trends of wetlands in the conterminous United States 1998 to 2004: Washington D. C., U. S. Fish and Wildlife Service report, 112 p.

Darst, M. R., Light, H. M. & McPherson, B. F. (1996). *Florida wetland resources, in Fretwell,* J. D., Williams, J. S. & Redman, P. J., eds., National water summary on wetland resources: U. S. Geological Survey Water-Supply Paper 2425, p. 153-160.

DeMort, C. L. (1991). The St. Johns River system, in Livingston, R. J., ed., *Rivers of Florida:* New York, Springer-Verlag, p. 97-120.

Dolan, T. J., Bayley, S. E., Zoltek, J. & Hermann, A. J. (1981). Phosphorus dynamics of a Florida freshwater marsh receiving treated wastewater: *Journal of Applied Ecology,* v. *18*, p. 205-219.

Duever, L. C. (1997). *Natural communities of Florida's wet prairies: Palmetto,* v. *7*, no. 2, 2 p.

Enfield, D. B., Mestas-Nunez, A. M. & Trimble, P. J. (2001). The Atlantic multidecadal oscillation and its relation to rainfall and river flows in the continental U. S. : *Geophysical Research Letters,* v. *28*, no. 10, p. 2077-2080.

Engeman, R. M., Smith, H. T., Severson, R. G., Seversen, M. M., Shwiff, S. A., Constantin, B. & Griffen, D. (2003). *Amount and economic valuation of feral hog damage to a unique basin marsh wetland in Florida*: Florida Park Service 2003 "Partnership" Technical Report, 5 p.

Ewel, K. C. (1990). Swamps, in Myers, R. L. & Ewel, J. J., eds., *Ecosystems of Florida*: Orlando, University of Central Florida Press, 765 p.

Fernald, E. A. & Purdum, E. D., eds., (1998). *Water resources atlas of Florida: Tallahassee,* Institute of Science and Public Affairs, 312 p.

Ficke, A. A. (2005). *The effects of global climate change on the fishes of the southeastern United States:* New York, World Wildlife Fund, 29 p.

Fitts, C. R. (2002). *Groundwater Science:* New York, Academic Press, 450 p.

Florida Department of Environmental Protection, (2008a). *Florida State of the Environment—Wetlands: A guide to living with Florida's wetlands,* accessed September 3, 2008, at http://www. dep. state. fl. us/water/wetlands/does/erp/fsewet.

Florida Department of Environmental Protection, (2008b). Wetland mitigation, accessed July 31, 2008, at http://www. dep. state. fl. us/water/wetlands

Florida Department of Environmental Protection, (2009). Florida Wetlands Delineation Manual, accessed June 29, 2009, at http://www. dep. state. fl. us/water/tmdl/index. htm.

Gilboy, A. E. (1985). *Hydrogeology of the Southwest Florida Water Management District: Brooksville,* Fla., Southwest Florida Water Management District Regional Analysis Section Technical Report 85-01, 18 p.

Haag, K. H., Lee, T. M. & Herndon, D. C. (2005). Bathymetry and vegetation in isolated marsh and cypress wetlands in the northern Tampa Bay area 2000-2004: U. S. Geological Survey Scientific Investigations Report 2005-5109, 49 p.

Hancock, P. J., Boulton, A. J. & Humphreys, W. F. (2005). Aquifers and hyporheic zones – towards an ecological understanding of groundwater: *Journal of Hydrogeology,* v. *13*, p. 98-111.

Houlahan, J. E., Keddy, P. A., Makkay, K. & Findlay, C. S. (2006). The effects of adjacent land use on wetland species richness and community composition: *Wetlands,* v. *26*, no. 1, p. 79-96.

Intergovernmental Panel on Climate Change, 2006, (2006). *IPCC guidelines for national greenhouse gas inventories, prepared by the National Greenhouse Gas Inventories Program*, Eggleston, H. S., Buendia, L., Miwa, K., Ngara,

T. & Tanabe, K., eds. : Hayama, Japan, Institute for Global Environmental Strategies.

Kentula, M. E., Brooks, R. P., Gwin, S. E., Holland, C. C., Sherman, A. D., Sifneos, J. C., (1993). *An approach to improving decision making in wetland restoration and creation:* Washington, D. C., Island Press, 151 p.

Kirk, J. A., Wise, W. R. & Delfino, J. J. (2004). Water budget and cost-effectiveness analysis of wetland restoration alternatives: A case study of Levy Prairie, Alachua County, Florida: *Ecological Engineering,* v. *22*, p. 43-60.

Kushlan, J. A. (1990). Freshwater marshes, in Myers, R. L. and Ewel, J. J., eds., *Ecosystems of Florida*: Orlando, University of Central Florida Press, 765 p.

Layne, J. N. (1983). Productivity of sandhill cranes in south central Florida*: Journal of Wildlife Management*, v. *47*, no. 1, p. 178-185.

Lee, T. M. (2002). Factors affecting groundwater exchange and catchment size for Florida lakes in mantled karst terrain: U. S. Geological Survey Water-Resources Investigations Report 02-4033, 54 p.

Lee, T. M. & Haag, K. H. (2006). *Strength in numbers; describing the flooded area of isolated wetlands*: U. S. Geological Survey Fact Sheet 2006-3118, 4 p.

Lee, T. M., Haag, K. H., Metz, P. A. & Sacks, L. A. (2009*). The comparative hydrology, water quality & ecology of selected natural and augmented freshwater wetlands in west-central Florida:* U. S. Geological Survey Professional Paper 1758, 152 p.

Lewelling, B. R. (2003). *Extent of areal inundation of riverine wetlands along Cypress Creek and the Peace,* Alafia, North Prong Alafia & South Prong Alafia Rivers, west-central Florida: U. S. Geological Survey Water-Resources Investigations Report 02-4254, 91 p.

Lewelling, B. R. (2004). *Extent of areal inundation of riverine wetlands along five river systems in the Upper Hillsborough River watershed,* west-central Florida: U. S. Geological Survey Scientific Investigations Report 2004-5133, 49 p.

Livingston, R. J., ed., (1990). *The rivers of Florida: New York*, Springer-Verlag, 289 p.

Main, M. B., Ceilly, D. W. & Stansly, P. (2007). Freshwater fish assemblages in isolated south Florida wetlands*: Southeastern Naturalist*, v. 6, no. 2, p. 343-3 50.

Marella, R. L. (2004). *Water withdrawals, use, discharge & trends in Florida* 2000: U. S. Geological Survey Scientific Investigations Report 2004-5 151, 136 p.

Martin, A. C., Hotchkiss, N., Uhler, F. M. & Bourn, W. S. (1953*). Classification of wetlands of the United States: Washington D. C., U. S. Fish and Wildlife Service Special Scientific Report—Wildlife*, no 20, 14 p.

Mendelson R. & Rosenberg, N. J., (1994). Framework for integrated assessments of global warming impacts: *Climate Change,* v. *28*, p. 15-44.

Metz, P. A. & Lewelling, B. R. (2009). *Hydrologic conditions that influence streamflow losses in a karst region of the upper Peace River*, Polk County, Florida: U. S. Geological Survey Scientific Investigations Report 2009-5140, 82 p.

Metz, P. A. & Sacks, L. A. (2002). *Comparison of the hydrogeology and water quality of a ground-water augmented lake with two non-augmented lakes in northwest Hillsborough County,* Florida: U. S. Geological Survey Water-Resources Investigations Report 02-4032, 74 p.

Middleton, B. A. (2003). Soil seed banks and the potential restoration of forested wetlands after farming: *Journal of Applied Ecology,* v. *40*, p. 1025-1034.

Middleton, B. A. (2006). *Bald cypress swamp management and climate change*: U. S. Geological Survey Open-File Report 2006-1269, 3 p.

Mullholland, P. J., Best, G. R., Coutant, C. C., Hornberger, G. M., Meyer, J. L., Robinson, P. J., Stenberg, J. R., Turner, R. E., VeraHerra, F. & Wetzel, R. G. (1997). Effects of climate change on freshwater ecosystems of the south- eastern United States and the Gulf Coast of Mexico: *Hydrological Processes,* v. *11*, no. 8, p. 949-970.

National Academy of Sciences. (1995). *Wetlands: Characteristics and Boundaries:* Washington D. C., National Academies Press, 308 p.

National Invasive Species Council. (2006). *Invasive species definition, clarification & guidance white paper,* accessed June 24 2009, at http://www. invasivespeciesinfo. gov/docs/ council/isacdef. pdf.

National Oceanic and Atmospheric Administration. (2008). NOAA Climatic Data Center temperature, precipitation, drought data for Florida, accessed July 17 2008, at http://www. ncdc. noaa. gov/oa/climate/regionalclimate centers. htmlt.

National Research Council. (1992). *Restoration of aquatic ecosystems—Science, technology & public policy:* Washington D. C., National Academy Press, 552 p.

National Research Council. (2001). *Compensating for wetland losses under the Clean Water Act:* Washington, D. C., National Academy Press, 322 p.

Neubauer, C. P., Hall, G. B., Lowe, E. F., Robison, C. P., Hupalo, R. B. & Keenan, L. W. (2008). Minimum flows and levels method of the St. Johns River Water Management District, Florida, USA: *Environmental Management*, v. *42*, no. 6, p. 1101-1114.

Ortiz, A. G. (2006). *Potentiometric surface of the Upper Floridan aquifer,* west-central Florida, September 2005: U. S. Geological Survey Open-File Report 2006-1128,1 sheet.

Ortiz, A. G. (2007). *Potentiometric surface of the Upper Floridan aquifer,* west-central Florida, September 2006: U. S. Geological Survey Open-File Report 2007-1228, 1 sheet.

Ortiz, A. G. (2009). *Potentiometric surface of the Upper Floridan aquifer*, west-central Florida, September 2008: U. S. Geological Survey Scientific Investigations Map 3071, 1 sheet.

PBS&J Science and Engineering. (2007). *Peace River Cumulative Impact Study*: Technical report prepared for the Florida Department of Environmental Protection, Tallahassee, Fla., variously paged.

Renken, R. A., Dixon, J., Koehmstedt, J., Ishman, S., Lietz, A. C., Marella, R. L., Telis, P., Rodgers, J. & Memberg, S. (2005). *Impact of anthropogenic development on coastal ground-water hydrology in southeastern Florida,* 1900- 2000: U. S. Geological Circular 1275, 77 p.

Richardson, J. L. & Vepraskas, M. J. (2001). *Wetland soils*: Boca Raton, Florida, Lewis Publishers, 417 p.

Riekerk, H. & Korhnak, L. V. (1992). Rainfall and runoff chemistry of Florida pine flatwoods: *Water, Air & Soil Pollution,* v. *65*, p. 69-68.

Riekerk, H. & Korhnak, L. V. (2000). *The hydrology of cypress wetlands in Florida pine flatwoods: Wetlands*, v *20,* no. 3, p. 448-460.

St. Johns River Water Management District. (2004). The Lake Apopka Marsh Flow-way, accessed on September 6 2008, at http://www. sjrwmd. com/publications. html.

St. Johns River Water Management District. (2006). *Lake Apopka—A decade of improvement now accelerating,* accessed on January 2 2008, at http://www. sjrwmd. com/ publications. html.

St. Johns River Water Management District. (2008). Hydro- geology of the St. Johns River Water Management District, accessed July 16 2008, at http://www. sjrwmd. com/springs/ hydrogeology. html

Schiffer, D. M. (1998). Hydrology of central Florida lakes— *A primer: U. S. Geological Survey Circular 1137,* 38 p.

Shaw, S. P. & Fredine, C. G. (1956). Wetlands of the United States—Their extent and their value to waterfowl and other wildlife: Washington, D. C., U. *S. Fish and Wildlife Service Circular 39,* 67 p.

Sinclair, W. C., Knutilla, R. L., Gilboy, A. E. & Miller, R. L. (1985). *Types, features & occurrence of sinkholes in the karst of west-central Florida*: U. S. Geological Survey Water Resources Investigations Report 85-4126, 81 p.

Southwest Florida Water Management District. (1996). *Northern Tampa Bay Water Resources Assessment Project,* Volume, *1,* Surface-water/groundwater interrelationships: Brooksville, Fla., variously paged.

Southwest Florida Water Management District. (2006). *Wetland treatment system recommended for Lake Hancock outfall,* accessed January 25 2009, at http://www. swfwmd. stste. fl. us/ news.

Southwest Florida Water Management District. (2008). *Hydrologic data summaries*, accessed September 29 2008, at http://www8. swfwmd. state. fl. us/WMIS/ResourceData/ ExtDefault. Aspx

Southwest Florida Water Management District (2009a), *West-central Florida's aquifers,* accessed March 5 2009, at http://www/swfwmd. state. fl. us/publications/files/flas_ aquifers. pdf.

Southwest Florida Water Management District (2009b). *Water Management Information System,* accessed January 6, 2009, at http://www. swfwmd. stste. fl. us/WMIS/ResourcedAta/ Extdefault. aspx.

Spechler, R. M. & Kroening, S. E. (2007). *Hydrology of Polk County,* Florida: U. S. Geological Survey Scientific Investigations Report 2006-5320, 114 p.

Stevenson, R. J., Bothwell, M. L. & Lowe, R. L. (1996). *Algal ecology:* New York, Academic Press, 753 p.

Sumner, D. M. (2001). *Evapotranspiration from a cypress and pine forest subjected to natural fires,* Volusia County, Florida, 1998-99: U. S. Geological Survey Water-Resources Investigations Report 01-4245, 56 p.

Sumner, D. M. (2006). *Evapotranspiration measurement and estimation in Florida—State of the art and future directions* [abs.], in Biennial Stormwater Research Symposium, 2nd, May 4-5 2006, Proceedings: Orlando, University of Central Florida, p. 125-138.

Sunquist, F., Sunquist, M. & Beletsky, L. (2002). Florida— *The ecotravellers' wildlife guide:* New York, Academic Press, 532 p.

Tihansky, A. B. (1999). Sinkholes, west-central Florida, in Galloway, Devin, Jones, D. R., Ingebritsen, S. E., *Land subsidence in the United States*: U. S. Geological Survey Circular 1182, p. 120-141.

University of Florida. (2009). All about wetlands: Institute of Food and Agricultural Sciences, Wetland Extension Office, Gainesville, Fla., accessed February 25 2009, at http:// wetlandextension. ifas. ufl. edu/exoticspecies. htm.

U. S. Army Corps of Engineers, (1987). *Wetland delineation manual*: Wetland Research Program Technical Report Y-87-1, 92 p.

U. S. Environmental Protection Agency. (2004). *Wetlands Regulatory Authority:* EPA 843-F-04-001, 2 p., accessed October 29 2009, at http://www. epa. gov/owow/wetlands pdf/reg_authority_pr. pdf.

U. S. Environmental Protection Agency. (2008). *Introduction to the Clean Water Act,* accessed October 29 2009, at http:// www. epa. gov/watertrain/cwa/.

U. S. Fish and Wildlife Service. (2009a). *National Wetlands Inventory,* accessed May 18 2009, at http://www. fws. giv/ wetlands/data/index. html.

U.S. Fish and Wildlife Service. (2009b). *National Wetlands Inventory Wetland Codes*, accessed June 24 2009, at http:// www. fws. gov/wetlands

U.S. Geological Survey. (2008a). *Facing tomorrow's challenges—An overview:* U. S. Geological Survey Fact Sheet 2008-3008, 4 p.

U.S. Geological Survey. (2008b). Groundwater availability in the United States: U. S. *Geological Survey Circular 1323,* 70 p.

U.S. Geological Survey. (2008c). *Hydrologic Data Web Portal – Florida potential and reference evapotranspiration* 2005-2008, accessed August 10 2009 at http://hdwp. er. gov/ et2005-2007. asp.

U.S. Geological Survey. (2009a). accessed April 17 2009, at http://waterdata. usgs. gov/fl/nwis/sw.

U.S. Geological Survey. (2009b). *Everglades Ecosystem Restoration – Florida Apple Snail,* accessed June 29 2009, at http://www. fl. biology. usgs. gov/sofla/apple_snail. pdf.

van der Valk, A. G. 2006, *The biology of freshwater wetlands: New York,* Oxford University Press, 173 p.

Wetland Solutions, Inc. (2007). *Infiltrating wetlands for reclaimed water recycling and nitrate removal at the Kanapaha Water Reclamation Facility—A preliminary feasibility assessment: Gainesville, Fla.,* Technical report prepared for Gainesville Regional Utilities, 29 p.

White, W. A. (1970). *Geomorphology of the Florida Peninsula: Tallahassee*, Florida Geological Survey Bulletin 51, 164 p.

Winter, T. C. (1998). Relation of streams, lakes & wetlands to groundwater flow systems: *Hydrogeology Journal,* v. *7*, p. 28-45.

Winter, T. C. (2000). The vulnerability of wetlands to climate change: A hydrological landscape perspective: *Journal of the American Water Resources Association*, v. *36*, no. 2, p. 305-311.

Winter, T. C., Harvey, J. W., Franke, O. L. & Alley, W. M. (1998). Ground water and surface water—*A single resource: U. S. Geological Survey Circular 1139,* 79 p.

Winter, T. C. & LaBaugh, J. W. (2003). Hydrologic considerations in defining isolated wetlands: *Wetlands*, v. *23*, no. 3, p. 532-540.

Winter, T. C. and Woo, M. K. (1990). *Hydrology of lakes and wetlands, in Wolman*, M. G. & Riggs, H. C., eds., Surface water hydrology: Boulder, Colo., Geological Society of America, v. *0-1*, p. 159-187.

Wise, W. R., Annable, M. D., Walser, J. A. E., Switt, R. S. & Shaw, D. T. (2000). A wetland-aquifer interaction test: *Journal of Hydrology*, v. *227*, p. 257-272.

Wright, J. O. (1907). Swamp and overflowed lands in the United States: Washington, D. C., U. S. Department of Agriculture, Office of Experiment Stations, *Circular, 76*, 23 p.

GLOSSARY

A

Acidic   Term applied to water or other substances with a pH less than 5.5.

Alkaline   Term applied to water or other substances with a pH greater than 7.4.

Alkalinity   A measure of the capacity of water to neutralize acids.

Aerobic   Having or providing oxygen.

Anaerobic   Lacking oxygen.

Aquatic   Living or growing in or on water.

Aquifer   A geologic formation, group of formations, or part of a formation that contains sufficient saturated, permeable material to be able to yield substantial quantities of water to wells and springs.

B

Bathymetry   The measurement of water depth at various places in a wetland, lake, or other water body.

Bioindicator   A species used to monitor the health of an environment or ecosystem.

Biomass   The amount of living matter, in the form of organisms, present in a particular habitat, usually expressed as weight per unit area.

Buffered   A solution that has the ability to resist a change in pH upon addition of an acid or a base.

C

Carbonates   Rock composed chiefly of carbonate minerals such as limestone and dolomite.

Confining layer A body of relatively impermeable or distinctly less permeable material stratigraphically adjacent to one or more aquifers that restricts the movement of water into and out of those aquifers.

Cypress wetland   A poorly drained to permanently wet depression dominated by cypress trees.

D

Discharge wetland A wetland that contains surface water at a lower elevation than the surrounding water table, causing an inflow of groundwater to the wetland.

Dissolved oxygen   Oxygen that is held in solution in water. Only a fixed amount of oxygen can be dissolved in water at a given temperature and atmospheric pressure.

Drainage basin A part of the surface of the Earth that drains into a body of water by way of overland flow or streamflow.

E

Ecology The science of the relations between organisms and their environment.

Emergent plants   Erect, rooted, herbaceous plants that may be temporarily to permanently flooded at their base but do not tolerate prolonged inundation of the entire plant.

Evaporation   The process by which water is changed from the liquid state into the gaseous state through the transfer of heat energy.

Evapotranspiration The sum of water lost from a given land area during any specified time by transpiration from vegetation; by evaporation from water surfaces, moist soil, and snow; and by interception (rainfall that never reaches the ground but evaporates from surfaces of plants and trees).

F

Flood duration The amount of time that a wetland contains standing water.

Flood frequency   The average number of times that a wetland contains standing water during a given period.

Flood plain   Flat or nearly flat land adjacent to a stream or river that experiences occasional or periodic flooding.

G

Groundwater Water below the land surface in the saturated zone.

H

Head   The measurement of water pressure above a common datum, usually measured as a water surface elevation, expressed in units of length, in a piezometer (a specialized type of water well).

Hydric soils   Soil that is wet long enough to periodically produce anaerobic conditions, thereby influencing the growth of plants.

Hydrologic cycle   A term describing the circulation of water from the ocean, through the atmosphere, to the land, and back to the ocean by overland and subterranean pathways and by way of the atmosphere; also includes the paths by which water is returned to the atmosphere without reaching the ocean.

Hydrology   The science of the water of the Earth.

Hydroperiod   The seasonal pattern of the water level in a wetland.

Hyporheic zone   The zone beneath a stream bottom where a mixture of surface water and groundwater can be found.

I

Infiltration   The flow of water into the Earth through pores in the soil at the land surface.

Invasive species   An exotic species that becomes established in natural or semi- natural ecosystems or habitats, is an agent of change, threatens native biodiversity (of species, populations and/or ecosystems), and whose introduction does or is likely to cause economic or environmental harm or harm to human health.

Isolated wetland   A wetland with no apparent surface-water connection to streams, rivers, estuaries, or the ocean.

J

K

Karst   A region underlain by limestone that contains solution cavities, and where the physical features of the land surface include large and small depressions.

L

M

Marsh   A frequently to continually wet depression characterized by emergent herbaceous vegetation.

N

O

Overland flow   Nonchannelized flow of water that usually occurs during and immediately following rainfall.

P

Percolation   The flow of water through a porous substance, usually in a vertical direction. Rainfall that reaches the land surface infiltrates the surface and percolates downward.

Permeability   The capacity of soil to conduct water flow; also known as hydraulic conductivity.

pH   A measure of the hydrogen ion concentration of a liquid.

Potentiometric surface   The surface that represents the level to which water will rise in a tightly cased (sealed) well.

Precipitation   Water from the atmosphere that reaches the land surface as rain, frozen rain, or snow.

Q

R

Recharge wetland   A wetland that contains surface water at a higher elevation than the adjacent water table, causing an outflow of wetland water to groundwater.

Residence time   The time necessary for the total volume of water in a wetland to be completely replaced by incoming water.

River mile   Measure of distance in miles along a river from its mouth. River mile numbers begin at zero and increase farther upstream.

Runoff   Nonchannelized surface-water flow.

S

Saturated zone   The zone below the land surface in which soil or rock is saturated with water under hydrostatic pressure.

Scrub   A general term for short, dense vegetation dominated by shrubs (woody plants less than 20 ft high), which typically forms an intermediate community between grass and forest.

Seasonally flooded   Wetlands that are flooded for extended periods during and following the wet season, but with no remaining surface water by the end of the dry season.

Seepage   A process in which water moves slowly through the surface and subsurface environments, or the actual water involved in this process.

Seepage wetland   A wetland on sloped or flat sands or peat with high moisture levels maintained by downslope seepage.

Shrub   A woody plant which at maturity is usually less than 20 ft high and generally exhibits several erect, spreading, or prostrate stems, and has a bushy appearance.

Sinkhole   A funnel-shaped depression in the surface of the Earth caused by dissolution of underlying limestones.

Slough   A slow moving body of water occupying a shallow, poorly-defined channel that is slightly deeper than the surrounding area. Sloughs may be intermittent.

Specific conductance   A measure of the property of water to conduct a current of electricity. Specific conductance is commonly used as an indicator of the dissolved solids content of water.

Surface runoff   That part of precipitation that does not infiltrate the land surface, but travels along the land surface.

Swamp   A water-saturated area, intermittently or permanently covered with water, vegetated with trees and shrubs.

T

Transpiration   The processes by which plants take water from the soil, use it in plant growth, and then transpire it to the atmosphere in the form of water vapor. Evaporation and transpiration are collectively referred to as evapotranspiration.

U

Unsaturated zone   The zone between land surface and the water table where the pores in the soil matrix are filled with both air and water.

V

W

Water budget   An accounting of the inflow to, outflow from, and storage within a wetland, lake, or drainage basin.

Water table   The upper surface of the zone of saturation in the ground. The water table commonly is at atmospheric pressure.

Well field   An area developed by a local or regional water authority where groundwater is withdrawn from the aquifer and sent to a treatment or distribution system.

Wetland   An ecosystem characterized by the presence of shallow water or flooded soils for part of the growing season, plants adapted to a wet environment, and soil indicators of flooding (hydric soils).

Wetland augmentation   The addition of water from an external source to increase the water level in a wetland.

X
Y
Z

CONVERSION FACTORS

Multiply	By	To obtain
inch (in.)	2.54	centimeter
foot (ft)	0.3 048	meter
mile (mi)	1.609	kilometer
square mile (mi^2)	2.590	square kilometer
acre	0.4047	hectare
cubic foot per second (ft^3/s)	0.02832	cubic meter per second
inch per year (in/yr)	2.54	centimeter per year
gallon per day (gal/d)	0.003 785	cubic meter per day
million gallons per day (Mgal/d)	0.04381	cubic meter per second

ACRONYMS AND ADDITIONAL ABBREVIATIONS

CAD	Computer Aided Design
DOQ	digital orthophoto quadrangle
DOQQ	digital orthophoto quarter quadrangle
ERP	Environmental Resource Permit
FLUCCS	Florida Land Use and Cover Classifications System
FNAI	Florida Natural Areas Inventory
GIS	Geographic Information System
GPS	geographic positioning system

LIDAR	light detection and ranging μS/cm microsiemens per centimeter
μg/L	micrograms per liter
mg/L	milligrams per liter
ppt	parts per thousand
USGS	U.S. Geological Survey

In: Wetlands in Central Florida: An Ecology and Hydrology...   ISBN: 978-1-61728-600-1
Editor: Samantha L. Elliot   © 2010 Nova Science Publishers, Inc.

Chapter 2

APPENDIX: HYDROLOGY AND ECOLOGY OF FRESHWATER WETLANDS IN CENTRAL FLORIDA

United States Geological Survey

This appendix includes maps showing the distribution of wetlands by type and pie diagrams showing the percent of each wetland type in each county of central Florida.

PIE CHART EXPLANATION

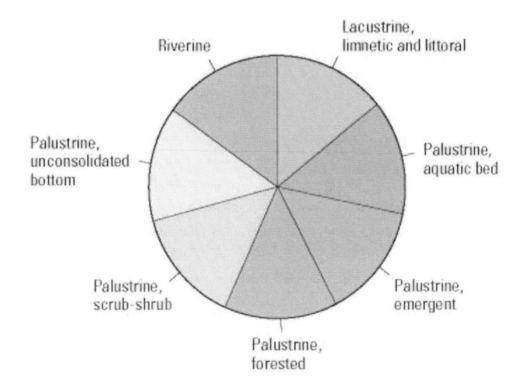

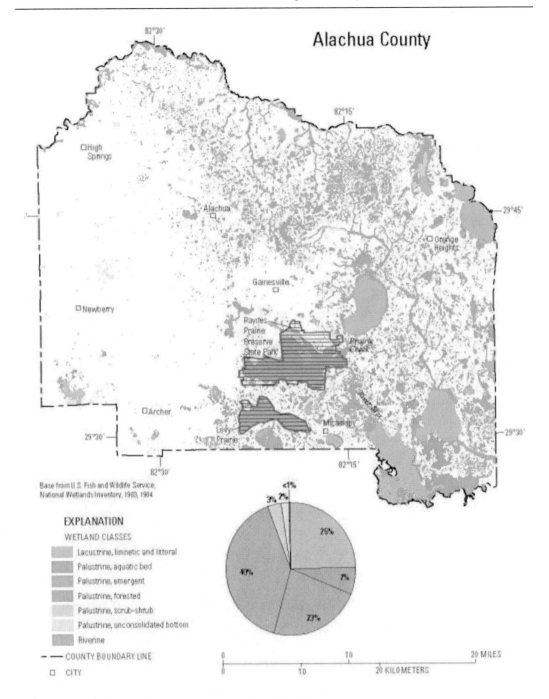

Map 1. The distribution of wetlands by type and pie diagrams showing the percent of each wetland type in Alachua County, Florida.

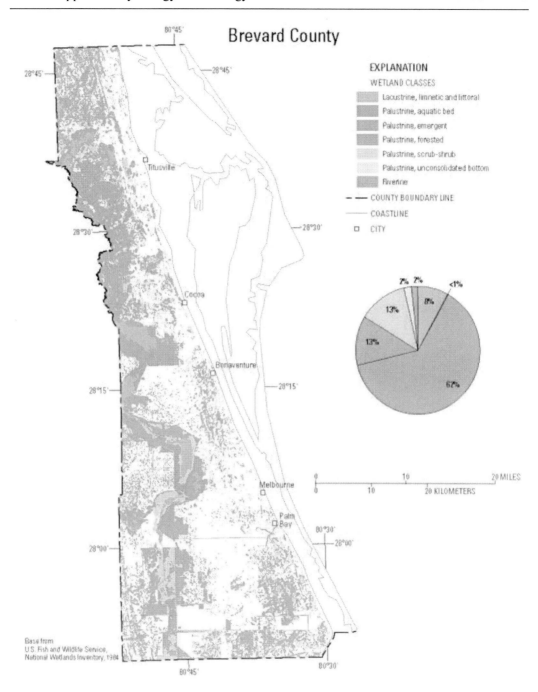

Map 2. The distribution of wetlands by type and pie diagrams showing the percent of each wetland type in Brevard County, Florida.

Citrus County

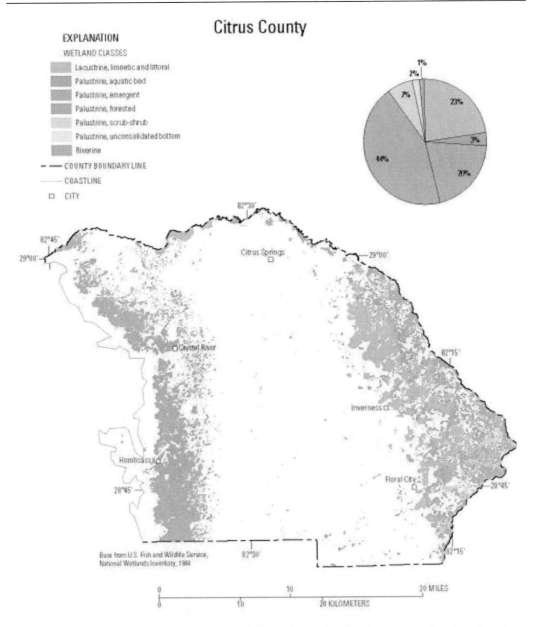

Map 3. The distribution of wetlands by type and pie diagrams showing the percent of each wetland type in Citrus County, Florida.

DeSoto County

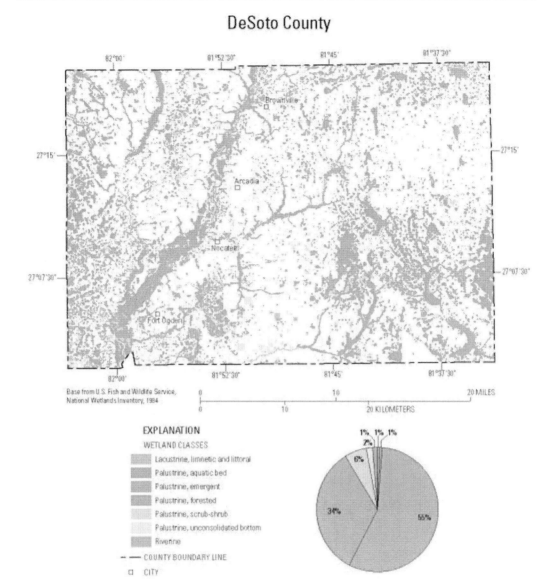

Map 4. The distribution of wetlands by type and pie diagrams showing the percent of each wetland type in DeSoto County, Florida.

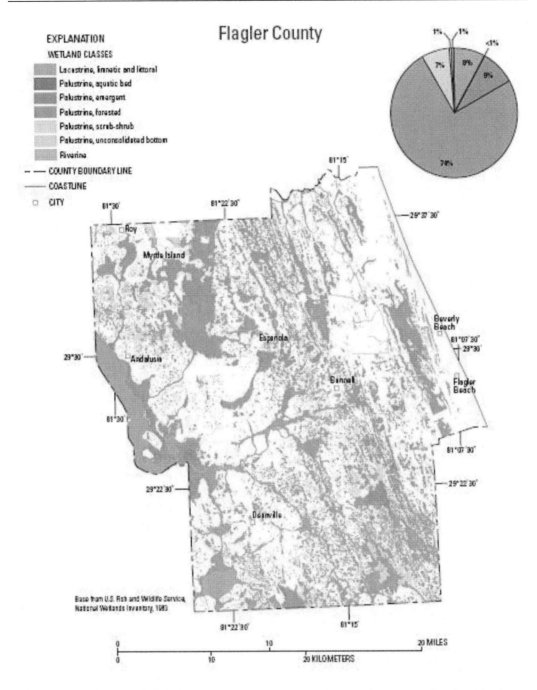

Map 5. The distribution of wetlands by type and pie diagrams showing the percent of each wetland type in Flagler County, Florida.

Hardee County

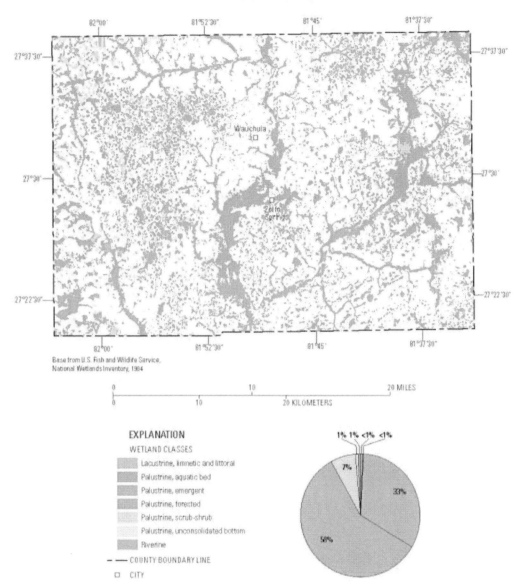

Base from U.S. Fish and Wildlife Service,
National Wetlands Inventory, 1984

EXPLANATION

WETLAND CLASSES

- Lacustrine, limnetic and littoral
- Palustrine, aquatic bed
- Palustrine, emergent
- Palustrine, forested
- Palustrine, scrub-shrub
- Palustrine, unconsolidated bottom
- Riverine
- — — COUNTY BOUNDARY LINE
- ☐ CITY

Map 6. The distribution of wetlands by type and pie diagrams showing the percent of each wetland type in Hardee County, Florida.

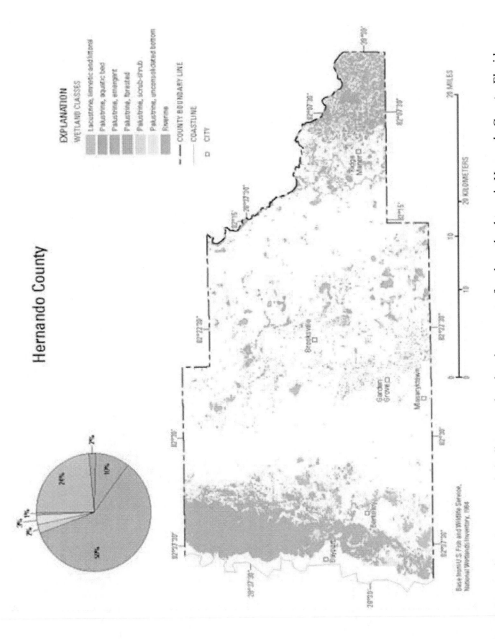

Map 7. The distribution of wetlands by type and pie diagrams showing the percent of each wetland type in Hernando County, Florida.

Highlands County

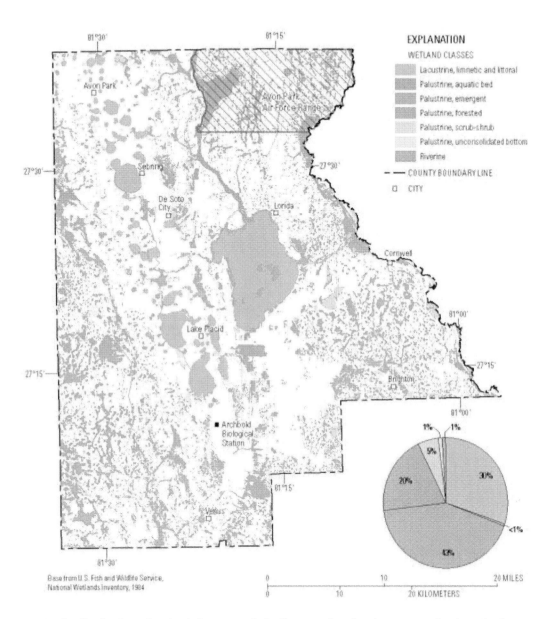

Map 8. The distribution of wetlands by type and pie diagrams showing the percent of each wetland type in Highlands County, Florida.

Hillsborough County

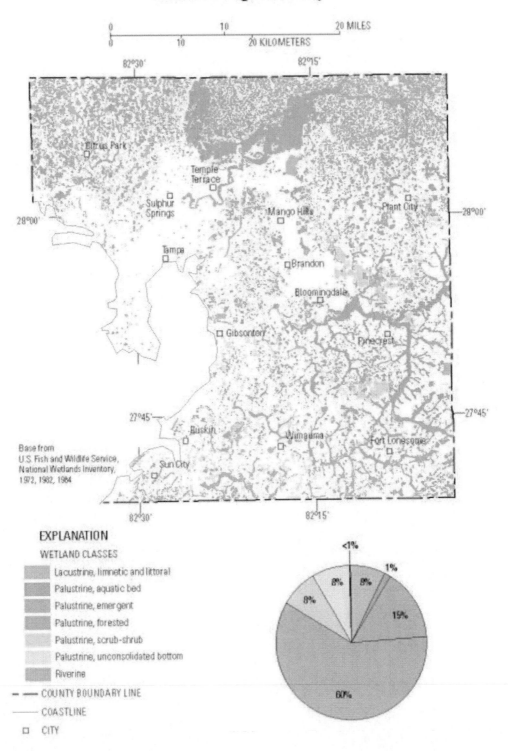

Map 9. The distribution of wetlands by type and pie diagrams showing the percent of each wetland type in Hillsborough County, Florida.

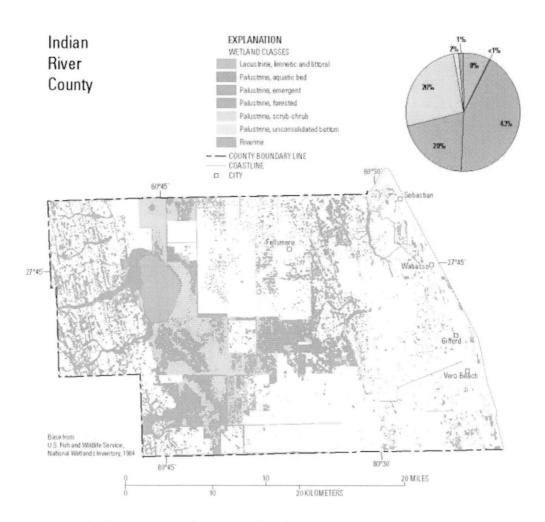

Map 10. The distribution of wetlands by type and pie diagrams showing the percent of each wetland type in Indian River County, Florida.

Lake County

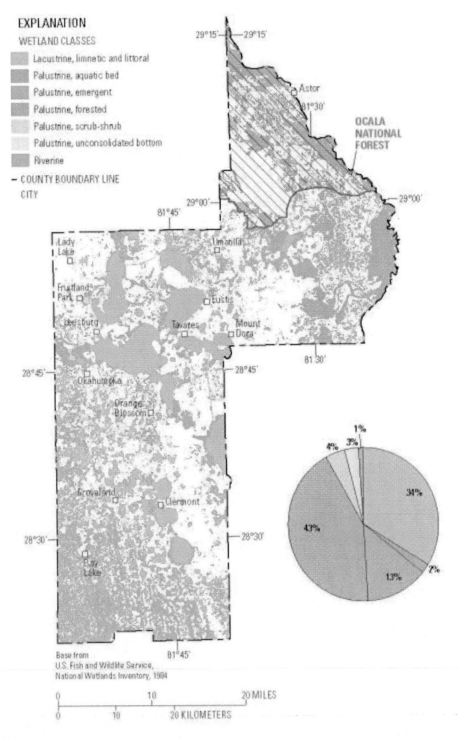

Map 11. The distribution of wetlands by type and pie diagrams showing the percent of each wetland type in Lake County, Florida.

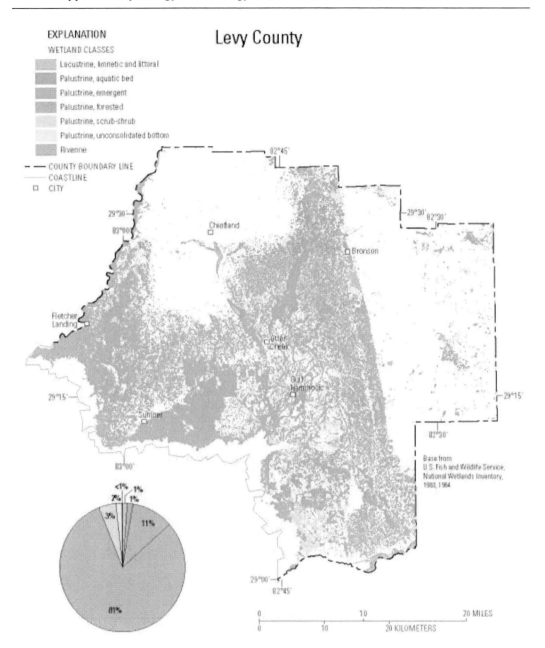

Map 12. The distribution of wetlands by type and pie diagrams showing the percent of each wetland type in Levy County, Florida.

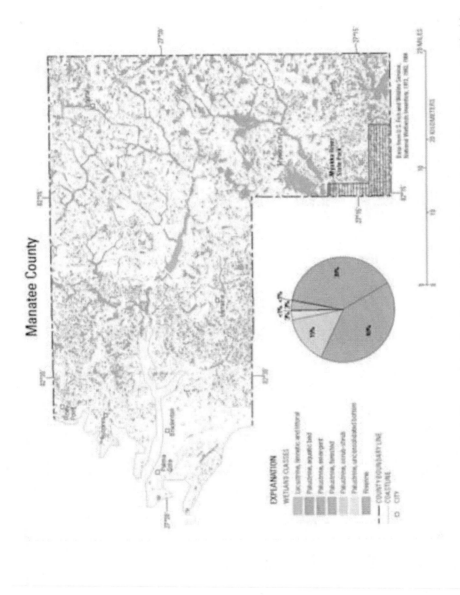

Map 13. The distribution of wetlands by type and pie diagrams showing the percent of each wetland type in Manatee County, Florida.

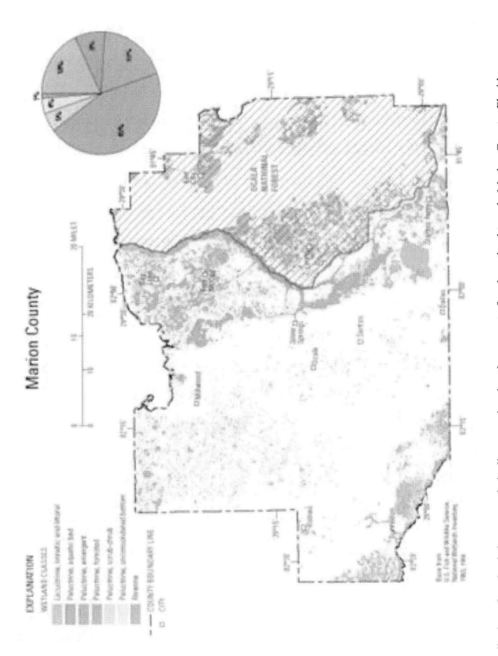

Map 14. The distribution of wetlands by type and pie diagrams showing the percent of each wetland type in Marion County, Florida.

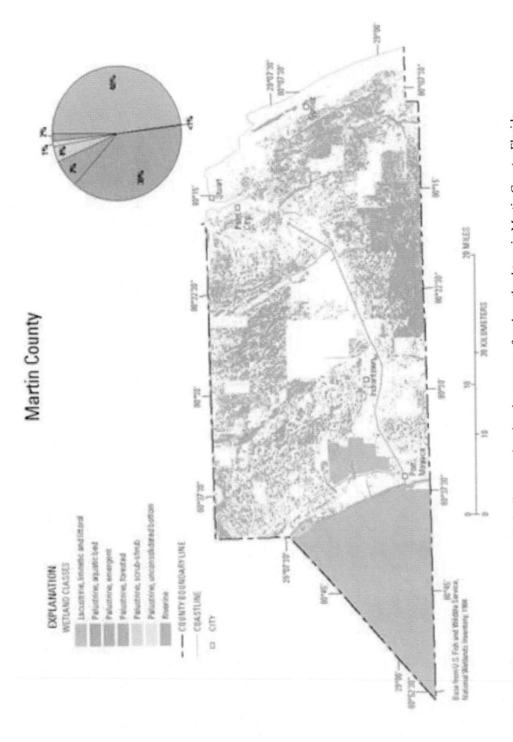

Map 15. The distribution of wetlands by type and pie diagrams showing the percent of each wetland type in Martin County, Florida.

Okeechobee County

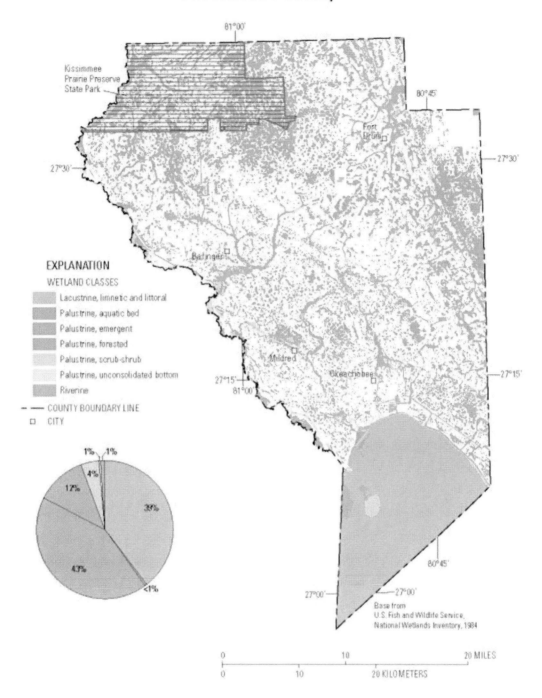

EXPLANATION

WETLAND CLASSES

Lacustrine, limnetic and littoral

Palustrine, aquatic bed

Palustrine, emergent

Palustrine, forested

Palustrine, scrub-shrub

Palustrine, unconsolidated bottom

Riverine

— — COUNTY BOUNDARY LINE

□ CITY

Base from
U.S. Fish and Wildlife Service,
National Wetlands Inventory, 1984

Map 16. The distribution of wetlands by type and pie diagrams showing the percent of each wetland type in Okeechobee County, Florida.

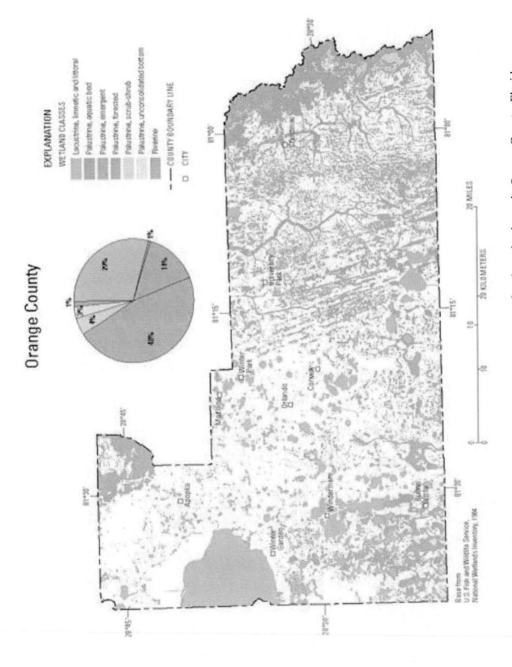

Map 17. The distribution of wetlands by type and pie diagrams showing the percent of each wetland type in Orange County, Florida.

Osceola County

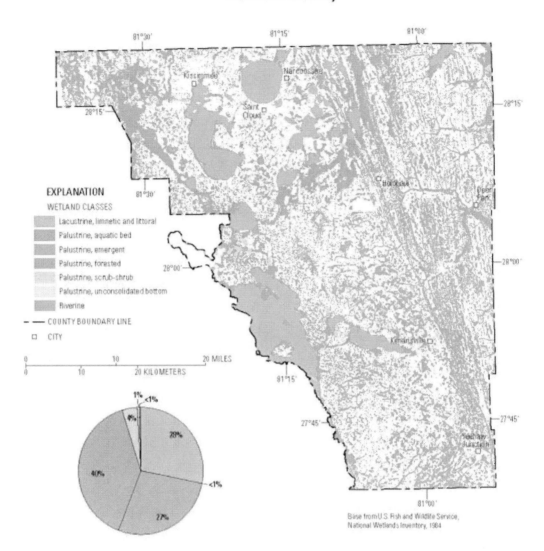

Map 18. The distribution of wetlands by type and pie diagrams showing the percent of each wetland type in Osceola County, Florida.

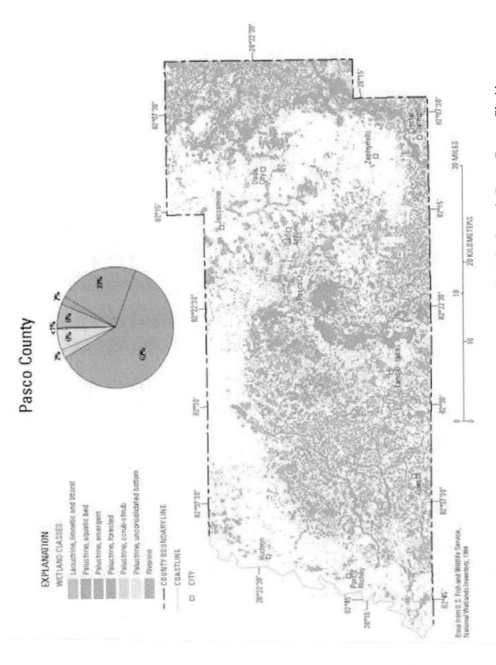

Map 19. The distribution of wetlands by type and pie diagrams showing the percent of each wetland type in Pasco County, Florida.

Pinellas County

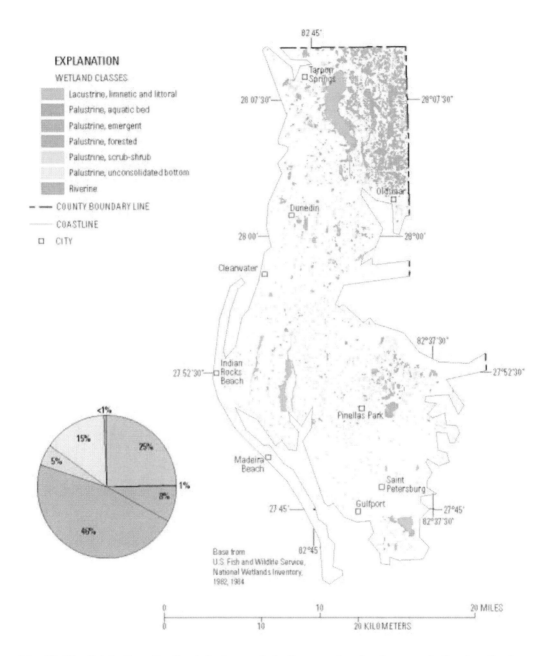

Map 20. The distribution of wetlands by type and pie diagrams showing the percent of each wetland type in Pinellas County, Florida.

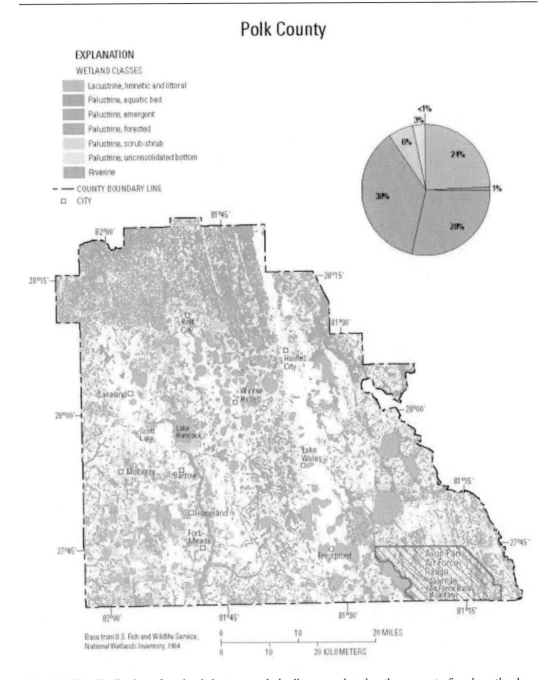

Map 21. The distribution of wetlands by type and pie diagrams showing the percent of each wetland type in Polk County, Florida.

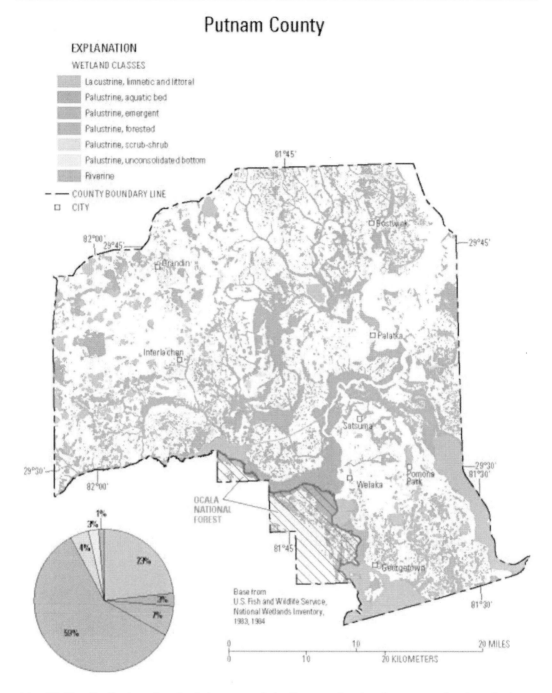

Map 22. The distribution of wetlands by type and pie diagrams showing the percent of each wetland type in Putnam County, Florida.

St. Lucie County

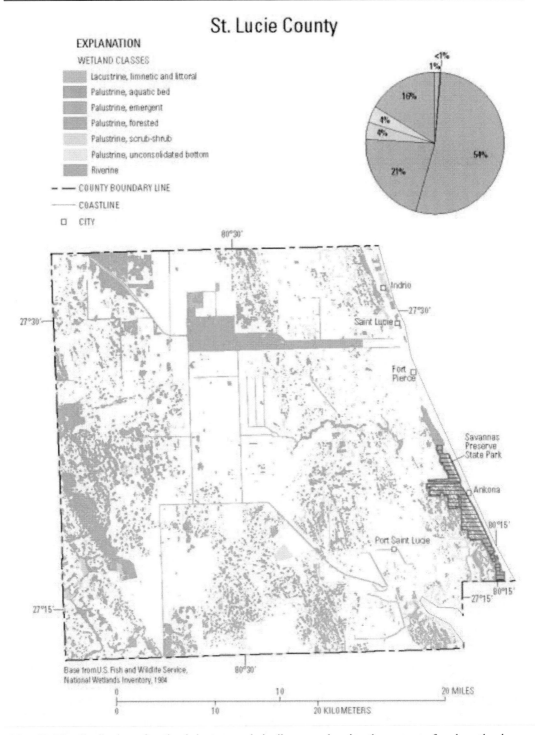

Base from U.S. Fish and Wildlife Service,
National Wetlands Inventory, 1984

Map 23. The distribution of wetlands by type and pie diagrams showing the percent of each wetland type in St. Lucie County, Florida.

Sarasota County

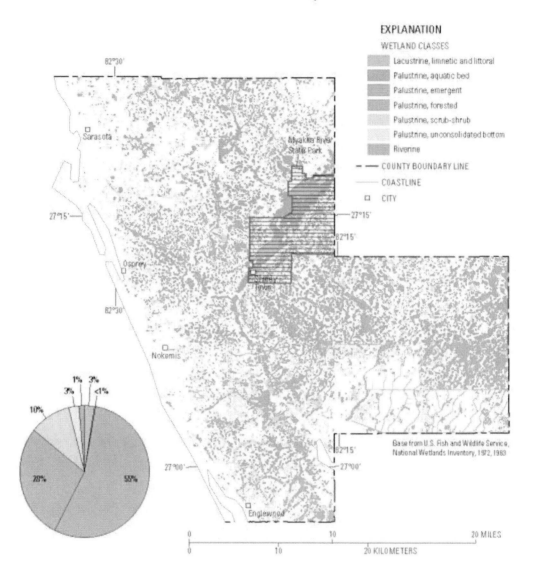

Map 24. The distribution of wetlands by type and pie diagrams showing the percent of each wetland type in Sarasota County, Florida.

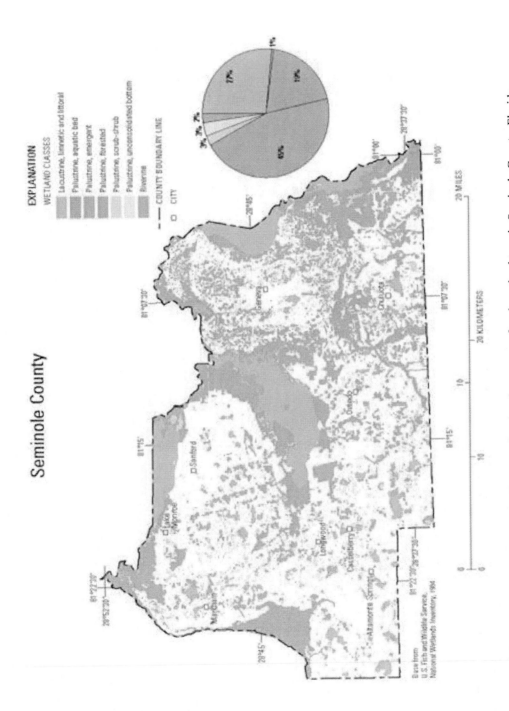

Map 25. The distribution of wetlands by type and pie diagrams showing the percent of each wetland type in Seminole County, Florida.

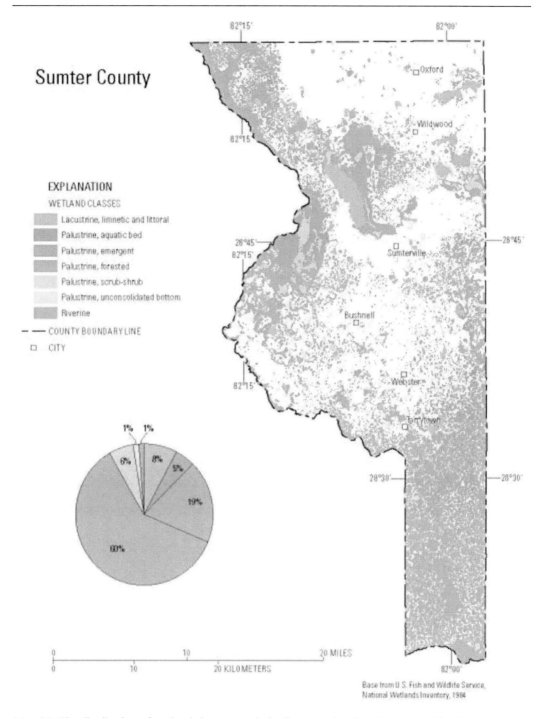

Map 26. The distribution of wetlands by type and pie diagrams showing the percent of each wetland type in Sumter County, Florida.

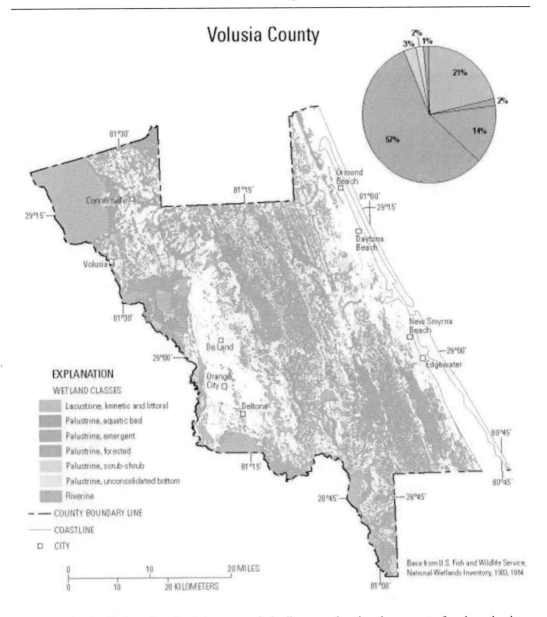

Map 27. The distribution of wetlands by type and pie diagrams showing the percent of each wetland type in Volusia County, Florida.

In: Wetlands in Central Florida: An Ecology and Hydrology...   ISBN: 978-1-61728-600-1
Editor: Samantha L. Elliot   © 2010 Nova Science Publishers, Inc.

Chapter 3

COMPARATIVE HYDROLOGY, WATER QUALITY, AND ECOLOGY OF SELECTED NATURAL AND AUGMENTED FRESHWATER WETLANDS IN WEST-CENTRAL FLORIDA

T.M. Lee, K.H. Haag, P.A. Metz and L.A. Sacks

ABSTRACT

Comparing altered wetlands to natural wetlands in the same region improves the ability to interpret the gradual and cumulative effects of human development on freshwater wetlands. Hydrologic differences require explicit attention because they affect nearly all wetland functions and are an overriding influence on other comparisons involving wetland water quality and ecology. This study adopts several new approaches to quantify wetland hydrologic characteristics and then describes and compares the hydrology, water quality, and ecology of 10 isolated freshwater marsh and cypress wetlands in the mantled karst landscape of central Florida. Four of the wetlands are natural, and the other six have water levels indirectly lowered by ground-water withdrawals on municipally owned well fields. For several decades, the water levels in four of these altered wetlands have been raised by adding ground water in a mitigation process called augmentation. The two wetlands left unaugmented were impaired because their water levels were lowered. Multifaceted comparisons between the altered and natural wetlands are used to examine differences between marshes and cypress wetlands and to describe the effects of augmentation practices on the wetland ecosystems.

In the karstic geologic setting, both natural and altered wetlands predominantly lost water to the surficial aquifer. Water leaking out of the wetlands created water-table mounds below the wetlands. The smallest mounds radiated only slightly beyond the vegetated area of the wetlands. The largest and steepest mounds occurred below two of the augmented wetlands. There, rapid leakage rates regenerated a largely absent surficial aquifer and mounds encompassed areas 7-8 times as large as the wetlands.

Wetland leakage rates, estimated using a daily water-budget analysis applied over multiple years and normalized as inches per day, varied thirtyfold from the slowest leaking natural wetland to the fastest leaking augmented wetland. Leakage rates increased as the size of the flooded area decreased and as the downward head difference between the wetland and the underlying Upper Floridan aquifer increased. Allowing one of the augmented wetlands to dry up for about 2.5 months in the spring of 2004, and then refilling it, generated a net savings of augmentation water despite the amount of water required to recreate the water-table mound beneath the wetland. Runoff from the surrounding uplands was an important component of the water budget in all of the unaugmented wetlands and two of the augmented wetlands. At a minimum, runoff contributed from half (45 percent) to twice (182 percent) as much water as direct rainfall at individual wetlands.

Wetland flooded areas, derived using wetland water levels and bathymetric data and presented as a percentage of total wetland area, were used to compare and contrast hydrologic conditions among the 10 wetlands. The percentages of the natural wetland areas that flooded during the study were comparable, despite differences in the sizes of the wetlands. The percent flooded area in each wetland was calculated daily over the study period and monthly for up to 16 years using historical water-level data. Historical flooding in the natural wetlands spanned a greater range in area and had more pronounced seasonality than historical flooding at either the impaired or augmented wetlands. Flooding in the impaired and natural wetlands was similar, however, during 2 years of the study with substantially reduced well-field pumping and above average rainfall.

Comparisons indicated several hydrologic differences between the marsh and cypress wetlands in this study. The natural and impaired marshes leaked at about half the rate of the natural and impaired cypress wetlands, and the marshes collectively were underlain by geologic material with lower vertical leakance values than the cypress wetlands. The natural marshes had higher evaporation rates compared to cypress wetlands, and their more isotopically- enriched surface waters indicated longer water residence times than the cypress wetlands. Over the same 8-year period, marshes spent from 16 to 30 percent more time (or about 15 to 29 months more) than cypress wetlands with greater than half of their total areas flooded. Cypress wetlands were nearly dry a greater percentage of time than marshes; however, more than 80 percent of their area was flooded a greater percentage of time than marshes. The water quality of natural marsh and cypress wetlands was similar, with a low pH, low conductivity, minimal alkalinity, and low concentrations of major ions; therefore, periphyton communities in natural marsh and cypress wetlands also were similar. Vegetation is inherently different between marsh and cypress wetlands, and among wetland sites of the same type there was a large variety and small overlap of vegetation species. Macroinvertebrate taxa richness and density were generally greater in natural marshes than in natural cypress wetlands.

The hydrology and water quality of augmented wetlands differed substantially from natural wetlands, but ecological differences were less apparent. Augmentation preserved between 40 and 80 percent of the original surface areas of four wetlands. The water levels in augmented wetlands, however, fluctuated less than in natural wetlands and augmented wetlands dried out far less frequently, accelerating sediment accumulation. Year-round augmentation of the deepest and fastest leaking wetland, Duck Pond Augmented Marsh, required a volume equivalent to a 60-foot column of water over an area of about 3 acres. The bottom sediments in augmented wetlands did not show enrichment of radium-226, as has been reported in augmented lakes in the area. Augmentation shifted wetland water quality from an acidic, dilute, and sodium-chloride dominated chemistry to a calcium-carbonate rich water with much higher alkalinity, specific conductance, and pH. The abundance of periphyton species known to prefer higher pH, conductivity, and nutrient concentrations was greater in augmented wetlands.

"Freshwater wetlands and their interaction with ground water play a pivotal role in the water resources of Florida"

Plant species richness and biomass were higher in the augmented wetlands than in unaugmented wetlands, most likely in response to more prolonged flooding and greater availability of nutrients released by accumulated decaying plant material. The natural variability of macroinvertebrate communities in marsh and cypress wetlands in this study exceeded the differences attributable to augmentation, although the presence of gastropods at augmented wetlands of both types was due to inherent water-quality differences. The comparisons of macroinvertebrate communities between natural and augmented wetlands would be more useful if a larger population of wetlands was available for study.

Quantifying wetland hydrology along with water quality and ecological indicators makes the results from the comparative analyses of these 10 wetlands generic. The approaches used in this study can be applied to future studies and those results can be compared to this initial study population, allowing the comparative analyses to describe an increasing number of wetlands.

INTRODUCTION

Freshwater wetlands and their interaction with ground water play a pivotal role in the water resources of Florida. Wetlands occupy a greater percentage of the land surface in Florida (29 percent) than any other state in the conterminous United States. A mantled karst terrain characterized by sinkhole subsidence and permeable aquifers, together with a wet subtropical to warm-temperate climate, produces a landscape where surface water and ground water can be viewed as a single resource (Winter and others, 1998). Ground water has been pumped in increasing quantities from below these surface waters in recent years, supplying more than 92 percent of the drinking water for more than 17 million Florida residents (in 2005) and 72 million tourists estimated to visit the State annually (in 2000) (Marella, 2004).

Large tracts of land, some containing numerous wetlands, have been set aside by municipalities across Florida for use as ground-water reservoirs and "well fields" where ground water is pumped for potable supply (Marella, 2004). Ground-water withdrawals at municipal well fields in west-central Florida have reduced the depth and duration of flooding in overlying wetlands (Mortellaro and others, 1995; Hancock and Smith, 1996). To mitigate the reduction in wetland flooding frequency and duration, a small fraction of the ground water pumped from a well field has been used to augment water levels in affected wetlands. The augmentation water thus replaces the water lost when leakage through the wetland bottom is accelerated by local ground-water withdrawal. Water levels in some of these mitigated wetlands have been augmented since the 1980s (Berryman and Hennigar, Inc., 2000). The augmentation rates needed to sustain targeted water levels depend on yearly climate conditions and ground-water pumping rates from the underlying aquifer.

Understanding the long-term effects of wetland augmentation and other mitigation practices on wetlands in Florida requires systematically comparing the hydrology, water quality, and ecology of both natural and augmented systems. A few comprehensive studies of natural wetlands in southern Florida have been published, including studies of Big Cypress Swamp (Klein and others, 1975; McPherson and others, 1976) and Corkscrew Swamp (Duever and others, 1975). Ewel and Odum (1984) presented a number of indepth studies of cypress wetlands in Florida and the eastern United States. The Florida Everglades has been studied in great detail (Davis and Ogden, 1994; Porter and Porter, 2002), and numerous

170 T.M. Lee, K.H. Haag, P.A. Metz et al.

studies are underway as part of the Comprehensive Everglades Restoration Plan (U.S. Army Corps of Engineers and South Florida Water Management District, 2000). In west-central Florida, however, conditions in marsh and cypress wetlands have not been rigorously studied using consistent methods uniformly applied to both natural wetlands and those wetlands that have experienced anthropogenic effects.

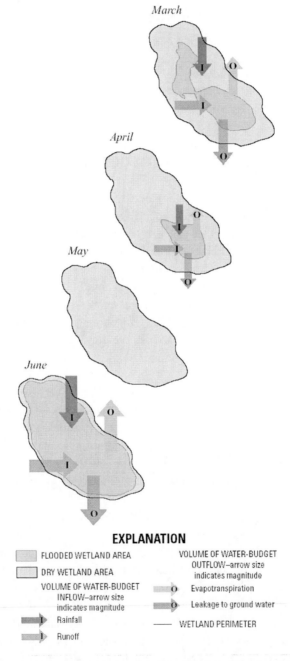

Figure 1. Conceptualized isolated wetland showing the changing size of the flooded area. The volumes of water- budget components change with the size of the flooded area, complicating hydrologic comparisons of isolated wetlands

Comparative assessments of vegetation in wetlands are numerous and have been documented in detail. In fact, names for different kinds of wetlands are often derived from the name of the dominant plant (for example, "maidencane marsh" and "cypress swamp"). In addition, a number of studies have focused on wetland water quality and biogeochemistry, although many of these studies were designed to assess the ability of wetlands, both natural and constructed, to assimilate and process nutrients and contaminants in wastewater (Mitsch and Gosselink, 2000), a focus outside the scope of this study.

In contrast, the hydrologic characteristics of isolated wetlands, particularly in the karst terrain of Florida, are not as well known (Kirkman and others, 1999). Methods used to compare the water budget and ground-water interactions in natural and augmented lakes in Florida provide a useful framework for studying wetlands (Metz and Sacks, 2002; Swancar and Lee, 2003). However, the classical goal of a lake water budget, namely, accounting for inflows and outflows to a permanent landscape feature, can lose its equivalence when applied to seasonally flooded or altered wetlands. In an isolated wetland, the ponded area that is subject to the conservation of mass principle can vary in size, disappear, and reappear over the timeframe of the water-budget analysis (figure 1). For multiple wetlands undergoing these processes in unsynchronized cycles, comparing wetland water budgets based on cumulative fluxes for a given time period can explain little about the intrinsic similarities and differences between individual wetlands. Water budgets have been applied to relatively few natural isolated wetlands (Carter, 1978; LaBaugh, 1986; Hayashi and others, 1998), usually over judiciously selected time periods with synchronized flooding. Water-budget analyses are more commonly available for constructed or mitigation wetlands that stay inundated year-round due to surface-water inflow or augmentation (Kadlec and Knight, 1996; Choi and Harvey, 2000; Biological Research Associates, Inc., and SDI Environmental Services, Inc., 2001).

To address the need for a greater understanding of the interactions among surface water, ground water, and wetlands ecosystems in karst terrain, the U.S. Geological Survey (USGS) initiated the current study in 1999 to compare and contrast:

The ponded area in isolated wetlands can vary in size, disappear, and reappear through time

(1) the hydrogeologic framework of wetlands and wetland/ ground-water interactions; (2) wetland water budgets, focusing on the role of leakage and runoff in the water budget; (3) the water quality of wetland surface waters and the geochemistry of underlying aquifers; (4) the frequency, duration, depth, and spatial extent of wetland flooding; and (5) wetland ecology as assessed by periphyton, aquatic vegetation, and macroinvertebrates. The current study was conducted in cooperation with Pinellas County, the Southwest Florida Water Management District (SWFWMD), and Tampa Bay Water.

The study conducted in west-central Florida examines the hydrologic behavior of 10 isolated wetlands in unprecedented detail at a daily timescale over a period of several years. The daily timescale makes it possible to interpret inundation patterns, rainfall/runoff relations, and wetland water budgets across a range of hydrologic conditions, and it generates comparable results whether a given wetland remains perennially flooded or is dry much of the year. In this approach, runoff entering the wetlands is quantified, but only until rainfall and runoff cause water to overflow the wetland perimeter.

Purpose and Scope

The purpose of this chapter is to distinguish and categorize the long-term effects of augmentation on the hydrology, water quality, and ecology of isolated wetlands in the mantled karst terrain of Florida. These effects were derived implicitly by comparing and contrasting selected natural and augmented wetlands to each other, and cataloguing differences.

The report is divided into five distinct (color coded) sections that collectively characterize the hydrology, water quality, and ecology of the 10 wetlands. A companion USGS scientific investigations report (Haag and others, 2005) and two USGS fact sheets (Haag and Lee, 2006; Lee and Haag, 2006) describe the bathymetry and vegetation in the 10 wetlands, and provide a framework for describing the flooded- area frequency of wetlands.

The first section begins the hydrologic characterization by defining the hydrogeologic setting of the wetlands and describing the interactions between wetlands and ground water. Hydrogeologic sections describe the hydrogeologic framework for 8 of the 10 wetlands and incorporate basin topography, wetland bathymetry, basin stratigraphy, groundwater flow patterns, and organic sediment thickness in the wetlands. Wetland water quality and the geochemistry of the underlying aquifers provide additional evidence of the wetland and ground-water interactions. Sediment cores taken in the center of three wetlands reveal the thickness and sequence of organic and mineralized layers beneath the wetlands. Surface geophysical surveys were made in two of the wetland basins, and the results are used to describe karst subsidence features that occur in these settings.

In the second section, the water-budget approach customarily applied to lakes and reservoirs was modified and adapted to characterize the small, periodically flooded wetlands in this study. The difference between the measured water volumes entering and leaving a wetland, and the observed change in the wetland volume is used to estimate the magnitude of two hydrologic fluxes that are difficult to directly quantify: the leakage of wetland surface water into the aquifer, and precipitation runoff the wetland receives from the surrounding upland area. The modified approach focuses on daily rates instead of cumulative volumes and, in doing so, generates results that are directly comparable for all 10 wetlands, regardless of how much the flooded wetland areas expand and contract, and whether or not all 10 wetlands remain continually flooded.

The third section presents wetland water-quality data from the 10 wetlands and describes the geochemistry of the wetland basins. The wetland water-quality data serve principally as supporting information, because surface-water quality is a strong determinant of many aspects of wetland ecology. Moreover, analyses of wetland water-quality data can be useful in describing various aspects of surface-water to ground-water interactions that are influenced by basin geochemistry. In addition, levels of radium-226 are measured in wetland water and sediment. This naturally occurring radioisotope has been found at elevated levels in lakes augmented with ground water in central Florida and may pose a human health risk for individuals who come in contact with it (Hazardous Substance and Waste Management Research, Inc., 2004).

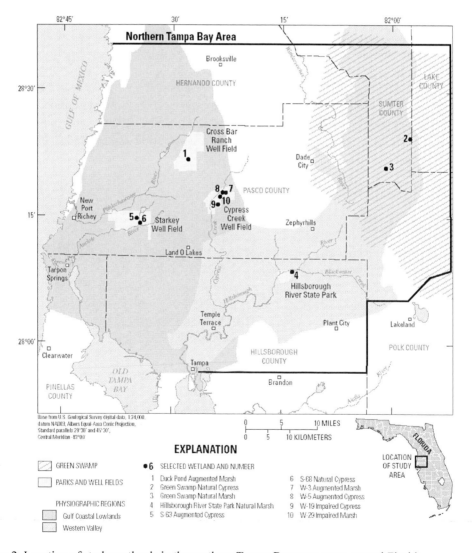

Figure 2. Location of study wetlands in the northern Tampa Bay area, west-central Florida

The fourth section continues the hydrologic characterization of the wetlands by comparing flooding patterns in the 10 wetlands. Flooded area is determined using detailed bathymetric maps of each wetland (described in Haag and others, 2005) and observations of wetland water levels. The per centage of the total wetland area that was flooded over time was compared among the 10 wetlands on a weekly basis over the period of study. Time-series data describing the size of the flooded area are then condensed to describe the duration of flooding over different regions of the total area of a wetland. The duration of flooding for the previous 8 to 16 years is reconstructed using long-term water-level data, and these flooding conditions are compared to the more recent flooding conditions in each wetland.

In the final section, three biological communities (algae, wetland plants, and macroinvertebrates) are assessed to interpret differences in ecological conditions between natural, impaired, and augmented wetlands. The variety and abundance of periphyton, the algae that grow on the surface of submersed plants and the wetland bottom, is an indicator of nutrient concentrations and overall water quality in wetlands. Periphyton communities were assessed quarterly, and differences in these communities are used to describe and compare ecological conditions in the 10 wetlands. Wetland vegetation communities are compared in the 10 wetlands, and differences in the macrophytes and woody vegetation are discussed in relation to hydrologic factors including water depth, water quality, and the spatial extent and duration of the flooding. Snails, crayfish, dragonfly nymphs, and other macroinvertebrates inhabiting the 10 wetlands were sampled quarterly, and macroinvertebrate community structure is compared and contrasted among the five marsh wetlands and among the five cypress wetlands. In accordance with the standard convention for ecological literature, all quantities in this section are reported in metric units.

Description of Study Area

The study area is located in west-central Florida and includes parts of Hernando, Hillsborough, Lake, Pasco, Pinellas, Polk, and Sumter Counties (figure 2). All 10 study sites are located in well fields or on publicly owned lands, such as wildlife management areas or parks, in two physiographic regions (figure 2). These regions, known as the Gulf Coastal Lowlands and Western Valley (White, 1970), have a relatively high water table and some surface drainage to rivers. In the subsurface, the Upper Floridan aquifer is the principal source of all local water supplies.

In west-central Florida, freshwater wetlands consist of forested and non-forested types, including riverine swamps, lacustrine swamps, cypress domes, marshes, and wet prairies (Southwest Florida Water Management District, 1999a). A 1986 inventory of 71 mi^2 in the northern Tampa Bay area indicates that wetlands account for about 23 percent of the total acreage surveyed (Manny Lopez, Southwest Florida Water Management District, written commun., 2002). About 92 percent of the total number of wetlands in the northern Tampa Bay area are isolated wetlands, and they constitute 68 percent of the total wetland acreage. Precipitation and shallow ground water supply the majority of water to isolated marshes and cypress swamps (Ewel and Odum, 1984; Myers and Ewel, 1990; Kirkman and others, 1999). In these isolated wetlands, where the water table seasonally approaches land surface under ambient conditions, the hydroperiod is largely determined by differences between precipitation and evapotranspiration, and is mediated by geology and topography. Small changes in wetland stage can cause large changes in wetland surface area because these wetlands are relatively shallow topographic features. Persistent changes in wetland water levels, due to changes in rainfall or human activities, could in turn cause a substantial change in the vegetation of hundreds or thousands of acres of land (Stewart and Kantrud, 1972; Poiani and others, 1996; Poiani and Johnson, 2003; Swanson and others, 2003).

Wetlands in the central Florida region typically follow a hydrologic pattern in which water levels decline during the winter and spring, with minimum water levels occurring in May and early June. During a year with average rainfall, wetland water levels typically begin rising in early summer and reach their highest levels in September (Berryman and Hennigar, Inc., 2000).

Rainfall Patterns and Regional Ground-Water Withdrawals

Surface water and ground water both respond relatively quickly to the distributed effects of rainfall and the more localized effects of ground-water withdrawals in the karst terrain of central Florida. Describing the hydrology of wetlands in the region requires identifying trends in both of these components of the hydrologic cycle. Rainfall in the region encompassing the study wetlands averages about 52 in/yr, based on 110 years of regional rainfall record from 1895 to 2005 for the two climate divisions that bisect the study area: Division 3 (52.26 in/yr) and Division 4 (51.84 in/ yr) (National Oceanographic and Atmospheric Administration, 2007). Annual rainfall during the study ranged substantially above and below the long-term average. Regional rainfall was about 12 to 15 in. below the average in 2000, and was close to the average in 2001 (figure 3). During the next 3 years (2002-04), annual rainfall was about 5 to 10 in. above average (figure 3). The above-average rainfall that began in late 2002 ended a 5-year drought in Florida (Verdi and others, 2006).

Rainfall was measured over 3 entire years at the study wetlands, and the annual totals measured at these sites followed the regional trend. The rainfall data are summarized monthly in appendixes 1 and 2. The annual rainfall measured at five wetland sites during 2001 ranged from below average to near the long-term average, whereas rainfall in 2002 and 2003 ranged from 3 to 15 in. above average at several of the wetlands (figure 4). The Hillsborough River State Park (HRSP) Natural Marsh was an exception, because the rainfall measured for 2003 was below (instead of above) the long-term average. In central Florida, where most of the annual rainfall occurs during the summer from small convective thunderstorms and larger tropical storms, spatial variability across a region can exceed the interannual variability (Chen and Gerber, 1990).

The increase in annual rainfall in the northern Tampa Bay area during 2002-04 was accompanied by a steep reduction in ground-water withdrawals from regional well fields (figure 5). Ground-water pumping from 11 well fields in the northern Tampa Bay area is coordinated by a regional water utility called Tampa Bay Water, which has been the principal provider of drinking water for Pasco, Hillsborough, and Pinellas Counties since 1998. Between 1998 and 2002, most of the regional water demand was supplied using ground water pumped from regional well fields. Well-field pumping decreased substantially beginning in late 2002 when nearly 66 Mgal/d of alternative water supply became available from a newly created surface-water reservoir. The reductions in well-field pumping complied with a master water plan that mandated reducing ground-water withdrawals in the 11 regional well fields from a historical annual average of about 158 Mgal/d to 90 Mgal/d by 2008 (Tampa Bay Water, 2004). The increased rainfall and decreased ground-water withdrawal during 2002-04 increased aquifer water levels and nearby wetland water levels; these effects are discussed in several chapters of the report.

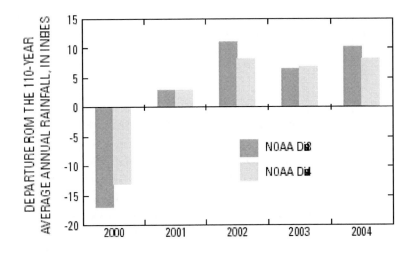

Figure 3. Regional annual rainfall departures from the long-term average, 2000 to 2004. (NOAA, National Oceanic and Atmospheric Administration.)

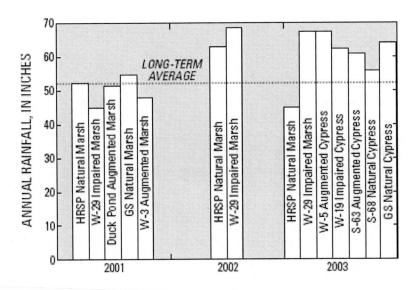

Figure 4. Annual rainfall measured at the marsh and cypress wetlands during 2001 to 2003 compared to the long-term average rainfall. NOAA Division 3 average is 52.26 in/yr and NOAA Division 4 average is 51.84 in/yr. (HRSP, Hillsborough River State Park; GS, Green Swamp.)

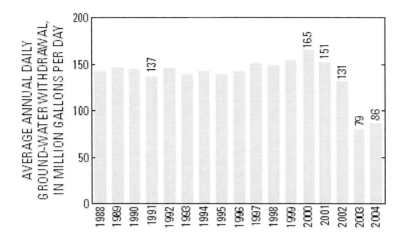

Figure 5. The average annual daily ground-water withdrawal from the 11 Tampa Bay Water well fields, 1988 to 2004

Table 1. Average Ground-Water Withdrawal Rates at Selected Tampa Bay Water Regional Well Fields during the Study. [all values are in million gallons per day]

Well-field name	Marsh data-collection period (Dec. 2000–Sept. 2002)	Cypress data-collection period (Nov. 2002–Aug. 2004)	Study wetlands on selected well fields
Cross Bar Ranch Well Field	20.7	11.6	Duck Pond Augmented Marsh
Cypress Creek Well Field	23.6	11.2	W-3 Augmented Marsh W-5 Augmented Cypress W-19 Impaired Cypress W-29 Impaired Marsh
Starkey Well Field	11.2	12.5	S-63 Augmented Cypress S-68 Natural Cypress
Total for all 11 well fields	148	85.5	

All of the augmented and impaired wetlands in this study were located on the three largest well fields operated by Tampa Bay Water, namely, Cross Bar Ranch Well Field, Cypress Creek Well Field, and Starkey Well Field (figure 2). Combined, these three well fields occupy more than 33 mi^2 of Pasco County and encompass hundreds of isolated wetlands. Although differences in rainfall and ground-water pumping affected all of the study wetlands over time, the effects were particularly evident in those three well fields where ground-water pumping was concentrated (table 1). Data for all five marshes were collected during 2001 and the first 9 months of 2002, prior to reductions in ground-water withdrawals and when rainfall was at or slightly below average (table 1 and figure 4). The five cypress wetlands were monitored during the remainder of 2002 and the subsequent 2 years, when rainfall was markedly above average and ground-water withdrawals had decreased sharply at

Cypress Creek Well Field and Cross Bar Ranch Well Field. Ground-water withdrawals, however, did not decline at Starkey Well Field (table 2). The timing of the pumping reductions provided a unique opportunity to examine their effects on wetland hydrology, because the reduction in ground-water withdrawals across the 11 Tampa Bay Water well fields was unprecedented.

Description of Study Design

Comparing the hydrology of isolated wetlands lacks a standardized method. Therefore, this study was designed to define approaches to compare the hydrologic condition of isolated wetlands equivalently, including wetlands with different vegetation types and in differing hydrologic settings. Augmentation has been used to mitigate environmental degradation in both isolated marshes and in cypress wetlands. To capture the potential differences in these two wetland types, five of the study wetlands are cypress wetlands and five are marsh wetlands [classified as forested wetlands and emergent wetlands, respectively, in the Palustrine System of Cowardin and others (1979)]. Equivalent methods were applied at the 10 study wetlands over a period of 4 years so that comparisons would be consistent across the range of hydrologic settings and for both wetlands types. Data were collected sequentially at the two wetland types, beginning with the five marshes during 2000-02. Data were collected at the five cypress wetlands (and continued at two of the marshes) during 2002–04 (figure 6).

The isolated wetlands selected for the study range in size from about 1 to 9 acres and maximum depth from about 1 to 8 ft (table 2). Isolated wetlands of this size are common throughout the region. Wetland sites with existing data collection programs were given preference in the selection process. All of the study wetlands belong to the hydrogeomorphic class of depression wetlands—naturally occurring topographic depressions with closed contours and low hydraulic energy in which the water sources are precipitation, ground water, and interflow (seasonal flow between wetlands when rainfall is abundant) (Brinson, 1993). Although these wetlands periodically flood beyond their respective perimeters, they lack a consistent surface outflow to a down-slope river, and they have little surface connectivity with other water bodies during years of typical rainfall.

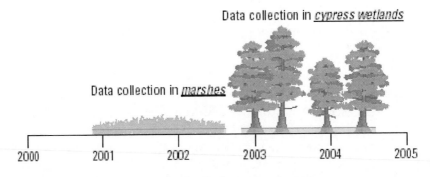

Figure 6. Approximate timeline of data collection in the two wetland types.

Table 2. Names, Locations, and Physical Characteristics of Study Wetlands.
[USGS, U.S. Geological Survey; N, North; W, West; E, East; Sec., Section; T, Township; S, South; R, Range; STA., Station; Latitude and Longitude in Degrees (°), Minutes (′), and Seconds (″)]

Wetland name, location, and USGS site identification number	Wetland name for this study	Period of hydro-logic record[1]	County	Latitude	Longitude	Map location[2]	Size (acres)	Maxi-mum depth (feet)	Mean depth (feet)
Duck Pond Marsh Cross Bar Ranch Well Field 282159082280400	Duck Pond Augmented Marsh	1978 - present	Pasco	28°21′59″N	82°28′02″W	Sec. 25, T. 24 S., R. 18 E Ehren	5.2	8.13	3.20
Green Swamp Cypress Green Swamp Wild-life Management Area 282445081574000	GS Natural Cypress	1979 - present	Sumter	28°24′47″N	81°57′40″W	Sec. 12, T. 24 S., R. 23 E Bay Lake	1.7	1.69	0.46
Green Swamp Marsh Green Swamp Wild-life Management Area 282114082100100	GS Natural Marsh	1995 - present	Sumter	28°21′16″N	82°01′02″W	Sec. 33, T. 24 S., R. 23 E Branchborough	1.6	1.07	0.62
Hillsborough River State Park Marsh Hillsborough River State Park 280848082134400	HRSP Natural Marsh	1977 - present	Hills-borough	28°08′49″N	82°13′41″W	Sec. 8, T. 27 S., R. 21 E Zephyrhills	2.2	2.65	0.67
S-63 Cypress Starkey Well Field 281455082350000	S-63 Augmented Cypress	1983 - present	Pasco	28°14′55″N	82°35′00″W	Sec. 2, T. 26 S., R. 17 E Odessa	1.3	1.47	0.58
S-68 Cypress Starkey Well Field 281415082343000	S-68 Natural Cypress	1983 - present	Pasco	28°14′21″N	82°34′31″W	Sec. 11, T. 26 S., R. 17 E Odessa	5.8	1.55	0.79

Table 2. (Continued)

Wetland name, location, and USGS site identification number	Wetland name for this study	Period of hydro-logic record[1]	County	Latitude	Longitude	Map location[2]	Size (acres)	Maxi-mum depth (feet)	Mean depth (feet)
W-3 Marsh Cypress Creek Well Field 281812082233800	W-3 Augmented Marsh	1978 - present	Pasco	28°18′13″N	82°22′40″W	Sec. 14, T. 25 S., R. 19 E Ehren	7.4	5.44	1.89
W-5 Cypress Cypress Creek Well Field 281820082225500	W-5 Augmented Cypress	1978 - present	Pasco	28°18′18″N	82°22′55″W	Sec. 14, T. 25 S., R. 19 E Ehren	8.8	2.11	0.52
W-19 Cypress Cypress Creek Well Field 281642082235000	W-19 Impaired Cypress	1978 - present	Pasco	28°16′42″N	82°23′52″W	Sec. 27, T. 25 S., R. 19 E Ehren	2.1	2.70	1.08
W-29 Marsh Cypress Creek Well Field 281754082231300	W-29 Impaired Marsh	1978 - present	Pasco	28°17′54″N	82°23′13″W	Sec. 22, T. 25 S., R. 19 E Ehren	6.5	2.76	1.44

[1] Historical data were collected by regional agencies (Southwest Florida Water Management District; Tampa Bay Water).

[2] USGS 1:24,000 topographic map name.

Photograph above provided by K. Haag, USGS; photograph at left provided by M. Hancock, SWFWMD

Pipeline delivering ground water to augment a marsh

The marsh and cypress wetlands were grouped depending on the principal hydrologic conditions that were used to describe them: natural wetlands, impaired wetlands, and augmented wetlands.

- Natural wetlands are defined as being unaffected or minimally affected by human activities including ground-water withdrawal. Four wetlands (two marsh and two cypress) were chosen as study sites to characterize this group.
- Impaired wetlands are defined as wetlands affected by ground-water withdrawals for several years that are typically dry for a longer period of the year than natural wetlands. These wetlands have never been augmented. Two wetlands (one marsh and one cypress) represent this group.
- Augmented wetlands are defined as wetlands affected by ground-water withdrawals and augmented with ground water for at least 5 years. Four augmented wetlands (two marshes and two cypress) were selected as study sites to characterize the altered hydroperiod and biota of augmented wetlands.

Defining the hydrologic and ecological conditions in the natural wetlands was fundamental to the study design. Conditions recorded in the four natural wetlands create a provisional baseline data set of typical conditions in regional wetlands in an undeveloped setting. Comparing and contrasting the conditions in the natural wetlands with the four historically augmented wetlands provides the basis for inferring changes resulting from wetland augmentation. A final aspect of the study design was to define conditions at two wetlands that are neither natural nor augmented, but are considered impaired because they are located in well fields and their water levels have been indirectly lowered by ground-water pumping. Studies of the two impaired wetlands are instructive, because these wetlands share attributes with both natural and augmented wetlands. In some respects, the impaired wetlands represent a more common contemporary hydrologic condition than the natural wetlands, because ground-water withdrawals affect wetlands to varying degrees throughout the northern Tampa Bay area, not just on its well fields.

Two of the ten wetlands, Green Swamp (GS) Natural Marsh and GS Natural Cypress, were studied less intensively than the others (figure 2) because of their remote location. Specifically, ground-water flow paths could not be defined and hydrogeologic sections could not be drawn at either site because new monitoring wells were not constructed.

Acknowledgments

The authors thank Ted Rochow and Michael Hancock of the Southwest Florida Water Management District, and Patty Fesmire and Chris Shea of Tampa Bay Water for providing historical hydrologic data and knowledgeable advice on area wetlands. Lauren Pusateri and Donald Herndon, formerly of the USGS Tampa office, provided valuable assistance with many aspects of data collection and analysis. Michael Deacon provided an excellent editorial review and Patty Fesmire, Michael Hancock, Warren Hogg, James LaBaugh, Chris Shea, Dave Slonena, Amy Swancar, and Douglas Wilcox provided technical review comments that greatly improved the report. Michael Hancock generously provided many of the wetland photographs used in the report. James Tomberlin and Kimberly Swidarski provided graphics support and layout design. Twila Darden Wilson provided guidance and evaluation in organization and design of the final product.

WETLAND HYDROGEOLOGIC SETTING

Wetland hydrology is strongly controlled by the geologic setting and the depth and direction of ground-water flow beneath wetland basins (Winter and Woo, 1990). The permeability of geologic deposits and the ground-water flow patterns around wetlands directly affect their rates of ground-water exchange and indirectly affect the magnitude of runoff they receive from the surrounding upland areas. The regional hydrogeology of the study area and the influence of karst terrain on wetland formation are addressed in this section, followed by a description of the hydrogeologic framework of 8 of the 10 wetland basins. The stratigraphy in the upland areas around the wetlands are compared and contrasted with the stratigraphy directly beneath wetlands. Groundwater flow patterns around the wetlands are described and contrasted for natural, impaired, and augmented wetlands, and the effects of augmentation on these differences are discussed.

Regional Hydrogeology

The regional landscape of west-central Florida is a mantled karst terrain, and in the low-lying areas north of Tampa Bay, wetlands are one of the dominant landforms (Schmidt, 1997; Sinclair and others, 1985). Mantled karst terrain is characterized by numerous topographic depressions, or sinkholes, that occur where thick, soluble limestone is overlain by a mantle of relatively insoluble sands and clays. Rainfall dissolves the limestone, forming sinkholes, solution pipes, and other karst features that are partially covered by the sand and clay deposits (Sweeting, 1973). Where the water table is close to land surface, the limestone dissolution is relatively shallow and the resulting land subsidence can create wetlands and lakes (figure 7) (Sinclair and others, 1985; Ewel, 1990; Winter and Woo, 1990). As the limestone dissolves and forms cavities, the overlying clay layer collapses and sand infiltrates or "pipes" into these openings (figure 8) (Sinclair and others, 1985; Tihansky, 1999). These sand-filled columns may increase the potential for leakage beneath wetlands if the underlying clay layer is substantially disrupted, and especially if water levels are relatively low in the underlying aquifers. Alternatively, the presence of organic-rich wetland sediments may impede leakage. Because of the long history of karstification in Florida, sinkholes exist in all stages of development, from ancient stable depressions formed during lower sea level stands to depressions formed recently.

The geologic framework of the study area is characterized by a thick sequence of Miocene to Eocene carbonate rock that is overlain by sand and clay sediments of Pliocene to Holocene age. The stratigraphic units, from oldest to youngest (deepest to shallowest), include the Avon Park Formation (Eocene), Ocala Limestone (Eocene), Suwannee Limestone (Oligocene), and Tampa Member of the Arcadia Formation of the Hawthorn Group (Miocene) (Miller, 1986; Metz and Sacks, 2002). Undifferentiated deposits of the Hawthorn Group and undifferentiated surficial deposits overlie the Tampa Member of the Hawthorn Group, except in the Green Swamp region where the Tampa Member and the Suwannee Limestone have been eroded (Tibbals and Grubbs, 1982).

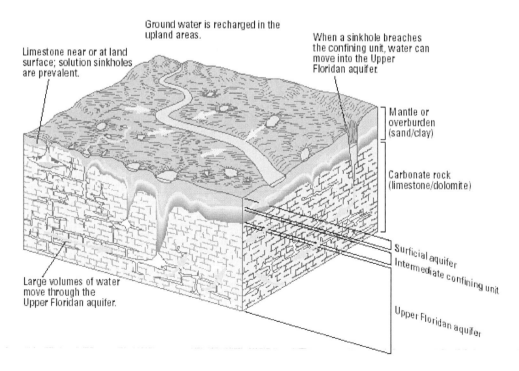

Figure 7. Landscape features and hydrogeologic framework of mantled karst terrain in west-central Florida. (Modified from Tihansky, 1999.)

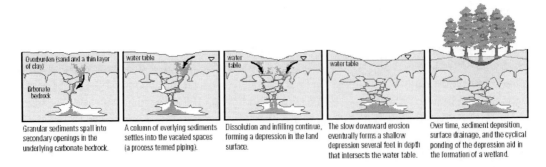

Figure 8. Example of dissolution and subsidence forming wetlands in mantled karst terrain. (Modified from Tihansky, 1999.)

A dense, plastic clay layer typically overlies the limestone below the study wetlands and is contained within the Miocene and Pliocene-age sediments of the Hawthorn Group. This layer is variable in extent, thickness, and permeability throughout the study area (Buono and others, 1979). The clay can be tan, greenish-gray, or blue-gray in color and can contain varying amounts of sand, phosphate grains, carbonate mud, and highly weathered limestone nodules (Sinclair, 1974). Clay minerals in the Hawthorn Group can contain potassium, radium, and radionuclides (Carr and Alverson, 1959). The radiogenic sediments in the Hawthorn Group yield elevated gamma radiation signatures that are used to identify the Group in borehole geophysical logs (Carr and Alverson, 1959; Scott, 1988).

The three principal hydrogeologic units in the study area, in descending order, are the surficial aquifer system, intermediate confining unit, and Upper Floridan aquifer. The surficial aquifer system is a permeable hydrogeologic unit contiguous with the land surface. It principally consists of unconsolidated to poorly indurated clastic deposits of sand and clayey sand (Southeastern Geological Society, 1986). Commonly, this unit is termed the surficial aquifer system where more than one permeable zone is present or where the deposits are interbedded. In this chapter, the deposits are considered to form a single homogeneous aquifer (Metz and Sacks, 2002), and are referred to as the surficial aquifer. Recharge to the water table by rainfall infiltration is relatively rapid because the surface soils are generally permeable and the water table is close to land surface. Although water recharged to the surficial aquifer can move laterally along short flow paths to points of discharge, most leaks downward into the underlying Upper Floridan aquifer.

The intermediate confining unit is a nonwater-yielding strata of undifferentiated deposits within the clay-rich Hawthorn Group (Metz and Sacks, 2002). The unit consists of dense, marine green-gray plastic clay that contains varying amounts of sand, chert, phosphate, organic material, and carbonate mud (Sinclair, 1974). The clay unit is variable in its extent and thickness throughout the study area. Although the intermediate confining unit impedes downward flow between the surficial aquifer and Upper Floridan aquifer in some areas, the hydraulic connection between the surficial and Upper Floridan aquifers is increased where the intermediate confining unit is thin or breached by sinkholes. The Upper Floridan aquifer is the primary source of water supply in the study area. The limestone and dolomites of the Upper Floridan aquifer contain many solution-enlarged fractures and typically yield large quantities of ground water to public and private wells (Metz and Sacks, 2002).

Table 3. Well Characteristics and Data Collected for Wells Used in the Study.
[USGS, U.S. Geological Survey; Hydrogeologic Unit: ICU, Intermediate Confining Unit;
SA, Surfical Aquifer; UFA, Upper Floridan Aquifer; Data Summary: CWR,
Continuous Water-Level Recorder; GSA, Grain-Size Analysis; QW, Water Quality;
WL, Periodic Water Level; --, Unknown Well or Casing Depth]

Well index number	USGS well identification number	Well name	Well depth[1] (feet)	Casing depth[1] (feet)	Hydro-geologic unit	Data summary
1	282201082280401	Crossbar Duck PD LNE	7	4	SA	GSA,QW,WL
2	282201082280701	Crossbar Duck PD LNW	14	9	SA	QW,WL
3	282157082280201	Crossbar Duck PD LSE	13	9	SA	GSA,QW,WL
4	282158082280601	Crossbar Duck PD LSW	11	7	SA	GSA,QW,WL
5	282202082280401	Crossbar Duck PD MNE	13	9	SA	GSA,QW,WL
6	282202082280801	Crossbar Duck PD MNW	14	10	SA	GSA,QW,WL
7	282156082280201	Crossbar Duck PD MSE	20	16	SA	GSA,QW,WL
8	282157082280701	Crossbar Duck PD MSW	15	11	SA	GSA,QW,WL
9	282203082280401	Crossbar Duck PD UNE	19	15	SA	QW,WL
10	282203082280901	Crossbar Duck PD UNW	14	10	SA	GSA,QW,WL
11	282157082280801	Crossbar Duck PD USW	21	17	SA	GSA,QW,WL
12	282202082280301	Crossbar Duck PD FLRD [2]	138	77	UFA	CWR,WL
13	282154082280401	Crossbar A-2 Deep [3]	700	152	UFA	WL
14	282154082280402	Crossbar A-2 Shallow[3] (USE)	23	19	SA	QW,WL
15	282157082280301	Crossbar Duck PD Aug [5]	--	--	UFA	QW
15a	282159082280301	Crossbar Duck PD Center	1	1	SA	WL
16	281641082235101	Cypress Creek W-19 B Center	7	--	SA	WL
17	281640082235201	Cypress Creek W-19 H	11	7	SA	QW,WL
18	281643082234901	Cypress Creek W-19 I	11	6	SA	QW,WL
19	281639082235201	Cypress Creek W-19 J	13	8	SA	QW,WL
20	281641082235401	Cypress Creek W-19 K	17	12	ICU	CWR,WL
21	281642082235401	Cypress Creek W-19 K2	10	6	SA	QW,WL
22	281641082235501	Cypress Creek W-19 L	17	12	SA	GSA,QW,WL
23	281644082234701	Cypress Creek W-19 M	7	2	SA	GSA,QW,WL
24	281644082235601	Cypress Creek W-19 N	13	8	SA	QW,WL
25	281645082234901	Cypress Creek W-19 O	9	4	SA	QW,WL
26	281645082235101	Cypress Creek W-19 Q	8	4	ICU	QW,WL
27	281642082235001	Cypress Creek W-19 P	7	3	SA	QW,WL
28	281642082235501	Cypress Creek W-19 FLRD [2]	117	80	UFA	CWR,WL
28a	281641082235301	Cypress Creek W-19 W	6	2	SA	WL
29	281758082231701	Cypress Creek W-29 B1CTR [4]	9	0	SA	GSA,QW,WL
30	281758082231601	Cypress Creek W-29 B1LNE	10	6	SA	GSA.WL
31	281759082231801	Cypress Creek W-29 B1LNW	7	3	SA	GSA.WL
32	281758082231602	Cypress Creek W-29 B1LSE	8	4	SA	GSA.WL
33	281758082231702	Cypress Creek W-29 B1LSW	10	6	SA	GSA.WL

Table 3. (Continued)

Well index number	USGS well identification number	Well name	Well depth[1] (feet)	Casing depth[1] (feet)	Hydro-geologic unit	Data summary
34	281759082231601	Cypress Creek W-29 B1MNE	11	7	SA	QW,WL
34a	281759082231802	Cypress Creek W-29 Ext [4] (B1MNW)	9	--	SA	WL
35	281758082231501	Cypress Creek W-29 B1MSE	8	4	SA	QW,WL
36	281757082231801	Cypress Creek W-29 B1MSW	11	7	SA	GSA,QW,WL
37	281800082231901	Cypress Creek W-29 B1UNW	15	11	SA	GSA.WL
38	281754082231301	Cypress Creek W-29 B2CTR	5	1	SA	GSA.WL
39	281754082231302	Cypress Creek W-29 B2CTRDP	11	8	SA	GSA.WL
40	281755082231301	Cypress Creek W-29 B2LNE	8	4	SA	GSA,QW,WL
41	281755082231401	Cypress Creek W-29 B2LNW	7	3	SA	GSA.WL
42	281754082231201	Cypress Creek W-29 B2LSE	10	6	SA	GSA,QW,WL
43	281753082231401	Cypress Creek W-29 B2LSW	9	5	SA	GSA.WL
44	281756082231201	Cypress Creek W-29 B2MNE	12	8	SA	GSA.QW,WL
45	281755082231601	Cypress Creek W-29 B2MNW	9	5	SA	GSA.WL
46	281753082231201	Cypress Creek W-29 B2MS	10	6	SA	GSA.WL
47	281754082231202	Cypress Creek W-29 B2MSE	17	13	SA	QW,WL
48	281753082231402	Cypress Creek W-29 B2MSW	18	14	SA	QW,WL
49	281757082231201	Cypress Creek W-29 B2UNE	14	10	SA	GSA.WL
50	281756082231601	Cypress Creek W-29 B2UNW	10	6	SA	GSA.WL
51	281750082231501	Cypress Creek W-29 B2USW	5	1	SA	WL
52	281759082231901	Cypress Creek W-29 FLRD [2]	136	59	UFA	CWR,WL
53	281810082223101	Cypress Creek W34 INT2 [4]	10	--	SA	WL
54	281813082224001	Cypress Creek W-03 DO Creek [4]	3	--	SA	WL
55	281814082223801	Cypress Creek W-03 UFA [2]	151	20	UFA	WL
56	281812082233801	Cypress Creek W-03 Augmentation [5]	--	--	UFA	QW
57	281817082224201	Cypress Creek W-04 INT [4]	6	--	SA	WL
58	281809082224403	Cypress Creek Shallow E-106	14	--	SA	WL
59	281817082223801	Cypress Creek BIO-1 [2]	15	2	SA	WL
60	281816082225301	Cypress Creek BIO-2 [2]	21	5	SA	WL
61	281804082224201	Cypress Creek BIO-3 [2]	16	2	SA	WL
62	281813082224202	Cypress Creek C2-S	19	2	SA	WL
64	281804082224202	Cypress Creek CCWFFUP [2]	5	2	SA	WL
65	281805082224201	Cypress Creek CCWFWTLD [2]	7	2	SA	WL
66	281817082223802	Cypress Creek CCWF E UPL [2]	12	2	SA	WL
67	281801082225201	Cypress Creek E107S [4]	20	15	SA	WL
68	281813082224501	Cypress Creek T1-A [2]	12	2	SA	WL
69	281816082224701	Cypress Creek T1-B [2]	12	2	SA	WL
70	281817082225001	Cypress Creek T1-C [2]	11	2	SA	WL

Table 3. (Continued)

Well index number	USGS well identification number	Well name	Well depth[1] (feet)	Casing depth[1] (feet)	Hydro-geologic unit	Data summary
71	281819082225401	Cypress Creek T1-D[2]	12	5	SA	WL
72	281821082225701	Cypress Creek T1-F [2]	12	2	SA	WL
73	281824082230101	Cypress Creek T1-H [2]	11	2	SA	WL
74	281817082225401	Cypress Creek W-05 No. 1 [2]	10	2	SA	CWR,QW,WL
75	281817082225101	Cypress Creek W-05 No. 2 [2]	23	3	SA	CWR,QW,WL
76	281821082225301	Cypress Creek W-05 No. 3 [2]	8	2	SA	QW,WL
77	281822082225901	Cypress Creek W-05 No. 4 [2]	8	2	SA	QW,WL
78	281821082225601	Cypress Creek W-05 No. 5 [2]	6	3	SA	QW,WL
79	281816082225701	Cypress Creek W-05 No. 6 [2]	14	2	SA	QW,WL
80	281818082225501	Cypress Creek W-05 Center [4]	8	--	SA	CWR,WL
81	281820082225001	Cypress Creek W-05 Aug. [5]	--	--	UFA	QW
82	281821082225302	Cypress Creek W-05 FLRD [2]	125	60	UFA	CWR,WL
83	282446081574201	Green Swamp Cypress 5 Upland 2	14	--	SA	WL
84	282447081574001	Green Swamp Cypress [5] Center	15	3	SA	WL
85	282118082010301	Green Swamp Marsh UPL [2]	9	1	SA	WL
86	282118082010401	Green Swamp Marsh FLRD [2]	122	44	UFA	WL
87	282116082010201	Green Swamp Marsh Center	6	1	SA	CWR,WL
88	280849082134101	Hillsborough River ST PK CTR	9	0	SA	CWR,GSA,QW,WL
89	280851082134001	Hillsborough River ST PK LN	12	8	SA	GSA,QW,WL
90	280850082134301	Hillsborough River ST PK LNW	11	7	SA	GSA,QW,WL
91	280849082134001	Hillsborough River ST PK LSE	13	9	SA	GSA,QW,WL
92	280847082134301	Hillsborough River ST PK LSW	14	10	SA	GSA,QW,WL
93	280854082134201	Hillsborough River ST PK UN	14	10	SA	GSA,QW,WL
94	280852082134301	Hillsborough River ST PK UNW	16	12	SA	GSA,QW,WL
95	280847082134001	Hillsborough River ST PK USE	11	7	SA	GSA,QW,WL
96	280846082134501	Hillsborough River ST PK USW	14	10	SA	GSA,QW,WL
97	280849082134401	Hillsborough River ST PK UW	16	12	SA	GSA,QW,WL
98	280852082135601	Hillsborough ST PK Parking Lot DP [2]	76	62	UFA	CWR,QW,WL
99	280852082135602	Hillsborough ST PK Parking Lot SH [2]	24	20	SA	QW,WL

Table 3. (Continued)

Well index number	USGS well identification number	Well name	Well depth[1] (feet)	Casing depth[1] (feet)	Hydro-geologic unit	Data summary
100	280846082134601	Hillsborough ST PK Boys Camp DP [2]	74	62	UFA	QW,WL
101	280846082134602	Hillsborough ST PK Boys Camp SH [2]	18	15	SA	QW,WL
102	281500082351101	Starkey S-10 FLRD Production [4]	750	165	UFA	QW
103	281454082345801	Starkey S-63 LMSE	14	10	SA	WL
104	281456082345901	Starkey S-63 LNE HTRN	16	12	ICU	QW,WL
105	281456082345902	Starkey S-63 LNE	6	2	SA	GSA,QW,WL
106	281456082350101	Starkey S-63 LNW	18	14	SA	QW,WL
107	281456082350102	Starkey S-63 LNW No. 2	10	6	SA	QW,WL
108	281455082345801	Starkey S-63 LSE	14	10	SA	QW,WL
109	281454082350001	Starkey S-63 LSW	14	10	SA	QW,WL
110	281457082345802	Starkey S-63 MNE	18	14	SA	QW,WL
111	281457082350201	Starkey S-63 MNW HTRN	22	18	ICU	QW,WL
112	281457082350202	Starkey S-63 MNW No. 2	11	7	SA	QW,WL
113	281453082350101	Starkey S-63 MSW HTRN	22	18	ICU	GSA.QW,WL
114	281453082350102	Starkey S-63 MSW NRSD	9	5	SA	QW,WL
115	281453082345701	Starkey S-63 UMSE	11	7	SA	QW,WL
116	281457082345801	Starkey S-63 UNE	16	12	SA	QW,WL
117	281457082350401	Starkey S-63 UNW HTRN	21	17	SA	QW,WL
118	281457082350402	Starkey S-63 UNW No.2 NRSD	12	8	SA	WL
119	281452082345501	Starkey S-63 USE	19	15	SA	QW,WL
120	281452082350301	Starkey S-63 USW HTRN	22	18	ICU	QW,WL
121	281452082350302	Starkey S-63 USW NRSD	10	6	SA	QW,WL
122	281452082350303	Starkey S-63 FLRD [2]	130	80	UFA	CWR,WL
122a	281455082350001	Starkey S-63 Center	4	0	SA	CWR,WL
123	281415082342401	Starkey S-68 LE	14	10	SA	QW,WL
124	281419082342601	Starkey S-68 LNE	14	10	SA	QW,WL
125	281420082343101	Starkey S-68 LNW	14	10	SA	QW,WL
126	281414082342701	Starkey S-68 LSE	12	8	SA	QW,WL
127	281417082343201	Starkey S-68 LW	13	9	SA	QW,WL
128	281413082342801	Starkey S-68 MSE HTRN	18	14	ICU	GSA,WL
129	281413082342802	Starkey S-68 MSE NRSD	7	3	SA	QW,WL
130	281417082343301	Starkey S-68 MW	13	9	SA	QW,WL
131	281422082342701	Starkey S-68 UNE	14	10	SA	QW,WL
132	281421082343101	Starkey S-68 UNW	14	10	SA	GSA,QW,WL
133	281410082342701	Starkey S-68 USE HTRN	21	17	ICU	QW,WL
134	281410082342702	Starkey S-68 USE NRSD	9	4	SA	QW,WL
135	281417082343601	Starkey S-68 UW HTRN	18	14	ICU	QW,WL
136	281417082343602	Starkey S-68 UW NRSD	11	7	SA	QW,WL

Table 3. (Continued)

Well index number	USGS well identification number	Well name	Well depth[1] (feet)	Casing depth[1] (feet)	Hydro-geologic unit	Data summary
137	281421082343102	Starkey S-68 FLRD [2]	130	80	UFA	WL
138	281418082343001	Starkey S-68 Center	4	4	SA	WL

[1] Depth values are in feet below land surface.
[2] Southwest Florida Water Management District well.
[3] Pinellas County well.
[4] Tampa Bay Water well.
[5] Tampa Bay Water augmentation outflow from well-field production pipeline.

Hydrogeologic Methods

The stratigraphy of the wetland basins was interpreted from existing geologic and borehole geophysical logs, grain- size analysis, and from the descriptions of well cuttings from more than 100 wells drilled for the study. Table 3 describes the construction and location of the wells used in the study, along with well index numbers and a summary of data collected at each well. The index numbers are provided to cross reference the wells shown in the maps of wetland basins and in the hydrogeologic sections of the eight wetlands with table 3. No new wells were drilled at the two most remote wetlands, namely, GS Natural Marsh and GS Natural Cypress; therefore, interpretation of stratigraphy and ground-water flow patterns in these two basins is limited.

Drilling a monitoring well for the study

Stratigraphy below the wetlands was reconstructed using information from bathymetry surveys (Haag and others, 2005) and from cores collected using a vibracore device (Lanesky and others, 1979). Stratigraphic data also were collected and interpreted using a multi-sensor down-core scanner (Gunn and Best, 1998), point measurements of the wetland soft-sediment thicknesses (Brenner and Whitmore, 1999), and ground- penetrating radar (GPR) (Barr, 1993; Kruse and others, 2006). The thickness of the organic-rich sediment in each wetland was measured by probing the sediments with a calibrated metal rod, following an approach used for shallow lakes in Florida (Brenner and Whitmore, 1999). Sediment thickness was measured at multiple points along at least one cross section through each of the 10 wetlands, and at additional points in several other wetlands.

The stratigraphic data beneath the wetlands were generally collected within 15 ft of land surface. Geologic samples were collected using a vibracore device at the five marshes (figure 9). At the cypress wetlands, samples were obtained using a hand auger or a small rotary drill rig (figure 10). The vibracores generated the most intact profile of the shallow stratigraphy; however, the maximum core length was either about 13 ft or to the depth of the first substantial clay layer. The coring device, powered by an air compressor, vibrated a 3-in. diameter aluminum core barrel into the wetland bottom (Lanesky and others, 1979).

Cores from three of the marshes were analyzed for changes in selected sediment properties with depth. A Geotek^{TM} multi-sensor scanner was used for down-core logging of saturated bulk density, also called gamma bulk density because it is determined by measuring the attenuation of gamma radiation from a Cesium-137 (^{137}Cs) source (J.M. Jaeger, University of Florida, written commun., 2003). Following the logging, cores were split and the sediments were photographed, described, and subsampled at 2-cm intervals for further analyses. Freeze-dried sediment samples were analyzed for radium-226 (^{226}Ra) activity as well as other associated radioisotopic activity using a gamma counter with an intrinsic low-energy germanium detector (J.M. Jaeger, University of Florida, written commun., 2003). Sediment grain sizes, or the relative mass percentages of sand, silt and clay, were analyzed to a depth of 19.7 in. (50 cm) in each core using the methods of Galehouse (1971).

In addition to vertical profiles of ^{226}Ra activity in sediment cores from the three marshes, ^{226}Ra activity also was measured in surface sediment grab samples taken from the 10 wetlands, as well as in surface water and augmentation water at selected wetlands. Samples for ^{226}Ra analysis were collected from the marsh wetlands in July 2002. A single 1-L subsurface grab water sample and a single 500-mL sediment sample were collected from inundated areas near the perimeter of each marsh in less than 6 in. of water (excluding W-29 Impaired Marsh, which was dry). A 1 -L sample of augmentation water was collected at each of the two augmented marshes. In May 2004, a second set of sediment samples was collected at all 10 wetlands for ^{226} Ra analysis.

Three sediment samples were collected at widely spaced locations in each wetland where the water depth was 6 in. or less. The water and sediment samples were collected using standard USGS methods described in Wilde and others (1998).

Water and sediment samples were analyzed through the USGS National Water Quality Laboratory (NWQL) in Lakewood, Colorado. The ^{226}Ra activity was reported for each sample, along with the minimum detectable concentration (MDC), and the combined standard uncertainty (CSU). The MDC at the time of analysis for ^{226}Ra activity was 1.8 dpm/g for sediment samples and 0.09 dpm/L for water samples. The uncertainty associated with the ^{226}Ra activity is 1 standard deviation of the CSU for ^{226}Ra determined by alpha spectrometry.

The uncertainty terms for the [226] Ra samples in this study were generally smaller than the measured values (16 – 53 percent of the measured values). Further explanations of these terms are found in Focazio and others (2001).

The GPR surveys were made at three wetlands (W-29 Impaired Marsh, Duck Pond Augmented Marsh, and S-63 Augmented Cypress) to provide evidence of karst subsidence in wetland basins. The surface-geophysical technique can profile the top of subsurface clay layers, identifying areas where the clays are deformed downward or breached by subsidence into sinkholes (Wilson and Garmen, 2002). Geophysical surveys included data collected over flooded wetlands (W-29 Impaired Marsh and Duck Pond Augmented Marsh) and across land. All GPR surveys were performed using a PulseEKKO 100[TM] system and in the manner of Barr (1993). The depth of reflected signals was correlated with geologic data at known reference points.

Ground-water levels were measured biweekly over varying time frames in a total of 118 surficial aquifer, 9 intermediate confining unit, and 11 Upper Floridan aquifer wells (table 3). At most of the wetlands, upland surficial aquifer wells were drilled at varying distances from the wetland perimeter to monitor the surrounding water table. One or more wells located near the center of each wetland were used to monitor either wetland stage during flooded periods, or the ground-water level as it receded below the land surface during dry periods. Because W-29 Impaired Marsh was frequently dry, numerous wells were drilled inside the perimeter of this wetland to map the underlying water table. The potentiometric level of the Upper Floridan aquifer also was monitored in the vicinity of each wetland. Water levels were recorded continuously at six Upper Floridan aquifer monitoring well locations, and biweekly in others (table 3). Upper Floridan aquifer water levels were then compared to the overlying surficial aquifer and wetland water levels. Continuous water-level monitoring for this study was done with submersible pressure transducers according to standard methods described in Freeman and others (2004). Biweekly ground-water levels and other hydrologic data for the wetlands are available online from the USGS National Water Information System database at http://waterdata.usgs.gov/fl/nwis/gw (U.S. Geological Survey, 2007).

Basin Stratigraphy

The wetlands showed no distinctive differences in basin stratigraphy that could be linked to the wetland type (marsh or cypress) or to the hydrologic conditions of the three wetland groups (natural, impaired, or augmented). For example, the unconsolidated surficial deposits surrounding the wetlands ranged from 20 to 40 ft thick and were mostly similar in composition (figures 11-18). Surficial deposits typically were composed of an uppermost fine- to medium-grained sand unit, a sequence of clayey sand, and a lower sequence of sandy clay. The sand is white to buff colored near the surface and contains a mixture of dark organic matter and silt. Based on grain-size analysis, Duck Pond Augmented Marsh and W-29 Impaired Marsh had the highest sand content in their surrounding surficial deposits. The clay content increased with depth below the sand and organic layer, creating a sequence of clayey sand. In some instances, iron staining and small limestone nodules were noted in this middle sequence (W-29 Impaired Marsh, W-3 Augmented Marsh, Duck Pond Augmented Marsh, W-

19 Impaired Cypress, 63 Augmented Cypress, S-68 Natural Cypress). A unit of sandy clay exists below the clayey sand sequence.

The description of the intermediate confining unit taken from drilling logs indicates it is variable in thickness, composition, and permeability throughout the 10 wetland basins. The thickness of the intermediate confining unit ranges from 5 ft at HRSP Natural Marsh (in areas where it is present) to 30 ft near W-19 Impaired Cypress. A grain-size analysis of samples from four of the basins where the intermediate confining unit is present indicates the clay fraction ranges from 30 to 80 percent.

The top of the limestone (and Upper Floridan aquifer) at the 10 wetland basins is relatively shallow and of irregular depth due to erosion. The limestone was encountered during drilling at depths ranging from 18 ft (W-5 Augmented Cypress) to 40 ft below land surface (W-19 Impaired Cypress). Historical geologic logs from wells near many of the wetlands indicate that sand and clay were encountered within the limestone unit far below the typical depth range of mantle deposits; for example, at 80 ft below land surface near S-68 Natural Cypress and S-63 Augmented Cypress, implicating potential sinkhole formation.

The HRSP Natural Marsh wetland, located along the Hillsborough River, is the only wetland in this study that currently is located in a regional ground-water discharge area. Large volumes of ground water seep upward from the Upper Floridan aquifer toward land surface in this area (Wolansky and Thompson, 1987). For example, a second magnitude spring (Crystal Springs) that discharges about 40 Mgal/d to the Hillsborough River is located about 6 mi northeast of HRSP Natural Marsh. Because of erosional processes in the vicinity of the Hillsborough River, the geology varies substantially and is characterized by an irregular weathered limestone surface and a thin to nonexistent intermediate confining unit (Trommer and others, 2007). Historical geologic logs and those from wells drilled during this study indicate substantial variability in the geology at HRSP. These logs indicate limestone at land surface near the river, as well as limestone deposits at a depth of 50 ft below land surface within the HRSP Natural Marsh basin.

The surficial deposits surrounding HRSP Natural Marsh differ in composition from the other wetlands and are composed of an upper fine sand unit underlain by a sandy clay, underlain by a sequence of white, medium-grained quartz sands, overlying a blue-green clay unit. Grain-size analyses indicate the surficial sediments around this wetland contain the highest percentage of clay (10-80 percent) of all the study wetlands. The mineralogy of the uppermost 20 ft of sediment indicated a high percentage of calcium carbonate (CaCO3) (10 to 60 percent) within the shallow mantle deposits. The shallow ground-water chemistry, sampled in wells less than 20 ft deep, indicated a substantial enrichment of calcium carbonate in the surficial aquifer.

Sub-Wetland Stratigraphy

Stratigraphy was examined to a depth of about 15 ft below the wetlands. All wetlands investigated share a common shallow stratigraphic sequence. An organic-rich wetland sediment layer is underlain by a sequence of sand and silt, underlain by a sandy-clay layer. However, differences in the nature of these layers distinguish one wetland from another. In particular, the wetlands differ in the (1) degree to which karst subsidence features are evident in the wetland basin, (2) thickness and composition of the organic-rich bottom sediments, (3) relative proportion of mud (silt and clay) in the shallow sediments, (4) [226]Ra enrichment in the sediments, (5) presence or absence of an iron hardpan in the underlying sand layers, and (6) depth of the intermediate confining unit below the wetland.

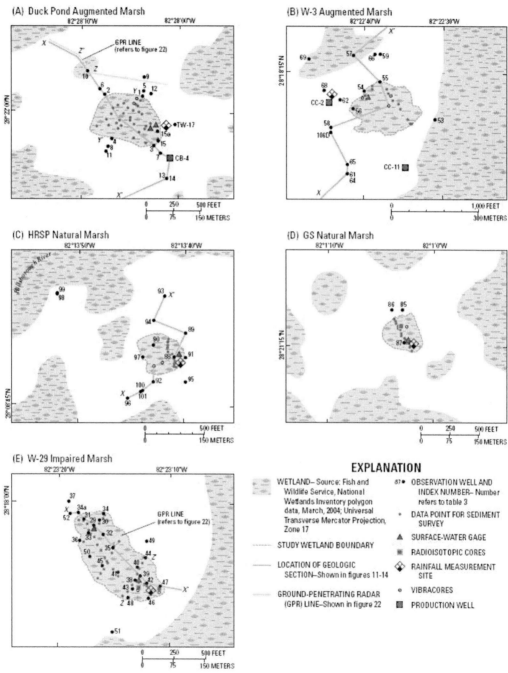

Note: Wells A1 shallow and deep are 900 feet beyond southern extent of map (A). Wells C3 and E107D are 280 and 580 feet, respectively, beyond southern extent of map (B). Well C1 is 525 feet beyond northern extent of map (B).

Figure 9. Location of data-collection sites for the marsh wetlands.

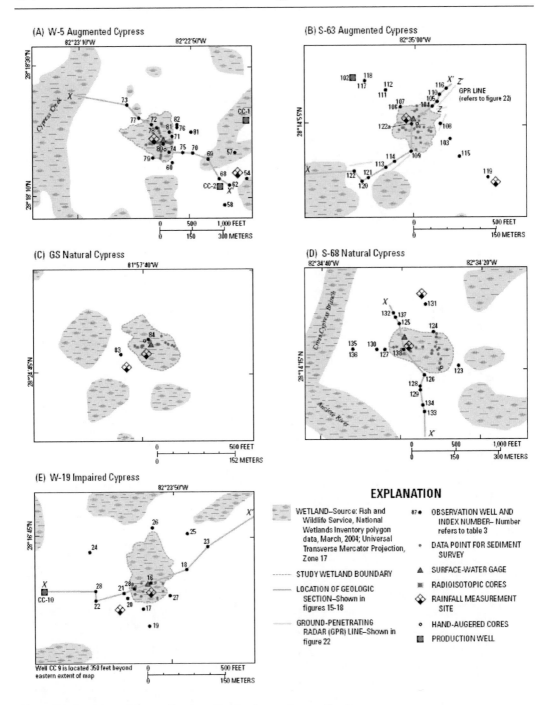

Figure 10. Location of data-collection sites for the cypress wetlands.

The organic-rich wetland sediments are composed of varying amounts of grayish-brown organic material, sand, and mud (silt and clay). The organic material varies in consistency from a fibrous, matted, turf-like material to a plastic, mud-like slime, resembling an early description of peat deposits in Florida marshes provided by Davis (1946). Organic sediment is thickest in the deepest areas of the wetlands and thinnest near the margins. The maximum sediment depth was similar in 8 of the 10 wetlands, ranging from 2.1 to 3.3 ft below land surface, and averaging 3.2 ft in thickness. The maximum sediment thickness was more than double this average in the two augmented marshes, namely, Duck Pond Marsh and W-3 Marsh (6.8 ft and 7.4 ft, respectively) (figures 12 and 13).

The thicker sediment encountered in the two augmented marshes is probably a consequence of ground-water augmentation. Both marshes are continually augmented, and have never been dry completely during their augmentation history. Instead, augmentation has maintained flooding over at least 40-60 percent of the marsh surface area. In contrast, the two augmented cypress wetlands, where the maximum sediment thickness was similar to the unaugmented wetlands, have each been dry during part of their augmentation history. The augmented cypress wetlands have been less than 20 percent flooded or completely dry during more than 30 percent of their respective periods of record. Further information about wetland flooding characteristics is provided in the section titled Wetland Flooding Characteristics.

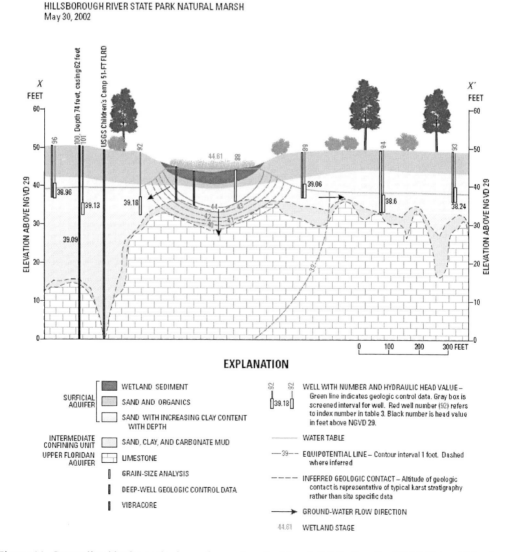

Figure 11. Generalized hydrogeologic section and vertical head distribution for HRSP Natural Marsh at Hillsborough River State Park.

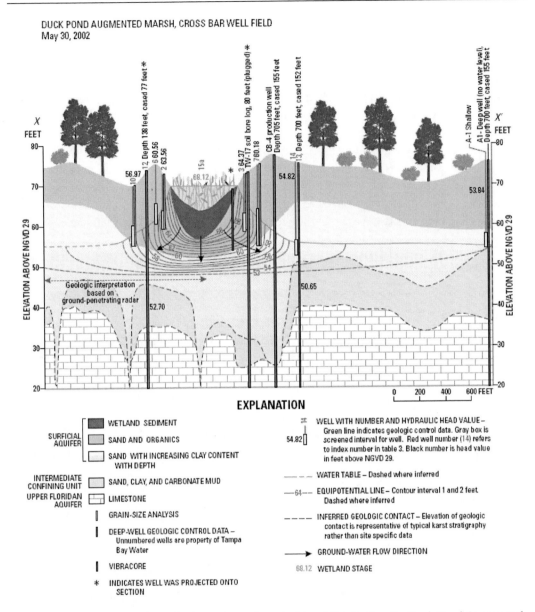

Figure 12. Generalized hydrogeologic section and vertical head distribution for Duck Pond Augmented Marsh at Cross Bar Well Field.

The W-29 Impaired Marsh wetland showed evidence of organic sediment loss, probably as a consequence of prolonged dry conditions in the wetland. Recurring exposure to the air oxidizes the organic matter in wetland sediments, limiting or greatly slowing their accumulation rate (Mitsch and Gosselink, 2000). Dry conditions prevailed at W-29 Impaired Marsh during the 16 years prior to this study, exposing wetland sediments over the majority of the wetland area to oxidation. The maximum sediment depth measured in W-29 Impaired Marsh (2.5 ft) was similar to the maximums recorded in the natural marshes, but was measured at an isolated deep point near the staff gage (figure 14). The remaining point measurements indicate much thinner sediment depths in other areas. Furthermore, the median sediment thickness for all points measured in W-29 Impaired Marsh was 0.4 ft—the smallest median value of any study wetland and about one-third of the median value for the wetland having the next thinnest sediments (HRSP Natural Marsh).

Vibracores are used to describe the stratigraphy below marsh wetlands

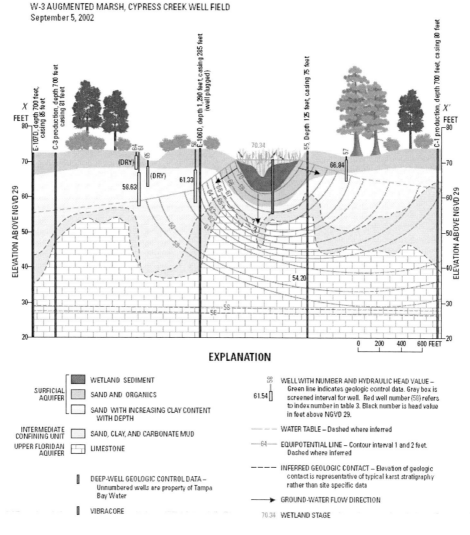

Figure 13. Generalized hydrogeologic section and vertical head distribution for W-3 Augmented Marsh at Cypress Creek Well Field.

W-29 IMPAIRED MARSH, CYPRESS CREEK WELL FIELD
May 16, 2002

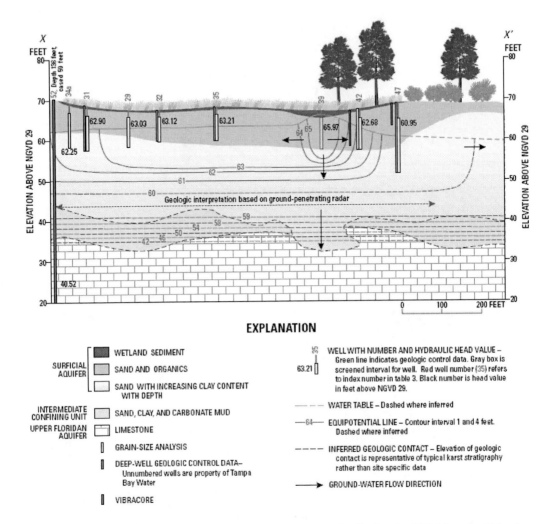

Figure 14. Generalized hydrogeologic section and vertical head distribution for W-29 Impaired Marsh at Cypress Creek Well Field.

Differences between the organic sediment profiles seen in vibracores taken from the three marshes probably also correlate to different durations of flooding and drying. Gamma bulk density provided a proxy for organic content in sediment cores. Increased organic content reduces the bulk density of soils compared to purely mineral or sandy soils. The bulk density of an organic soil is generally 0.2 to 0.3 g/cm^3, whereas values for unlithified sands generally range from 1.5 to 1.8 g/cm^3 (Mitsch and Gosselink, 2000). Bulk density data from the sediment core from GS Natural Marsh indicated the maximum organic matter content is near the land surface (figure 19A). The maximum clay content also is near land surface, and both clay and organic matter decrease sharply with depth. Clay and organic matter can accumu late in low-energy aquatic environments such as wetlands, where fragments of organic matter may act as a substrate for adherence of settling clay particles (Mitsch and Gosselink, 2000). In contrast, the surface sediments taken from a historically drier area of W-29 Impaired Marsh are much sandier (figure 19B). The upper 1.6 ft (0.5 m) of this core has a much higher bulk density and less organic matter, and the percentages of clay and silt are markedly lower than those measured in the GS Natural Marsh. A core taken from a perpetually flooded area of W-3 Augmented Marsh has dark organic-rich sediment at a depth of 6.6 ft (2 m). Because the sand content increases substantially below a depth of about 1.6 ft (0.5 m), the gamma bulk density values are only slightly lower than values in the underlying sand despite the black organic appearance of the sediment. For all four cores described here, the gamma bulk density values below about 1.6 ft (0.5 m) depth are between 1.6 and 2.0 g/cm^3.

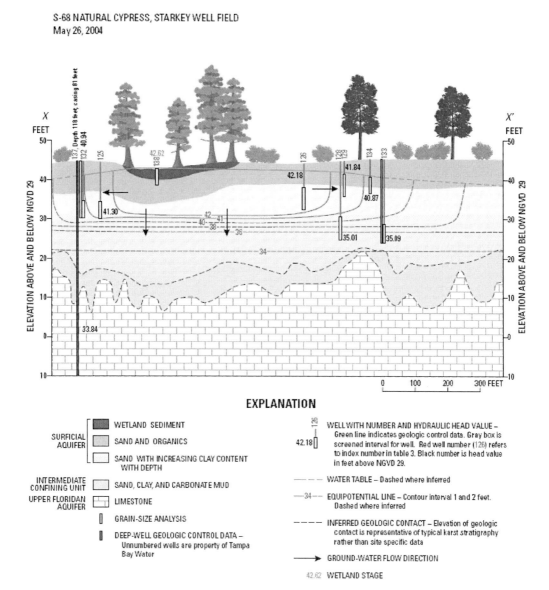

Figure 15. Generalized hydrogeologic section and vertical head distribution for S-68 Natural Cypress at Starkey Well Field.

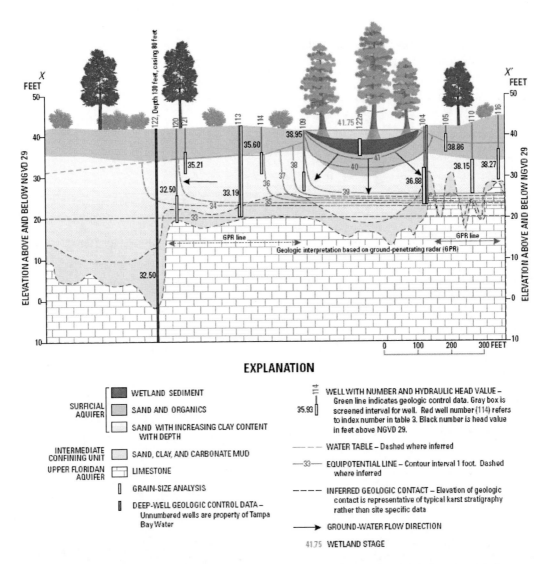

Figure 16. Generalized hydrogeologic section and vertical head distribution for S-63 Augmented Cypress at Starkey Well Field.

Vibracores from Duck Pond Augmented Marsh, W-3 Augmented Marsh, and W-29 Impaired Marsh show iron staining in the sandy zones that occurs below the shallow organic-rich sediments, suggesting available oxygen in the water leaking out of the wetland. Similar iron staining is absent in the core from GS Natural Marsh. Vibracores encountered the clay intermediate confining unit below several of the wetlands. The clay has a green-gray color and a dense plastic consistency that is characteristic of the Hawthorn Group (Sinclair, 1974; Scott, 1988). Because the vibracore device could not penetrate the dense clay layer, only the depth to the layer was established. A clay layer was encountered below the following wetlands: W-3 Augmented Marsh, W-5 Augmented Cypress (well 74, by drilling), HRSP

Natural Marsh, and GS Natural Marsh. The presence of a clay layer at a shallow depth beneath at least some part of these wetlands may indicate better confinement than at wetlands where the clay layer is either deeper or entirely absent. The vibracore device did not encounter the clay layer beneath W-29 Impaired Marsh, and vibracores were not collected at the four other cypress wetlands. Consequently, the depth of the confining unit directly below these wetlands could not be determined.

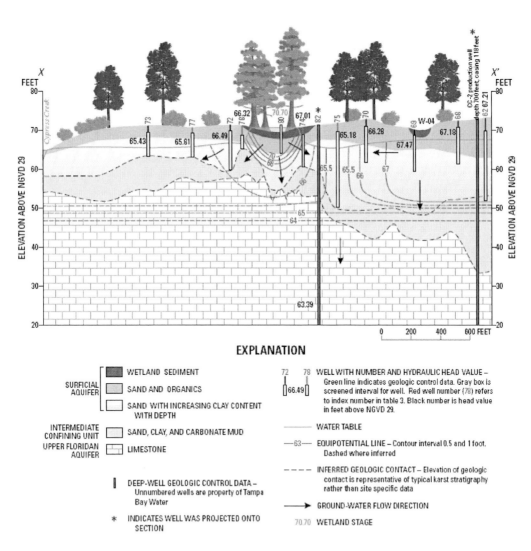

Figure 17. Generalized hydrogeologic section and vertical head distribution for W-5 Augmented Cypress at Cypress Creek Well Field.

W-19 IMPAIRED CYPRESS, CYPRESS CREEK WELL FIELD
May 18, 2004

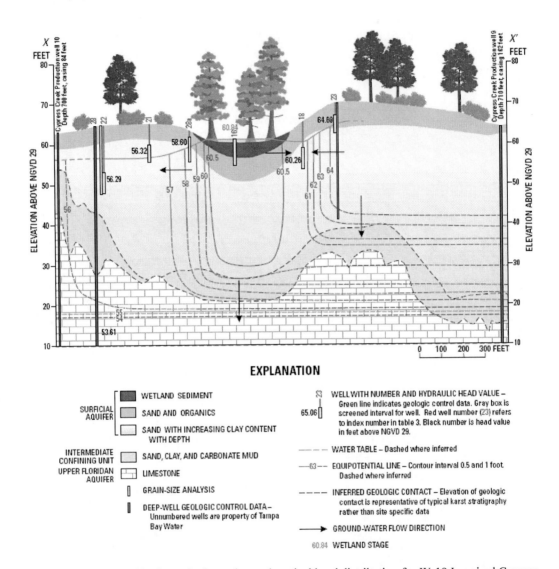

Figure 18. Generalized hydrogeologic section and vertical head distribution for W-19 Impaired Cypress at Cypress Creek Well Field.

Radium-226

Collectively, ^{226}Ra activity in shallow sediment samples and in water samples from both unaugmented and augmented wetlands was relatively low. In shallow sediment samples, average ^{226}Ra activities were 0.16-0.56 dpm/g at unaugmented sites and 0.14-0.77 dpm/g at augmented sites. The augmentation water supplied to the two augmented marshes had ^{226}Ra activities typical of Upper Floridan aquifer ground water in the area, ranging from 1.5 to 2.7 dpm/L. These ^{226}Ra activities were similar to the ^{226}Ra activity in ground water (0.82-3.26

dpm/L) from wells used to augment four nearby lakes (Brenner and others, 2006). As a result of the augmentation in the present study, ^{226}Ra activity in the surface water of the two augmented marshes (1.1-2.1 dpm/L) was higher than in the two natural marshes (0.2-0.4 dpm/L).

Augmenting lakes with ground water has been shown to elevate the ^{226}Ra activity in the lake sediment and lake water (Brenner and others, 1997; Smoak and Krest, 2006). The results of the present study, however, indicate that the ^{226}Ra activities in the surface sediment samples were similar in augmented and unaugmented wetlands (figure 20). Radium-226 activities in sediment from natural and impaired wetlands ranged from about 0.1 to 1.2 dpm/g, and most activity levels were less than 0.3 dpm/g (figure 20). In the augmented wetlands, ^{226}Ra activities in the sediment ranged from 0.1 to 1.4 dpm/g. The augmented wetlands generally appeared to have higher ^{226}Ra activity, although non-parametric statistical tests indicated no significant difference (p = 0.06). The wetland with the lowest average ^{226}Ra activity in the surface sediment was S-68 Natural Cypress (average 0.2 dpm/g), whereas the site with the highest ^{226}Ra activity was the nearby S-63 Augmented Cypress (average 0.8 dpm/g). These sites are about 1 mi apart, and have the most similar geology of any of the augmented/natural wetland pairs. Based on these observations, the difference in sediment ^{226}Ra activity is probably related to augmentation practices.

Sediments cores taken from ground-water-augmented lakes indicate recent enrichment of ^{226}Ra, and ^{226}Ra levels in shallow sediment 0 to 4 cm (0-1.6 in.) deep were an order of magnitude greater than the deeper background values (Brenner and others, 2006). However, vertical profiles of ^{226}Ra activity in sediment cores from one augmented marsh and two unaugmented marshes in the present study provided little or no evidence of this effect (J.M. Jaeger and L.M. Mertz, University of Florida, written commun., 2003). Radium-226 activities in the surface sediments of the cores ranged from less than 1 to about 4 dpm/g (figure 21). GS Natural Marsh had the highest ^{226}Ra activity at the sediment surface (4.3 dpm/g), which was probably due to the presence of radiogenic clays of the Hawthorn Group near the surface (figure 21D). The next highest ^{226}Ra activity was in the core from W-3 Augmented Marsh (3.9 dpm/g). Peak values in the core (figure 21A) were substantially greater than the average of the surface sediment samples (figure 20), although ^{226}Ra activity in surface samples resembled values deeper in the core. The cores from W-29 Impaired Marsh showed low ^{226}Ra activities and little change with depth (figure 21B-C).

The ^{226}Ra activity measured in sediments of natural, impaired, and augmented wetlands in this study were similar in magnitude to those reported for other natural wetlands in central Florida (about 0.4 dpm/g) (Brenner and others, 2004). The values were considerably lower, however, than those measured in many augmented lakes in central Florida (Brenner and others, 2000; 2004). Concern about the accumulation of ^{226}Ra in lake sediments and biota (DeArmond and others, 2006; Smoak and Krest, 2006; Brenner and others, 2007) has resulted in closer scrutiny of the practice of augmenting lakes with water from the Upper Floridan aquifer. Results from this study indicate that ^{226}Ra activity is low in sediments beneath the augmented wetlands, and is considerably lower than the U.S. Environmental Protection Agency action level of 11 dpm/g (5 pCi/g) above background levels (U.S. Environmental Protection Agency, 1999; Hazardous Substance and Waste Management Research, Inc., 2000).

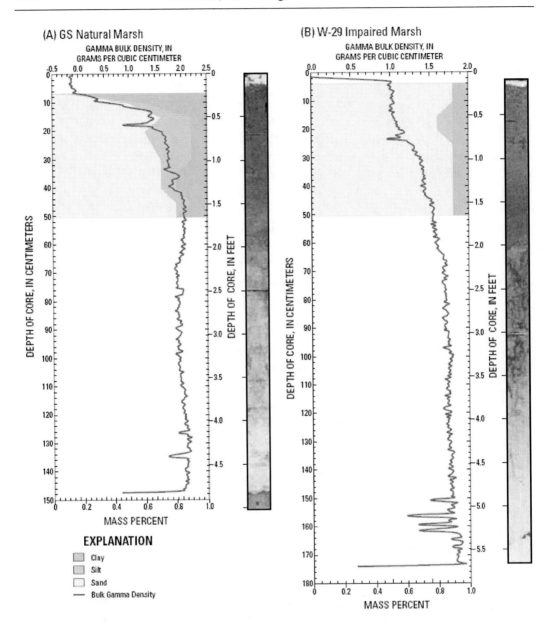

Figure 19. Vertical profiles of bulk gamma density and grain size in sediment cores from (A) GS Natural Marsh and (B) W-29 Impaired Marsh.

There is concern in central Florida that ^{226}Ra in water and sediment may enter the food chain and bioaccumulate in aquatic organisms (Brenner and others, 2007). Mussels in lakes receiving ground-water augmentation have been shown to bioaccumulate ^{226}Ra at rates many orders of magnitude greater than those for lake sediments (Brenner and others, 2007). Over a 2-3 month study period, these mussels (primarily the unionid mussel *Elliptio buckleyi*) accumulated ^{226}Ra relatively rapidly in their soft tissues, and larger mussels showed greater ^{226}Ra activity than smaller mussels. These large, long-lived mussels were not found in the augmented wetlands, probably because the wetlands are not as hydrologically stable as lakes, and may dry out completely during some years. Augmented wetlands in the present study do harbor filter-feeding bivalves in the Family Sphaeriidae, but these small mussels have much shorter life spans, typically 1 year or less, and they do not build up large amounts of soft tissue because they are adapted to devote resources toward rapid and early reproduction rather than attaining a large body size. Therefore, although no tissue samples were analyzed from Sphaeriidae in this study, it is expected that bioaccumulation of ^{226}Ra activity in these mussels would be substantially less than that reported for the large mussels living in augmented lakes.

Several factors could contribute to the lower ^{226}Ra activity observed in augmented wetlands compared to augmented lakes. Factors generally affecting the amount of ^{226}Ra adsorbed to recent sediments include: (1) ^{226}Ra activity in the augmentation water, (2) water residence time in the wetland, (3) the proportional contribution of ground water to the water budget of the wetland (Brenner and others, 2006), (4) the organic matter content of the sediment (DeArmond and others, 2006), and (5) cycling between wet and dry wetland soil conditions. Some factors are comparable in both wetlands and lakes, whereas others favor ^{226}Ra accumulation in wetlands, suggesting other considerations (Mark Brenner, University of Florida, written commun., 2007). For one, the apparent levels of ^{226}Ra activity per gram of dry weight could be "diluted" in the sediment of augmented wetlands by greater primary productivity and faster sediment deposition rates in augmented wetlands compared to augmented lakes. In addition, lake sediment may contain smaller particles (including algae), which are preferential binding sites for ^{226}Ra. Wetlands may tend to have larger particle sizes, contributed from coarse plant material, with less surface area for binding. It is also possible the ^{226}Ra could remain in solution because of the shorter residence time of augmentation water in wetlands compared to lakes, and could be washing out of the wetlands either by overflow or by downward leakage.

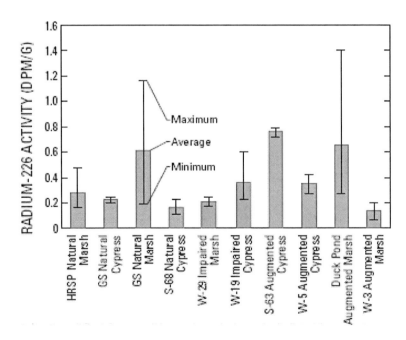

Figure 20. Average, minimum, and maximum radium-226 activity from surface sediment samples collected in July 2002 and May 2004.

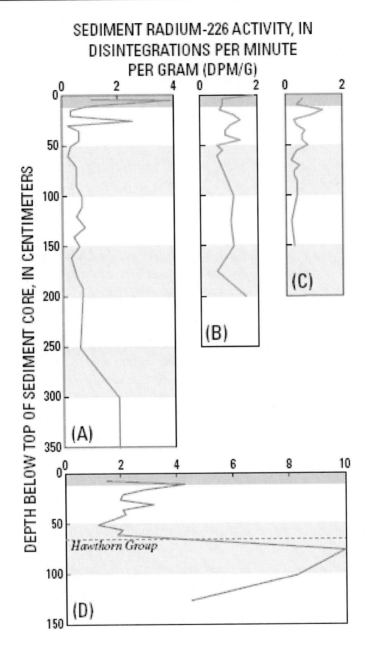

Figure 21. Vertical profiles of radium-226 activity in sediment cores taken from (A) W-3 Augmented Marsh, (B) W-29 Impaired Marsh #1, (C) W-29 Impaired Marsh #2, and (D) GS Natural Marsh.

Cycling between wet and dry conditions also could lower the ^{226}Ra activity in the surficial sediments of augmented wetlands compared to those of augmented lakes ^{226}Ra is only slightly particle reactive and is susceptible to desorption from inorganic particles under changing Eh and pH conditions (Frissel and Koster, 1990). Cycling between wet and dry wetland soil conditions alters the Eh/pH conditions, which controls the distribution of ^{226}Ra between the particulate and dissolved phases. This inherent cycling could limit the ^{226}Ra accumulation in augmented wetlands that periodically dry out.

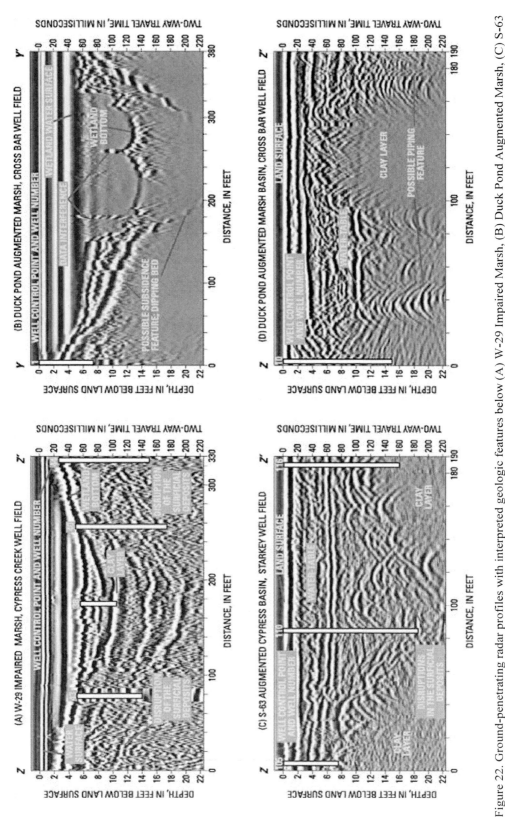

Figure 22. Ground-penetrating radar profiles with interpreted geologic features below (A) W-29 Impaired Marsh, (B) Duck Pond Augmented Marsh, (C) S-63 Augmented Cypress basin, and (D) Duck Pond Augmented Marsh basin. (Locations of ground-penetrating radar transects are shown in figures 9 and 10.)

Evidence of Karst Features in Wetland Basins

The circular shape of most of the wetlands in this study is similar to the general shape of many lakes in the study area, which is consistent with sinkhole formation (Sinclair and others, 1985; Metz and Sacks, 2002). Depressional features in the bottom of the wetlands provide further evidence of karstification in the study area. The small circular depressions along the wetland bottom range in depth from 1.07 ft at GS Natural Marsh to 8.13 ft below the wetland perimeter at Duck Pond Augmented Marsh (app. 3). The deepest areas of these depressions may overlie sand columns or "piping features" created by localized subsidence beneath the wetlands. Duck Pond Augmented Marsh had the deepest depression in the wetland bottom, and this may be a factor affecting its leakage rate.

Analysis of GPR data at three wetlands (W-29 Impaired Marsh, Duck Pond Augmented Marsh, and S-63 Augmented Cypress) revealed well-defined reflectors in areas of the basins where the lateral bedding within the surficial deposits was intact. In other areas of the record, discontinuous reflectors and dipping reflectors indicate that the surficial deposits have been disrupted by karst subsidence (figure 22). The most notable geologic features beneath W-29 Impaired Marsh and Duck Pond Augmented Marsh are the steeply dipping reflectors that indicate subsidence in the underlying layers and may signify sinkhole activity (figure 22). For W-29 Impaired Marsh, the bathymetry indicates the wetland has two distinct basins (Haag and others, 2005), which suggests that multiple sinkholes form the wetland. The GPR data indicate that the southern basin of W-29 Impaired Marsh has a more intact clay layer than the northern basin, which shows a more intact sandy layer and thus a higher permeability zone (figure 22A). The GPR data for Duck Pond Augmented Marsh show a reflection-free or attenuated zone near the center, which is surrounded by steeply dipping reflectors on both sides of the wetland bottom (figure 22B). These steeply dipping reflectors indicate subsidence or sinkhole activity. The reflection-free zone in the middle is probably interference caused by gases in the thick, organic sediments (figure 22B).

Smaller infilled or buried sinkholes not evident as depressions in the land surface were found to be abundant in the GPR record, along with possible piping features where reflective layers in the surficial deposits are disrupted or are deformed downward by karst subsidence (figure 22C-D). In these areas, the surficial aquifer has the potential to leak faster to the underlying Upper Floridan aquifer, creating a depression in the water table despite a level or inclining land surface (Lee, 1996).

Ground-Water Flow Patterns in Wetland Basins

Mapping ground-water flow patterns around wetlands over time reveals the changeable interactions between wetlands and their underlying aquifers, as demonstrated by studies of the prairie potholes of North Dakota (Winter and Rosenberry, 1995). In the present study, ground-water flow patterns around two natural wetlands are characterized and compared to the ground-water flow patterns around four augmented wetlands and two impaired wetlands. Commonly observed flow patterns are presented from two perspectives—by contouring the water- table elevations around the wetlands, and by contouring the vertical distribution of hydraulic head between the wetland stage, water table, and potentiometric level in the Upper Floridan aquifer. Time-series graphs of wetland stage and selected ground-water levels in each basin are used to show how the relation between wetland water levels and ground-water levels fluctuate seasonally, and how typical ground-water flow patterns could be altered during seasonal extremes.

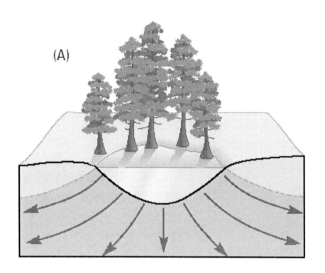

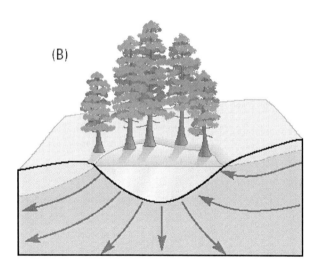

EXPLANATION

☐   WATER TABLE

──▶   GROUND-WATER FLOW PATH

Figure 23. Conceptualized interactions of wetlands with (A) ground-water recharge and (B) ground-water flow through. (Modified from Winter and others, 1998.)

Wetlands, like lakes, can experience either recharge, discharge, or flow through with respect to the surrounding ground water (Winter and others, 1998). For instance, several marshes in the ridge areas of central Florida were found to be in flow-through settings (Knowles and others, 2005). The wetlands in this study, whether they were natural, impaired, or augmented, routinely recharged the underlying aquifer. The water levels in wetlands typically were higher than the water-table altitude in the surficial aquifer, causing water to leak into and recharge the aquifer (figure 23A). Only one of the eight wetlands (W-19 Impaired Cypress) in which groundwater flow paths were established experienced persistent flow- through conditions (figure 23B). During the wettest conditions of the study, however, several marsh and cypress wetlands briefly switched from a recharge condition to a flow-through condition. When this occurred, the areas of ground-water flow into the wetland often mirrored areas of surface-water inflow.

Augmented wetlands experienced the most extreme recharge conditions because their stages were highest above the background ground-water levels. The two augmented marshes were perched on top of steep, conical, ground-water mounds that radiated out from the wetland perimeter as much as 500 ft (figure 24A-B). During May 2002, the ground-water mound below Duck Pond Augmented Marsh was about 15 ft high. The water-table contours encircling the wetland dropped from the wetland water level to an elevation slightly above the potentiometric surface of the Upper Floridan aquifer (figure 12), indicating that wetland leakage was recharging the surficial aquifer below the wetland. The intermediate confining unit slowed the vertical flow between the wetland and Upper Floridan aquifer, causing the base of the recharge mound to spread outward over the top of the confining clays until it blanketed an area large enough to transmit flow at the augmentation rate. The size of the mound stayed relatively consistent year-round because the wetland water level and Upper Floridan aquifer potentiometric surface tracked each other seasonally (figure 25A). The recharge mound covered about 40 acres during May 2002, including the 5.2-acre wetland area. The roughly symmetrical mound had a steeper slope in the direction of the nearest production well, located southeast of the marsh (figures 24A and 7). Similar water-table mounds have been documented below augmented lakes in the northern Tampa Bay region, although their sizes were considerably greater (Metz and Sacks, 2002).

At W-3 Augmented Marsh, the water-table mound had a total height of about 12 to 13 ft during September 2002 (figure 24B), with the steepest slope in the direction of the ground-water production well located south of the wetland. The surficial aquifer is probably dewatered near the production well, causing the level of the water table to approach the head of the Upper Floridan aquifer (figure 13). In September 2002, the mound at W-3 Augmented Marsh was about 52 acres in size, including the 7.4-acre wetland area, but unlike Duck Pond Augmented Marsh, the shape and size of the mound changed substantially over time. The Upper Floridan aquifer levels at W-3 Augmented Marsh changed by more than 15 ft during the study period. There were corresponding changes in the water table, but little change in wetland stage (figure 25B). As a result, when the Upper Floridan aquifer level was lowest (in spring 2001), the water table fell below the monitoring well depths and could not be mapped. Under these conditions, a steeper mound with a smaller footprint probably existed under the wetland, and more leakage probably flowed straight downward instead of radially outward from the wetland.

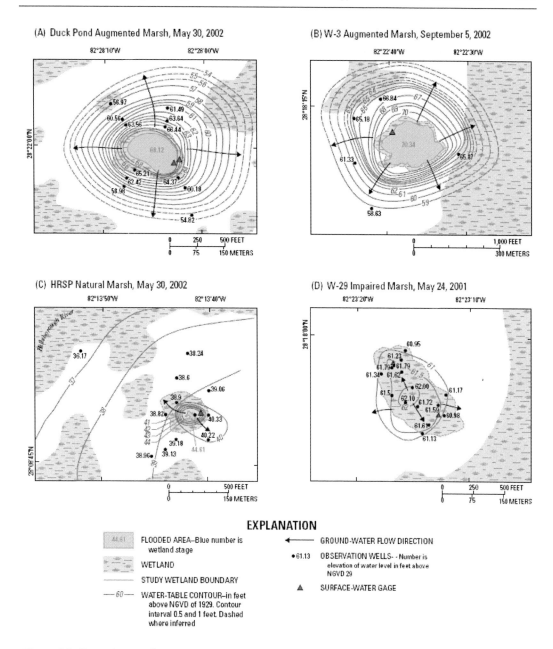

Figure 24. Ground-water flow patterns around the marsh wetlands during representative dry-season conditions. Wetter conditions are shown at W-3 Augmented Marsh, because monitoring wells were dry during the dry season.

A compact and steep recharge mound also was observed below HRSP Natural Marsh in May 2002 (figure 24C). The 5-ft mound created only a slightly larger footprint than the wetland flooded area. The base of the mound did not expand outward as it approached the water level in the Upper Floridan aquifer, probably due to the lack of confining clays overlying the limestone of the Upper Floridan aquifer in the basin (figure 11). During the dry seasons, such as in late May and early June of 2001 and 2002, the potentiometric surface of the Upper Floridan aquifer, which also constitutes the water table in this basin, dropped well below the wetland stage, causing wetland water levels to decline (figure 25C). In contrast, during the late summer and early fall of 2001 and 2002, the Upper Floridan aquifer head approached land surface, rising above the wetland bottom elevation in 2001. The HRSP Natural Marsh became a flow-through wetland during the wet seasons of 2001 and 2002. Ground-water levels toward the southeast rose higher than the wetland, whereas those toward the northwest were lower (wells 91 and 95), creating a flow-through setting for the wetland and effectively making the basin part of the regional ground-water flow pattern toward the Hillsborough River (Wolansky and Thompson, 1987) (figure 9C).

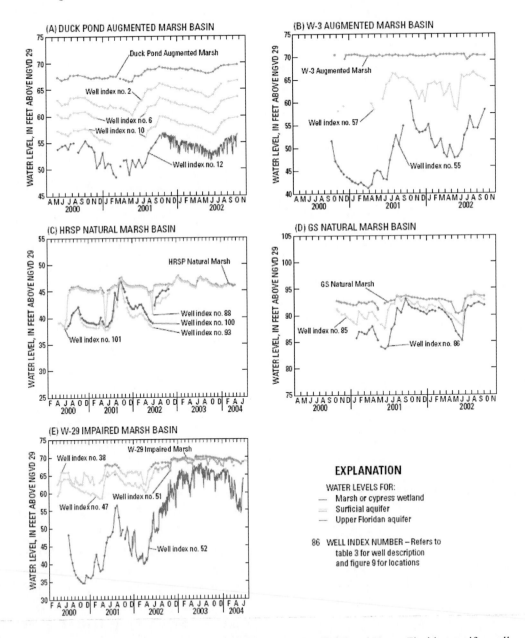

Figure 25. Wetland stage and ground-water levels in selected surficial and Upper Floridan aquifer wells in the marsh wetland basins.

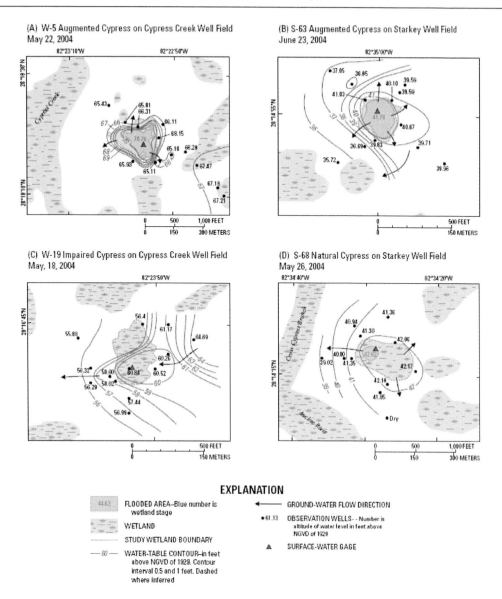

Figure 26. Ground-water flow patterns around cypress wetlands during representative dry-season conditions.

A recharge mound also was present in the water table beneath W-29 Impaired Marsh, even though the wetland was dry and the peak of the recharge mound was several feet below the wetland bottom (figure 24D). Although rainfall and runoff were insufficient to flood W-29 Impaired Marsh for more than several months during the first 2 years of the study, recharge still created a water table mound beneath the wetland (figure 14). Water levels in the Upper Floridan aquifer were much lower than those in the surficial aquifer (figure 25E); however, the surficial aquifer was not dewatered during the lowest water-level conditions, suggesting restricted flow across the intermediate confining unit. Persistent flooding in W-29 Impaired Marsh occurred only after mid-2002, after water levels in the Upper Floridan and surficial aquifers had risen substantially.

The two augmented cypress wetlands had smaller, lower recharge mounds compared to the two augmented marshes because the regional water table had risen closer to land surface during the cypress study period. In May–June 2004, stage in the augmented cypress wetlands S-63 and W-5 was only 3 to 5 ft higher than the background water table, and the recharge mounds radiated outward about 200 ft from the water's edge (figure 26A-B). The water-table mound was even lower around S-68 Natural Cypress (figure 26D).

The pattern of ground-water flow around W-19 Impaired Cypress reflected the geologic setting of the wetland basin and the effect of ground-water pumping from a nearby production well (figure 26C). Most of the time, ground-water inflow occurred on the eastern side of the wetland through an area where the surficial deposits contain more clay and the Upper Floridan aquifer is better confined compared to the western side. This observation is supported by lithologic and grain size analyses of two geologic cores (29 and 17 ft deep) on the eastern side of W-19 Impaired Cypress, and two index wells (22 and 23) on the western side (table 3). Wetland water leaked outward from the western side where the surficial deposits are sandier and the clay confining unit appears to be discontinuous (figure 26D). Pumping from a production well lowered surficial aquifer and Upper Floridan aquifer heads on the western side of the wetland, and also induced outflow from the wetland (figure 18). During May 2004, a seasonal minimum in water-table elevation briefly caused potential for outflow along the eastern perimeter of the wetland, putting the entire wetland in a ground-water recharge setting.

Although the most commonly observed ground-water interaction displayed by the wetlands was one of ground-water recharge, all four natural wetlands had the potential to receive ground-water inflow from the surficial aquifer during brief periods. The water-table elevation in areas adjacent to the natural marshes rose above the wetland stage briefly during the summers of 2001 and 2002 (figure 25C-D), and at the natural cypress wetlands during the summer of 2003 (figure 27C-D). The pattern suggests that the natural wetlands may receive some ground-water inflow during high rainfall periods. Ground-water inflow conditions never occurred at the four augmented wetlands, even during the wettest periods of the study, but did occur at W-29 Impaired Marsh in February 2003 and April 2004 (figure 25E). Water tables were high in the wetland basins when the Upper Floridan aquifer head also was high and the difference between the wetland stage and Upper Floridan aquifer head was minimal (figs. 25 and 27). The head differences between the wetlands and the Upper Floridan aquifer differed in the three groups of wetlands over time, and substantially affected wetland leakage losses.

Overview of Wetland Hydrogeologic Settings

Isolated wetlands are one of the dominant landforms in the low-lying areas north of Tampa Bay. The geologic setting of these wetlands, and the depth and direction of ground water flowing below their basins, directly affect their rate of ground-water exchange and indirectly affect the runoff they receive from the surrounding upland areas. The wetlands in this study showed no distinctive differences in basin stratigraphy that could be linked to the wetland type (marsh or cypress) or to the hydrologic conditions of the three wetland groups (natural, impaired, or augmented). All investigated wetlands shared a common stratigraphic sequence, whereby an organic-rich wetland sediment layer was underlain by a sequence of sand and silt, and then by a sandy clay layer. However, differences in the thickness and composition of these stratigraphic layers distinguished one wetland from another. The thicker sediment encountered in the two augmented marshes is probably a consequence of augmentation. The W-29 Impaired Marsh showed evidence of organic sediment loss, probably as a consequence of prolonged dry conditions in the wetland.

Although augmenting lakes with ground water has been shown to elevate the ^{226}Ra activity in the lake water and sediment, results of the present study indicate that the ^{226}Ra activities in the surface sediment samples were similar in augmented and unaugmented wetlands. The ^{226}Ra activities measured in sediments of natural, impaired, and augmented wetlands in this study were similar in magnitude to those reported for other natural wetlands in central Florida, and they were considerably lower than activities measured in many augmented lakes in central Florida. Factors that could contribute to the lower ^{226}Ra activity observed in augmented wetlands compared to augmented lakes include the ^{226}Ra activity in the augmentation water, short water residence time in the wetland, proportional contribution of the augmentation water to the water budget of the wetland, organic matter content of the wetland sediment, and cycling between wet and dry wetland soil conditions.

Analysis of GPR data at three wetlands (W-29 Impaired Marsh, Duck Pond Augmented Marsh, and S-63 Augmented Cypress) indicated well-defined reflectors in areas of the basins where the lateral bedding within the surficial deposits was intact. In other areas of the record, discontinuous reflectors and dipping reflectors suggest that the surficial deposits have been disrupted by karst subsidence. The most notable geologic features beneath W-29 Impaired Marsh and Duck Pond Augmented Marsh are the steeply/dipping reflectors that indicate subsidence in the underlying layers and signify sinkhole activity. Smaller infilled or buried sinkholes not evident as depressions in the land surface were found to be abundant in the GPR record, along with possible piping features where reflective layers in the surficial deposits are disrupted or are deformed downward due to karst subsidence. In these areas, the surficial aquifer has the potential to leak faster to the underlying Upper Floridan aquifer, causing a low in the water table despite a level or rising land surface.

Thick organic sediment in an augmented wetland

The wetlands in this study, whether they were natural, impaired, or augmented, routinely recharged the underlying aquifer. The water levels in wetlands typically were higher than the water-table elevation in the surficial aquifer, causing water to leak into and recharge the aquifer. None of the wetlands were observed in a discharge setting, where wetland water levels are lower than the encircling water table. Only one of the eight wetlands where ground-water flow paths were established was persistently in a flow-through setting. However, during the wettest conditions of the study, several marsh and cypress wetlands briefly alternated from a recharge condition to a flow-through condition. When this occurred, the areas of ground-water flow into the wetland often mirrored areas of surface-water inflow.

Recharge mounds were observed below all the wetlands. The recharge mounds were generally compact and steep at the natural wetlands, often with a footprint only slightly larger than the wetland flooded area. A recharge mound was even present beneath W-29 Impaired Marsh, despite the fact that the wetland was usually dry and rainfall was insufficient to flood the wetland for more than a few months. Augmented wetlands had the most extreme recharge settings. The two augmented marshes were perched on top of steep, conical, ground-water mounds that radiated out from the wetland perimeter as much as 500 ft. During May 2002, the ground-water mound below Duck Pond Augmented Marsh was about 15 ft high and covered about 40 acres, including the 5-acre wetland area. The concentric water-table contours encircling the wetland dropped from the wetland water level to an elevation slightly above the potentiometric surface of the Upper Florida aquifer, indicating that wetland leakage had recharged the surficial aquifer below the wetland. The two augmented cypress wetlands had smaller, lower recharge mounds compared to the two augmented marshes because the regional water table was closer to the land surface during the latter part of the project when the cypress wetlands were studied.

WETLAND WATER BUDGETS

The water-budget approach was used in this study primarily to quantify ground-water interactions with the wetlands. The approach was adapted from studies designed to quantify the interaction of ground water with lakes in mantled karst terrain (Sacks and others, 1992; Lee, 1996; Lee and Swancar, 1997; Swancar and Lee, 2003). The lake water-budget studies typically shared four traits: (1) terms in the water-budget equation were defined at the weekly or monthly timescale over a year or more; (2) lake evaporation was quantified independently; (3) net ground-water exchange was derived as a residual term to the water-budget equation; and (4) detailed hydrogeologic descriptions of the lake basin, including aquifer geochemistry, were used to help interpret the timing and magnitude of ground-water exchanges. The water-budget approach used for the wetlands in this study is analogous, except that evaporation was estimated instead of measured, and wetland water-budget components were analyzed at the daily timescale instead of being summed over weekly or monthly time periods.

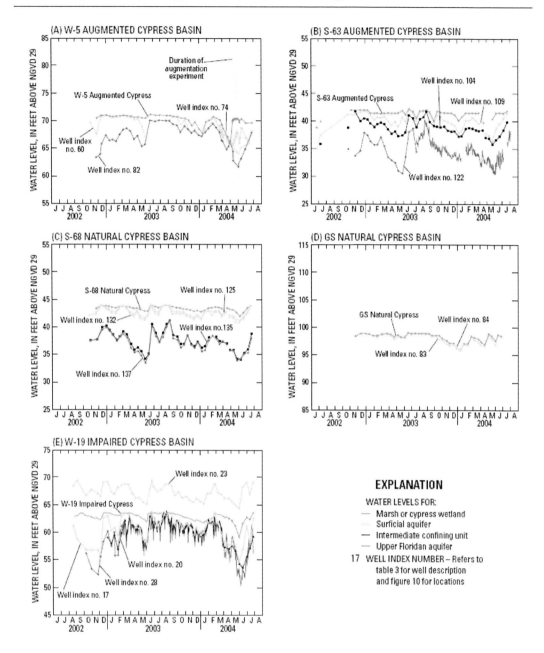

Figure 27. Wetland stage and ground-water levels in selected surficial and Upper Floridan aquifer wells in the cypress wetland basins.

The water-budget analysis quantifies all of the water exchanges with a wetland volumetrically, and compares these exchanges to the measured change in the wetland water volume. The wetland volume change is computed using daily stage data and wetland bathymetric data. Describing all flows volumetrically was required to (1) compare wetland groups in this study, because augmentation inflows were volumetric, not areal flux rates; and (2) quantify runoff into wetlands. Bathymetric data for wetlands often are not available, and stage changes alone are used to evaluate the water budget of wetlands. This approach is valid only if all water exchanges of interest are areal fluxes (for example, rainfall, evaporation, or leakage), or if the size of the flooded area remains constant despite changes in stage, as can occur in artificial retention ponds (for example, Choi and Harvey, 2000). Stage changes alone were used to describe the earliest water budgets created for isolated wetlands in the United States, such as the prairie pothole wetland in North Dakota during the 1960s (Shjeflo, 1968; Eisenlohr, 1972), and the earliest water budgets created for isolated wetlands in the mantled karst terrain in Florida (Heimburg, 1976; 1984).

Methods of Computation

For a wetland not connected by streams to other surface-water bodies, the change in the water volume over an interval of time equals the difference between the inflow and outflow volumes:

$$\Delta S = P - ET + A + R + Gi - L \ [\mathrm{L}^3], \tag{1}$$

where:

ΔS	is change in wetland volume,
P	is precipitation,
ET	is evapotranspiration,
A	is augmentation water added to the wetland,
R	is runoff into the wetland,
G_i	is ground-water inflow, and
L	is leakage—the wetland water that leaks out to the underlying ground water.

All terms in equation 1 are expressed in units of volume and are quantified daily.

Four of the terms in equation 1 (ΔS, P, ET, A) were directly quantified using the methods described in this section. These four terms were used to compute a residual term equal to the difference between the two dominant unknown terms, namely, R and L:

$$\text{Residual Term} = R - L \pm e\text{Residual Term}$$

$$= \Delta S - P + ET - A. \tag{2}$$

Ground-water inflow, G_i, is not included in the residual term because it probably makes a negligible contribution to the wetlands during their water-budget periods. The water quality of the wetlands and ground-water flow patterns around them support this assumption at all of the wetlands except W-19 Impaired Cypress, where some ground-water inflow is interpreted to occur, although at a daily rate that is small compared to other budget terms. The residual term has an associated error or uncertainty ($e\text{Residual Term}$) that is derived from the various measurement errors present in the directly quantified terms on the right hand side of equation 2.

Table 4. Water-Budget Characteristics and Selected Flux Rates for the Study Wetlands.
[NGW, Net Ground-Water; in/d, Inches Per Day]

Water-budget characteristics	Natural				Augmented				Impaired	
	GS Natural Marsh	HRSP Natural Marsh	GS Natural Cypress	S-68 Natural Cypress	Duck Pond Augmented Marsh	W-3 Augmented Marsh	S-63 Augmented Cypress	W-5 Augmented Cypress	W-29 Impaired Marsh	W-19 Impaired Cypress
Dates of hydrologic data collection	12/11/00-10/02/02	12/12/00-04/05/04	11/22/02-08/01/04	12/11/02-08/04/04	12/08/00-10/14/02	12/07/00-10/09/02	11/05/02-08/04/04	10/11/02-07/27/04	12/07/00-07/01/04	08/23/02-07/26/04
Total data collection days	661	1,211	619	602	676	672	638	656	1,303	704
Total water budget days	295	607	225	452	635	47	463	333	687	460
Dry days	171	31	59	10	0	0	76	91[1]	484	24
Overflow days	133	227	265	120	0	0	21	196[2]	121	99
Positive NGW days "Runoff Days"	123	211	41[3]	121	0	0	34	41	173	93
Negative NGW days "Leakage Days"	172	396	184	331	635	47	429	292	514	367
Leakage rate, median, in/d	0.07	0.11	0.26	0.14	2.0	0.6	1.17	0.40	0.09	0.18
Leakage rate, mean, in/d	0.10	0.16	0.28	0.16	2.2	0.71	1.27	0.56	0.13	0.22
Rainfall sum for leakage days, inches	3.22	20.86	2.62	4.55	87.04	17.48	28.9	13.11	13.72	7.79
Rainfall sum for runoff days, inches	31.50	67.52	17.45	41.08	0	0	30.59	22.25	96.92	39.89

[1] Dry days at W-5 Augmented Cypress were part of an augmentation experiment.

[2] Overflow occurs at W-5 Augmented Cypress when the wetland stage exceeds a road cut elevation at 71.20 ft above NGVD 29. At all other sites, it occurs when the elevation exceeds the wetland perimeter.

[3] The number of "Runoff Days" appears low at GS Natural Cypress because the water budget (and runoff) could not be computed for the numerous "overflow" days when the wetland was overflowing its perimeter, despite the fact that the potential for runoff was high.

The residual term computed from the water-budget equation can be either positive or negative, depending primarily upon whether the runoff (R) or the leakage (L) predominates. For unaugmented wetlands in this study, the majority of the water-budget days with a negative residual value had no rainfall to generate runoff (table 4). Negative residual values on these days, therefore, were interpreted to represent gross leakage. Similarly, because most days with a positive residual term were days with rainfall, the positive residual values were equated with runoff. Wetland leakage does occur on days when runoff generates a positive residual value and, therefore, the runoff estimate is actually the difference between runoff and leakage, or a net runoff estimate, meaning the positive residuals underestimate the runoff. For this reason, the large daily leakage rates of augmented wetlands can mask smaller runoff events by generating a negative residual term, even on days when runoff may have occurred. Positive residual values may be generated for augmented wetlands, although only for days when large rainfall events create enough runoff to exceed leakage.

A positive or negative residual value also could be an artifact of residual error that is greater than the L and R terms. Although the actual error is unknown, the maximum probable uncertainty in the residual term can be estimated by adding together (as a root mean square) the errors ascribed to each of the directly quantified terms of the water-budget components in equation 2 (Ramette, 1981; Winter, 1981; Lee and Swancar, 1997). This cumulative error can itself be positive or negative, functionally adding to or subtracting from the runoff and leakage. When the residual error is large, it masks the hydrologic information contained in the residual term, making the term physically meaningless for interpreting runoff or leakage.

In this analysis, the uncertainty in the residual term is acknowledged but is not estimated using the maximum probable error approach. Error estimates were not available for the daily values of the water-budget components, and the use of conservatively large error estimates can discourage further examination of the residual values and their potentially valuable physical information (Lee and Swancar, 1997). Instead, the size of error and, conversely, the physical importance of the residual term were checked by correlating the population of daily residual values to external environmental variables. The positive water-budget residuals considered to reflect runoff were examined in relation to rainfall. The negative water-budget residuals considered to reflect leakage were examined for correlation to head values in the underlying Upper Floridan aquifer. If the residual terms were significantly correlated to an independently measured physical variable, then their values were assumed to retain physical meaning despite residual errors, and the errors were concluded to be, on average, substantially smaller than the residual values.

The daily volume of leakage from each wetland was expressed as a linear flux rate in inches per day by dividing it by the average size of the flooded area in the wetland on that day. In this way, the linear leakage rates from each of the wetlands (or at an individual wetland over time) could be compared without regard to the size of the respective flooded areas. Collectively, the daily linear leakage rates calculated for each wetland were viewed as a sample population with statistical properties that could be compared among wetlands. The median value of the daily leakage rate was compared for the 10 wetlands, and the first and third quartiles were interpreted to be plausible ranges for the daily leakage of a given wetland. Leakage values that fell outside the first and third quartiles were considered less physically representative and possibly artifacts of residual error.

The box plots used for descriptive analysis of linear leakage rates include a vertical box that represents the 25th through the 75th percentiles of the data (50 percent of the data), and a horizontal line or symbol that represents the median of the data (that is, the middle observation). The height of the box from top to bottom is a representation of how much variability or "spread" is present in the data. The length of this spread is called the interquartile range. The long lines extending from the boxes are called "whiskers." The whiskers extend up to 1.5 times the interquartile range, indicating the spread of additional data beyond the 25th and the 75th percentiles. If data do not extend to or beyond 1.5 times the interquartile range, the whiskers extend to the outermost upper and lower data points from the median. Stars and open circles are "outlier" data points beyond the 1.5 and 3.0 interquartile ranges, respectively.

A subset of the daily data collected at each wetland was used for the water-budget analysis (table 4). Days were eliminated if the (1) wetland was flooded beyond the wetland perimeter, making the change in volume unquantifiable; (2) wetland was dry; or (3) flooded area was less than 0.06 acres (about 2,600 ft^2), making it difficult to accurately describe the change in volume term (ΔS). Additional days were lost if augmentation flow rates were not available (163 days for S-63 Augmented Cypress), or if equipment or power failures resulted in missing data. Between 225 and 687 daily residual values were available for 9 of the 10 wetlands (table 4). At W-3 Augmented Marsh, the location of the stage recorder within the wetland limited the population of interpretable water-budget days to the 47 days with the highest stage.

Rainfall and Evapotranspiration

At each wetland, rainfall was measured hourly to the nearest 0.01 in., using 6-in.-diameter rain gages (Texas Electronics, Inc.) with automated tipping-buckets, and cumulative rainfall was measured every 2 weeks in 4-in.-diameter storage rain gages. The rainfall totals at the different sites are summarized in appendixes 1 and 2. The tipping-bucket gages onsistently over- reported rainfall by several percent and were corrected using the storage rain gage observations. At the five cypress wetlands, rainfall under the tree canopy was measured using both tipping- bucket and storage rain gages. Rainfall outside the wetland tree canopy was measured with a storage rain gage. The biweekly rainfall totals under the canopy were consistently lower, ranging from 85 to 95 percent of the rainfall totals outside the canopy (app. 3). Rainfall measured under the canopy was used in water budgets for the cypress wetlands.

Because evapotranspiration was not measured at the study wetlands, a synthetic daily time series was created based on published weekly to monthly wetland evapotranspiration data in Florida. Evapotranspiration losses from marshes were based on three comprehensive field studies of marshes in Florida (Abtew, 1996; German, 2000; and Mao and others, 2002). Monthly average marsh evapotranspiration was derived by averaging all of the published evapotranspiration values for a given month (app. 4). German (2000) used the Bowen-ratio/energy-budget method to compute annual evapotranspiration from seven marsh sites distributed in the Everglades area of southern Florida during 2 years. The monthly average evapotranspiration for all seven sites for 1996 and 1997 was used in this study (E.R. German, U.S. Geological Survey, written commun., 2005). Monthly evapotranspiration from a cattail marsh in southern Florida for 1993 and 1994 was measured by Abtew (1996) using continuously saturated lysimeters. Mao and others (2002) also used lysimeters to record evapotranspiration losses from three marshes in the Upper St. Johns River Basin in east-central Florida from May 1996 through December 1999.

Beneath the tree canopy in a cypress wetland

Daily evapotranspiration from the cypress wetlands was based on work by Sumner (2001). The study used tower-mounted instruments above the tree canopy, and the energy-budget variant of the eddy correlation method, to describe evapotranspiration from an extensive area of cypress wetland with fragmented areas of pine-forested upland in east-central Florida. Cypress wetland evapotranspiration estimates used in the current study were based on daily, and daily maximum, unburned evapotranspiration rates obtained from D.M. Sumner (U.S. Geological Survey, written commun., 2005). Daily values were summed to create monthly totals (app. 4). The annual cypress evapotranspiration rate of 38.19 in/yr (970 mm/yr) estimated by Bidlake and others (1996) in a similarly instrumented study in west-central Florida compares closely with the annual total of 37. 80 in/yr (960 mm/ yr) determined by Sumner (2001). Measured evapotranspiration rates in Sumner (2001) declined during spring months when wetlands were dry. Because evapotranspiration was needed only for flooded cypress wetlands in this study, values for the dry- season months of May and June were adjusted slightly upward.

Synthetic daily evapotranspiration values were created by assigning the monthly average daily value to the middle day of each month and interpolating the values for intervening days. Although the actual daily variability in evapotranspiration is lost, the information that is preserved provides the water budget with a daily evapotranspiration signal of appropriate magnitude to minimize the error in the largest number of residual values. The validity of using synthetic evapotranspiration in an annual sine curve to minimize budget errors has gained credibility in recent water budget studies and rainfall-runoff models (Oudin and others, 2005; Sumner, 2006).

Marsh and cypress wetland evapotranspiration rates for this study were lower than the open-water evaporation rate for Lake Starr, a lake in central Florida with 10 years of continuous, energy-budget evaporation estimates, the longest for any lake in the southeastern United States (Swancar and Lee, 2003; Swancar, 2006). The monthly Lake Starr evaporation rates shown in appendix 4 are averages for a 4-year period from 1997 to 2000.

Wetland Stage, Volume, and Area

Bathymetric survey results described in Haag and others (2005) were used to determine the water volume and flooded area in each wetland for a given stage value. The daily volume and flooded area were interpolated to the nearest 0.01 ft of stage. Volume and area were computed at midnight of each day, and the daily volumes of evapotranspiration and rainfall were computed by multiplying the linear flux rate of these terms by the daily average size of the flooded area of the wetland. The daily change in wetland volume was the forward difference between successive midnight volumes.

The daily augmentation volumes at the four augmented wetlands were provided by Tampa Bay Water and were typically rounded to the nearest 10,000 gal (0.01 Mgal/d) (Chris Shea, Tampa Bay Water, written commun., 2004).

Wetland Leakage

Wetland linear leakage rates varied nearly thirtyfold among the 10 sites (figure 28). GS Natural Marsh had the lowest median leakage rate (0.07 in/d). Duck Pond Augmented Marsh had the greatest median leakage rate (2.00 in/d), with an interquartile range of 1.74 to 2.74 in/d (table 5). The four natural wetlands and two impaired wetlands shared similarly low leakage rates, ranging from 0.07 to 0.26 in/d.

Among the six unaugmented wetlands, the three marshes leaked more slowly than the three cypress wetlands. This finding is not attributable to the different evapotranspira- tion rates used for the two wetland types, because when the lower cypress evapotranspiration rates were assumed for both wetland types, the three marshes still leaked, on average, at about half the rate of the three cypress wetlands (table 5). In addition, climate differences during the marsh and cypress wetland water-budget periods support this result. Marsh leakage rates were slower than cypress leakage rates even though the lower ground-water conditions during the marsh water-budget period theoretically should have favored faster leakage rates.

The augmented wetlands had the widest range in linear leakage rates, and these rates were not related to wetland type; that is, the two augmented cypress wetlands did not leak faster than the two augmented marshes. Differences in leakage rates, however, suggested differences in hydrogeologic conditions at the individual wetlands. For example, the two augmented wetlands located within the Cypress Creek Well Field (W-3 Augmented Marsh and W-5 Augmented Cypress), leaked at rates equal to about 20 to 50 percent of the rates of S-63 Augmented Cypress and Duck Pond Augmented Marsh.

Wetland leakage rates can change through time depending on rainfall and ground-water levels, and natural or augmentation-related changes in wetland stage. The changing ground-water head gradients surrounding the wetland interact with the hydraulic conductivity of the underlying sediments to determine the magnitude and direction of leakage flow. For example, as a group, augmented wetlands are expected to leak more than natural or impaired wetlands because the vertical head differences that drive leakage become amplified when ground-water levels are lowered by well-field pumping and wetland stage is raised through augmentation. But are augmented wetlands intrinsically leakier than their natural wetland counterparts? To address this question, wetland leakage rates were analyzed further to distinguish the effects of downward head conditions and hydraulic conductivity on the leakage rate of individual wetlands.

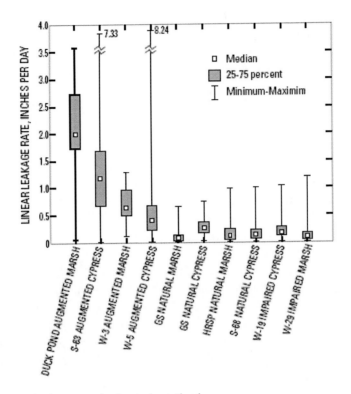

Figure 28. Daily linear leakage rates in the study wetlands.

Table 5. Wetland Leakage Rate Statistics.
[in/d, Inches Per Day. Leakage Rates in Parentheses Were Computed Using the Same Evapotranspiration Rates for All Wetlands. Results Reveal Higher Leakage Loss Rates in the Unaugmented Cypress Wetlands Compared to the Marsh Wetlands Whether Evapotranspiration in Marshes is Set to be Either Equal to or Greater Than in Cypress Wetlands]

Wetland group and/or type		Wetland name	Leakage rate, median (in/d)	Leakage rate, 1st quartile (in/d)	Leakage rate, 3rd quartile (in/d)
Augmented		Duck Pond Augmented Marsh	2.00	1.74	2.74
		S-63 Augmented Cypress	1.17	0.67	1. 68
		W-3 Augmented Marsh	0.67	0.49	0.96
		W-5 Augmented Cypress	0.40	0.23	0.67
Unaugmented	Marsh	GS Natural Marsh	0.07 (0.06)	0.03	0.13
		HRSP Natural Marsh	0.11 (0.09)	.05	0.24
		W-29 Impaired	0.09 (0.07)	0.04	0.16
	Cypress	GS Natural Cypress	0.26 (0.22)	0.17	0.37
		S-68 Natural	0.14 (0.11)	0.06	0.22
		W-19 Impaired Cypress	0.18 (0.16)	0.12	0.28

Effect of Downward Head Differences on Wetland Leakage

To compare the effect of hydrogeologic conditions on leakage estimates, the vertical, or downward, head difference between each wetland and the underlying aquifer was evaluated. The downward head difference, dh, provides the potential for vertical flow, and is part of the Darcy formula for one-dimensional, laminar ground-water flow (Bear, 1979)

$$Q_v = K_v * A (dh/dz), \tag{3}$$

where:

Q_v | is the volumetric flow rate in the vertical direction or leakage [L^3/T];

K_v | is the vertical hydraulic conductivity of the geologic material the leakage flows through;

A | is the projected area perpendicular to the flow [L^2], which is assumed to equal the flooded area of the wetland; and

dh/dz | is a dimensionless vertical head gradient.

All leakage is assumed to exit the wetland vertically, through a projected area equal to the flooded area of the wetland.

The daily linear leakage rate, q_v, is the volumetric leakage rate divided by the daily average flooded area.

$$q_v = Q_v/A = K_v(dh/dz) \quad [L/T]. \tag{4}$$

In these wetlands, the vertical head difference, dh, is equal to wetland stage minus the Upper Floridan aquifer head. The head difference occurs across the vertical interval, dz, equal to the vertical distance between the wetland bottom and the top of the persistent limestone of the Upper Floridan aquifer. Head differences at 9 of the 10 wetlands were calculated using biweekly measurements of wetland stage and the head in an adjacent Upper Floridan aquifer well. GS Natural Cypress lacked an Upper Floridan well and was, therefore, excluded from the analysis.

Wetlands with the greatest leakage rates were not necessarily those with the greatest downward head difference during their water budgets, as shown by a comparison of figures 28 and 29. Although W-3 Augmented Marsh experienced the largest head difference, it leaked more slowly than the two fastest leaking wetlands, Duck Pond Augmented Marsh and S-63 Augmented Cypress. W-29 Impaired Marsh, which like W-3 Augmented Marsh experienced large downward head differences and also was on Cypress Creek Well Field, had the second to lowest leakage rate. Head differences in the nine wetlands also were not clearly distinguished by wetland group or type. For example, head differences at the two natural marshes were among the lowest, as might be expected. Head differences at W-19 Impaired Cypress and W-5 Augmented Cypress, however, were both comparable in magnitude to those of the natural wetlands (figure 29). The typically greater head differences at the augmented wetlands reveal two aspects of their condition. First, the potentiometric level of the Upper Floridan aquifer can range farther below these wetlands due to well-field pumping than it ranges at the natural wetlands. Second, the water budget could be calculated throughout the dry season because these wetlands are augmented, whereas unaugmented wetlands would become dry as ground-water levels declined.

The contrast in head differences at wetland groups becomes more evident when comparisons are based on the entire data-collection time period, rather than the subset of days used for calculating the wetland water-budgets. To do this, a surrogate for the hydraulic head difference was calculated using the bottom elevation of the wetland instead of wetland stage, reflecting the physical distance of the potentiometric surface below the wetland bottom. Because wetlands are typically shallow, the elevation difference computed using the wetland bottom elevation is generally only several feet less than the head difference derived using wetland stage when the wetland is flooded.

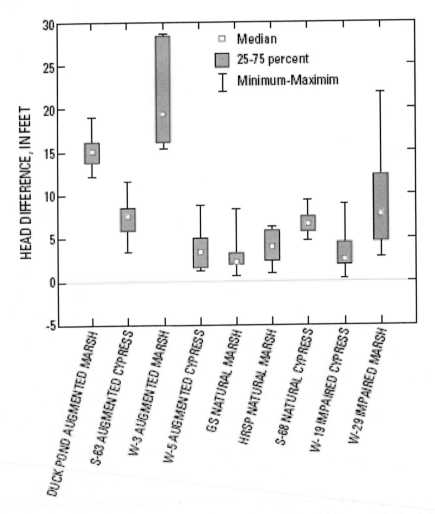

Figure 29. Downward head differences at each wetland during its water-budget period. Head difference is between wetland stage and the head of the Upper Floridan aquifer.

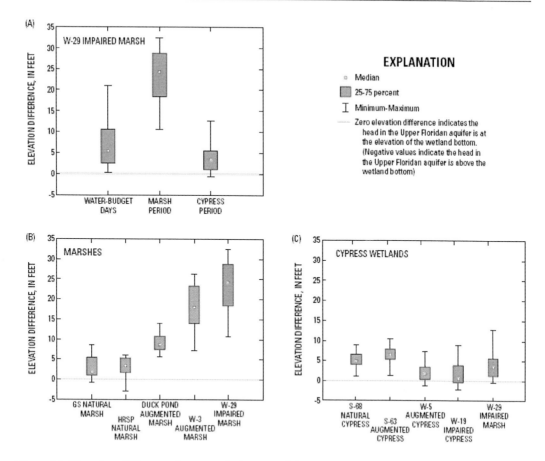

Figure 30. Elevation differences between the bottom of the wetland and the head in the Upper Floridan aquifer at (A) W-29 Impaired Marsh for three time periods, (B) marshes from December 2000 through September 2002, and (C) cypress wetlands from November 2002 through July 2004.

The elevation difference between the bottom of the wetland and the potentiometric surface of the Upper Floridan aquifer at W-29 Impaired Marsh contrasted sharply during the marsh and cypress data-collection periods, and revealed the importance of head conditions in underlying aquifers to wetland flooding (figure 30). During the nearly 2-year marsh data-collection period, with rainfall slightly below average, the potentiometric surface was a median distance of 24.36 ft below the bottom of W-29 Impaired Marsh while the interquartile range was 18.41 to 28.75 ft below the wetland (figure 30A). Above average rainfall and pumping reductions during the cypress data-collection period raised the potentiometric surface to a median distance of only 3.39 ft below the bottom of W-29 Impaired Marsh, with an interquartile range of 1.10 to 5.53 ft. During this period, W-29 Impaired Marsh exhibited a characteristic seen only at the natural marshes during the previous marsh period—the potentiometric surface briefly rose above the wetland bottom, and the elevation difference became negative (figure 30A).

If only those days when W-29 Impaired Marsh was inundated and the water budget could be calculated ("water- budget days") are examined, the median distance between the wetland bottom and the potentiometric surface in the Upper Floridan aquifer was 5.35 ft, with an interquartile range from 2.52 to 10.59 ft (figure 30A). This range overlaps the lower values observed during the marsh period, but more closely resembles the range and median value occurring during the cypress period. There is one exception: the water-budget days do not include any days when the potentiometric surface of the Upper Floridan aquifer was above the wetland bottom elevation because, when these conditions occurred, the wetland was overflowing its perimeter and the water budget could not be calculated (figure 30A).

During the marsh data-collection period, the potentiometric surface of the Upper Floridan aquifer was substantially closer to the bottom elevations of the two natural marshes than to the bottom elevations of the impaired and augmented marshes (figure 30B). The median elevation differences in GS Natural Marsh and HRSP Natural Marsh were 1.78 and 3.42 ft, respectively, and the interquartile range at both sites was between 1.00 and 5.41 ft. The potentiometric surface of the Upper Floridan aquifer also was occasionally above the bottom of each of the natural wetlands. In contrast, the median distance of the potentiometric surface below W-3 Augmented Marsh was large (17.94 ft), and similar in magnitude to the median value at W-29 Impaired Marsh (24.37 ft), probably because both are located on the same well field and are subject to similar ground-water pumping regimes. The median distance of the potentiometric surface below Duck Pond Augmented Marsh is less (8.57 ft), in part because the marsh is substantially deeper than the other two marshes (figure 30B).

With pumping reductions and above average rainfall during 2002-04, the surrogate head differences in the natural, impaired, and augmented cypress wetlands, as well as W-29 Impaired Marsh, resembled those measured earlier in the two natural marshes (compare figure 30B with figure 30C). The potentiometric surface of the Upper Floridan aquifer was a median distance of between 0.61 ft. and 3.40 ft below W-5 Augmented Cypress, W-19 Impaired Cypress, and W-29 Impaired Marsh, while the interquartile range was -0.34 to 5.53 ft. All three wetlands showed negative surrogate head differences at their minimum values, or within the lower quartile at W-19 Impaired Cypress. The potentiometric surface remained a greater distance below the two wetlands located on the Starkey Well Field where ground-water pumping had not been reduced. The median elevation difference at the natural wetland S-68 Natural Cypress (4.80 ft) was slightly less than the median at S-63 Augmented Cypress (6.63 ft), and the inter- quartile range was smaller. The potentiometric surface of the Upper Floridan aquifer was never above the bottom elevation of either wetland.

Effect of Hydraulic Conductivity on Wetland Leakage

Wetland leakage rates also are proportional to the vertical hydraulic conductivity (K_v), a constant and intrinsic property of the geologic material beneath a wetland. By assuming that all of the wetland leakage flowed vertically, the Darcy formula was used to derive a vertical leakance coefficient below each of the wetlands. Leakance, expressed as K_v/b (1/day), is a term used to describe the properties of a semipervious layer of thickness b capping a leaky confined aquifer (Anderson and Woessner, 1992). The property usually applies to a confining bed, or semipervious layer, because the layer with the lowest hydraulic conductivity tends to dictate the flow rate through the entire geologic interval. In this study, the precise stratigraphy beneath the wetlands was not known and the vertical thickness of the clastic deposits separating the bottom of each wetland from the top of the transmissive limestone was comparable (typically 20-40 ft); therefore, the entire thickness, dz, was equated to b and leakance was derived by rearranging equation 4 as follows:

$$q_v/(dh) = K_v/dz \quad [T^{-1}]. \tag{5}$$

A population of leakance coefficients was derived for each wetland by solving equation 5 using daily linear leakage rates, (q_v), and daily vertical head differences (dh). The statistical properties of these populations of leakance coefficients should reflect the constant and intrinsic properties of the subsurface beneath the wetlands. Daily average Upper Floridan aquifer head values were computed from hourly readings at Duck Pond Augmented Marsh, W-5 Augmented Cypress, W-19 Impaired Cypress, W-29 Impaired Marsh, and S-68 Natural Cypress. Daily aquifer levels were interpolated from biweekly measurements at HRSP Natural Marsh, W-3 Augmented Marsh, S-68 Natural Cypress, and GS Natural Marsh. The number of daily leakance coefficient estimates at each site ranged from 48 (W-3 Augmented Marsh) to 418 (W-29 Impaired Marsh).

Based on the median and interquartile range of the leakance coefficient estimate, S-63 Augmented Cypress on Starkey Well Field has the leakiest geologic setting of all the wetlands (figure 31). Duck Pond Augmented Marsh has a lower leakance coefficient, but a faster linear leakage rate than S-63 Augmented Cypress because it was subjected to larger downward head differences. S-63 Augmented Cypress is about 4,000 ft northwest of S-68 Natural Cypress, a natural cypress wetland with one of the lowest leakance coefficients in the study. Although S-68 Natural Cypress was subjected to downward head differences similar to those at S-63 Augmented Cypress, it maintained a flooding pattern most similar to those of the natural wetlands, probably because of its low- permeability setting.

A comparative analysis of wetland leakage rates alone would have been misleading. During the cypress water-budget period, the downward head differences at both W-5 Augmented Cypress and W-1 9 Impaired Cypress resembled those in the natural wetlands (figure 30B-C). As a result, the leakage rate for W-1 9 Impaired Cypress was one of the slowest, and the leakage rate for W-5 Augmented Cypress was the slowest for the augmented wetlands (figure 28). These two wetlands, however, have leakance coefficients that fall in a high-intermediate range, less than the two leakiest wetlands, but substantially greater than the values in the remaining five wetlands (figure 31). The leakance coefficients for W-5 Augmented Cypress and W-19 Impaired Cypress indicate the vulnerability of these two wetlands to larger leakage rates when head differences are larger than those observed during this study. This vulnerability explains the augmented and impaired status, respectively, of these two wetlands.

The comparison of leakance coefficients reinforces the conclusion that the marshes occupied less leaky settings than the cypress wetlands. The five wetlands with the lowest leakance values include all four of the shallow marshes (even W-3 Augmented Marsh), even though the marshes were located in three different parts of the study area. Duck Pond Augmented Marsh, the deepest wetland with the greatest potential for lateral flow, was the only exception (figure 12). The results indicate that the relatively fast leakage rate observed in W-3 Augmented Marsh during this study was due more to the large downward head differences it experienced than to a highly conductive setting. The distinction between marshes and cypress wetlands also was evident in neighboring wetlands for the two marshes and two cypress wetlands within Cypress Creek Well Field (figure 31).

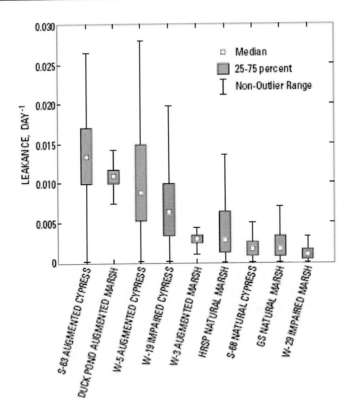

Figure 31. Leakance values below the study wetlands.

By assuming that vertical leakage always predominates over lateral leakage, both physical processes become incorporated in the vertical leakance coefficient. At each wetland, some leakage flows laterally away from the flooded perimeter, propelled by the slope in the surrounding water table and by the horizontal hydraulic conductivity of the surficial aquifer. The vertical exaggeration used in the hydrogeologic sections (figs. 11-18) exaggerates the appearance of horizontal flow near the wetlands. In fact, the wetlands are expansive, shallow features. Their large horizontal dimensions are typically exposed to vertical head gradients that far exceed the water- table slope. For this reason, horizontal leakage losses are considered negligible compared to vertical leakage losses.

Case Studies of Wetland Leakage

Leakage rates from all 10 wetlands were affected by a range of physical and environmental conditions. The effects of these conditions on wetland leakage, however, are easiest to show using the water-budget results for the augmented wetlands, rather than corresponding results for natural and impaired wetlands. Augmented wetlands leaked the most, making daily leakage values less subject to residual error and more robust for statistical analysis. In addition, they typically did not flood beyond the wetland perimeter during the wettest season or dry up during the driest season, although S-63 Augmented Cypress is a notable exception. As a result, the water budgets of augmented wetlands could be calculated for the greatest number of days per year, and for the greatest range in seasonal ground-water levels. This permitted detailed analyses of regression relations between leakage losses and environmental variables such as head in the Upper Floridan aquifer.

In the following three case studies, processes affecting wetland leakage rates are examined at three augmented wetlands: Duck Pond Augmented Marsh, S-63 Augmented Cypress, and W-5 Augmented Cypress. The three case studies examine, respectively, the relation between linear leakage rate and three factors: (1) head in the Upper Floridan aquifer; (2) size of the flooded area in the wetland; and (3) the effect of unsteady/unsaturated flow conditions when a dry wetland is initially augmented.

Duck Pond Augmented Marsh

Duck Pond Augmented Marsh provided the most continuous water-budget record of the 10 wetlands, and the most direct evidence of Upper Floridan aquifer head effects on wetland leakage rates. More than 90 percent of the 21-month water-budget period produced usable daily residual values, and all residual values were leakage (table 4). The nearly continuous record of daily leakage provided the opportunity to describe an annual wetland water budget for 2001. At Duck Pond Augmented Marsh, the magnitudes of augmentation and leakage overshadow all other water-budget components (figure 32). The annual volume of augmentation was equal to 65.52 vertical ft of water, covering an annual average flooded area of 2.87 acres. The annual leakage volume was only slightly less at 64.49 ft/yr, indicating the majority of the augmentation water (98 percent) exits the wetland as leakage. Annual rainfall and evaporation volumes, in comparison, totaled 4.36 and 3.95 ft/yr, respectively. Because the daily augmentation volume was relatively constant at Duck Pond Augmented Marsh, the daily leakage volume was relatively constant. However, the velocity of the leakage exiting the marsh, reflected in the linear leakage rate, was not constant. Instead, the leakage velocity accelerated and decelerated with fluctuations in the potentiometric surface of the Upper Floridan aquifer.

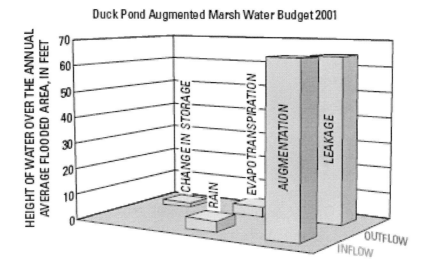

Figure 32. Annual water budget for Duck Pond Augmented Marsh in 2001. Volume is shown as height of water above the annual average flooded area.

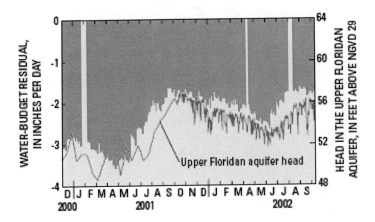

Figure 33. Daily water-budget residual for Duck Pond Augmented Marsh and head in the Upper Floridan aquifer during December 2000 through September 2002. Gaps reflect missing data. Negative residual values represent leakage.

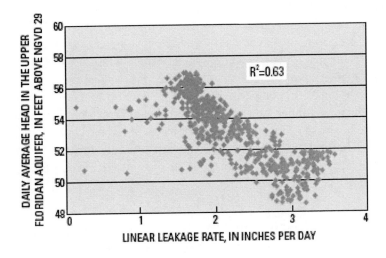

Figure 34. Daily average head in the Upper Floridan aquifer in relation to daily linear leakage rate from Duck Pond Augmented Marsh.

Daily linear leakage from Duck Pond Augmented Marsh varied by a factor of 2 during the water-budget period, ranging from a minimum of about 1.7 in/d in September of both 2001 and 2002 to a maximum of 3.7 in/d in April of 2001, and its magnitude closely tracked the head in the Upper Floridan aquifer (figure 33). Daily leakage rates were correlated with the average head in the Upper Florida aquifer for the same day (R2 = 0.63, confidence interval 95 percent), indicating that leakage from Duck Pond Augmented Marsh responds rapidly to head changes in the Upper Floridan aquifer (figure 34). The statistically significant relation between the heads measured in the Upper Floridan aquifer, and leakage derived as a residual term to the water-budget equation, validates the physical significance of the daily residual term. The relation also shows that the rate of leakage loss could be reduced by raising the Upper Floridan aquifer level near the wetland.

S-63 Augmented Cypress

Unlike the continuous leakage seen at Duck Pond Augmented Marsh, S-63 Augmented Cypress wetland periodically dried out and rewetted, and had more than 30 days with runoff (table 4 and figure 35). These variations caused additional processes to affect leakage rates at S-63 Augmented Cypress. The water budget still generated more than 420 linear leakage values that correlated with the head in the nearby Upper Floridan aquifer well, although at a lower R^2 value (0.44) than Duck Pond Augmented Marsh (figure 36). The maximum linear leakage rate at S-63 Augmented Cypress was typically around 3 in/d, similar to the maximum linear leakage rate at Duck Pond Augmented Marsh. However, exceptionally high linear leakage rates were evident in S-63 Augmented Cypress when the wetland was drying out or rewetting.

Dry conditions at S-63 Augmented Cypress wetland when augmentation stopped

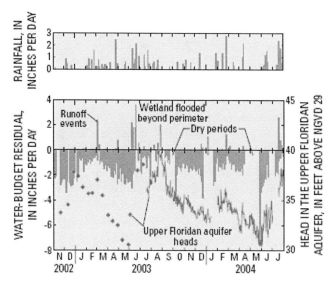

Figure 35. Daily rainfall, daily water-budget residual, and head in the Upper Floridan aquifer at S-63 Augmented Cypress wetland during November 2002 through July 2004. Data are missing when the wetland was dry or flooded beyond its perimeter. Positive and negative residual values represent runoff and leakage, respectively.

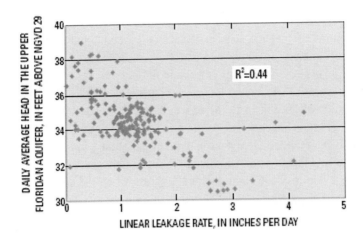

Figure 36. Daily average head in the Upper Floridan aquifer in relation to daily linear leakage rate at S-63 Augmented Cypress wetland. Four leakage values greater than 3.5 in/d are omitted from the regression relation.

On repeated occasions when S-63 Augmented Cypress dried out, linear leakage rates increased exponentially in the last few days before the wetland became dry. Similarly, when S-63 Augmented Cypress rewetted after having been dry, the initial linear leakage rate was highest and decreased exponentially during the next few days. For example, S-63 Augmented Cypress dried up on four occasions, each lasting one to several weeks. Each time, in the final days before completely drying or in the first days of being rewetted, the daily linear leakage rate peaked at from 4 to 7 in/d, substantially higher than the typical background leakage rates of 1 to 2 in/d (figure 35). The peaks in the linear leakage rate were not proportional to changes in the Upper Floridan aquifer, suggesting that processes other than saturated, vertical ground-water flow were important.

The apparent increase in linear leakage rate could, in part, reflect increased lateral leakage along the perimeter of the flooded area. During drying periods, as the flooded area shrinks and the surrounding water table drops, the slope of the wetland water-table mound increases, and as a result, lateral leakage also increases. At the same time, the decrease in flooded area increases the perimeter-to-area ratio, increasing the relative importance of lateral flow to vertical flow (Millar, 1971). If the water-table slope reaches a maximum and the flooded area reaches a minimum immediately before S-63 Augmented Cypress wetland dries out, or immediately after it rewets, the resulting increase in the lateral leakage could be interpreted as increased vertical leakage.

Increases in the linear leakage rate as the flooded area contracts also could be due to more permeable geologic material below the deepest region of the wetland. The deepest region of the wetland, and therefore, the last area to dry up or first to rewet, could overlie a collapse feature breaching the confining unit of the Upper Floridan aquifer—an association documented in Florida lakes (Tihansky and others, 1996). If this is the case, the linear leakage rate would increase when only this lowest region is flooded.

Finally, the rise in linear leakage rates could reflect a shift from saturated flow to infiltration into unsaturated soil. Evidence for this process can be found during an 8-day period in late December 2003, when S-63 Augmented Cypress alternated between flooded and dry conditions every day (discussed later). Augmentation flow to S-63 Augmented

Cypress was sufficient to flood only the deepest area of the wetland for 4 to 14 hours each day. When inflow was turned off, the wetland rapidly dried up and the water table dropped below the wetland bottom. Linear leakage rates from the small area that flooded were exceptionally high. Hourly water budgets were used to estimate the hourly linear leakage rates during these 8 days. The median leakage rate was 0.9 in/hr with a range of 0.48 to 1.2 in/hr across a median flooded area of 0.18 acre. This is comparable to a daily linear leakage rate of about 21 in/d. When computed with the daily water budget, the highest daily value of leakage for S-63 Augmented Cypress was 7.3 in/d occurring on the second day of flooding after it had been dry for a month and a half during April-May 2004 (figure 35). (The change in volume from the initial dry condition cannot be computed for the first day.) The higher linear leakage rates on an hourly basis most likely reflect infiltration into unsaturated soil, and this rate becomes attenuated as pore spaces in the soil fill and infiltration transitions to saturated ground-water flow.

At S-63 Augmented Cypress, days with positive residual values (runoff) generally coincided with rainfall days when the potentiometric level of the Upper Floridan aquifer was high (figure 35). They also coincided with periods when the water table on the north-northeast side of the wetland was higher than wetland stage, creating the potential for S-63 Augmented Cypress to receive lateral ground-water inflow. Most days with rainfall did not generate a positive residual term, and ground-water inflow was not large enough to generate a positive water-budget residual on days without rainfall (figure 35). The elevated water table and potentiometric surface apparently predisposed the wetland to receive substantial runoff, as indicated by the positive residual terms on days with rainfall. These "runoff days" typically appeared as solitary events on days with rainfall, and were surrounded by days with net leakage.

W-5 Augmented Cypress

An augmented wetland would mimic the hydrology of natural wetlands more closely if it dried up periodically rather than being perpetually flooded, and would gain several ecological benefits. Drying reduces the thickness of accumulated organic sediments in the bottom of wetlands by allowing sediments to oxidize and consolidate. In addition, the regeneration of cypress is enhanced because cypress seedlings can germinate only in dry conditions (Demaree, 1932). In addition to ecological benefits, allowing certain augmented wetlands to dry out could potentially conserve water. Although periodic drying is recommended in regulatory permits (for example, once every 5 years at Duck Pond Augmented Marsh), none of the augmented wetlands in this study have been intentionally allowed to dry up. No standard method currently exists for drying and rewetting augmented wetlands, and additional monitoring and other assistance would be needed to implement such a regime. Moreover, the potential exists that rewetting a dry wetland would require an unacceptably large volume of augmentation water compared to maintaining an existing flooded area. Specifically, rewetting an impaired wetland involves first mounding the water table to land surface, then flooding the wetland. Field experiments are needed to quantify the amount of water and time rewetting actually requires. These experiments could be used to determine the feasibility of increasing the similarity of flooding patterns in augmented and natural wetlands.

Several of these uncertainties were explored using the water-budget analysis of W-5 Augmented Cypress. In addition to the regular water-budget period, leakage losses were quantified during a controlled experiment to rewet the wetland. During the late spring of 2004,

W-5 Augmented Cypress was allowed to dry out by not augmenting the wetland for 79 days. The wetland was completely dry for the last 40 days, and during this time the water table declined about 4.5 ft below the wetland bottom. Augmentation water then was added in a prescribed manner for 22 days, from May 10 until June 1, 2004. The augmentation flow rate and ground-water levels around the wetland were monitored twice a day, and wetland stage was monitored continuously. The prescribed augmentation rates flooded two different areas used to calculate leakage. First, 1.3 acres (flooded area 1) were flooded to an elevation of 70.65 ± 0.02 ft. The flooded area was then increased to 2.3 acres (flooded area 2) at an elevation of 70.75 ± 0.02 ft. No substantial rain fell during this period, and water budgets were calculated daily.

Augmentation of W-5 Augmented Cypress quickly reestablished flooding conditions. About 12 hours after augmentation flow was started, the water table below the deepest area of W-5 Augmented Cypress was mounded to the land surface, and a small pond formed. Thereafter, the size of the pond increased along with the size of the water-table mound (figure 37A-B). About 5 days of augmentation were required to reach the first of the two prescribed flooded areas (figure 38). After 11 days of augmentation, a recharge mound radiated out about 150 ft from the flooded area, engulfing part of a water-table trough that had been below the southeast corner of W-5 Augmented Cypress when the wetland was dry (figure 37B).

As the mound became established, the augmentation volume required to maintain the first flooded area steadily declined and leveled off at about 6,000 ft^3/d (figure 38). The time required to form the water-table mound is evident in the response of individual wells that were located closest to the wetland. Before augmentation began on May 10, water levels in all of the shallow wells were dropping at the same rate as the head in the Upper Floridan aquifer well (figure 39). Afterwards, the ground-water levels in wells closest to the edge of the flooded area rose first (well index numbers 71, 74, 78, figs. 37 and 39). After 22 days of augmentation, the mound had reached its full height at wells 71 and 74, but was continuing to rise at well 78. The mound extended outward to wells 75, 76, and 77, but instead of raising the water table at these wells, the recharge slowed the decline of the water table compared to the Upper Floridan aquifer level (figure 39). During the first 4 or 5 days of rewetting, as the recharge mound grew in size and flooded area expanded to the first target area, the daily linear leakage rate declined exponentially, dropping from 8.24 in/d to a rate between 1.0 and 1.5 in/d. When the flooded area was increased in size to the second target area, the linear leakage rate declined again, reaching a rate between 0.5 and 1.0 in/d (figure 40).

The rapid response of W-5 Augmented Cypress to augmentation was due in part to the high augmentation flow rate. The maximum daily rate of augmentation flow into W-5 Augmented Cypress was about 11,200 ft^3/d (1.9 acre-ft/d), and thus the water deliverable in a day was 40 percent of the total wetland volume (as listed in app. 9 of Haag and others, 2005). At Duck Pond Augmented Marsh, by comparison, the normal daily augmentation rate was about 3.6 percent of the total volume of the wetland. This small daily rate would require far more time to refill Duck Pond, and could potentially prevent successful refilling under certain conditions.

Drying out and refilling W-5 Augmented Cypress was feasible for ground-water conditions similar to the case study, and has the potential to conserve augmentation water. Refilling W-5 Augmented Cypress to the first flooded area and establishing a steady rate of augmentation took about 10.5 days and required 93,430 ft^3 of water. This was about 30,000 ft^3 more water than would have been needed for uninterrupted augmentation of the wetland for the same 10.5 days (at 6,000 ft^3/d). This 30,000 ft^3 "investment" of water could have been recouped during a 5-day period with no augmentation. If additional days without augmentation conserved water at the same 6,000 ft^3/d maintenance rate, then not augmenting W-5 Augmented Cypress for the 79-day period of this experiment conserved about 440,000 ft^3/d, or 10.10 acre-ft, of water. The water conserved during the dry phase could be viewed as reserve to be used if needed in W-5 Augmented Cypress wetland at some later time period, for example, to achieve the ecological benefits of seasonal maximum water levels.

Additional augmentation experiments and numerical ground-water flow modeling studies could be used to understand the ground-water conditions and augmentation rates that are optimal for drying down and refilling augmented wetlands most strategically, and similarly to natural wetlands. For example, the augmentation experiment of W-5 Augmented Cypress wetland took place in May 2004 when the potentiometric surface of the Upper Floridan aquifer was higher than in previous years (figure 27A). Additional augmentation volume and time would have been required to refill W-5 Augmented Cypress for the lower ground-water conditions that prevailed at Cypress Creek Well Field during 2001 and much of 2002 (for example, figure 25E).

Augmentation water flooding W-5 Augmented Cypress Wetland

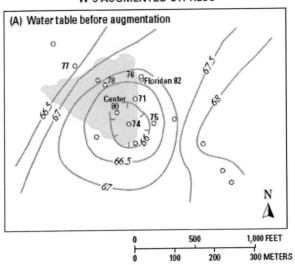

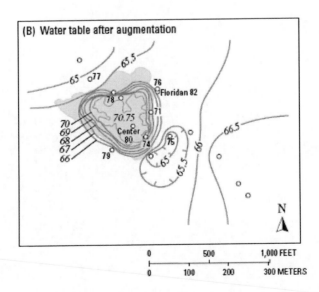

Figure 37. Water-table configuration at W-5 Augmented Cypress wetland (A) on May 10, 2004 before augmentation, and (B) on June 1, 2004 after 23 days of augmentation.

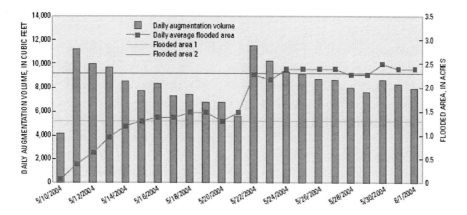

Figure 38. Daily augmentation volume and flooded area in W-5 Augmented Cypress wetland during the augmentation experiment.

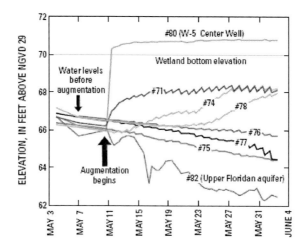

Figure 39. Response of the water table below W-5 Augmented Cypress wetland to augmentation. Well index numbers refer to table 3 and figure 37.

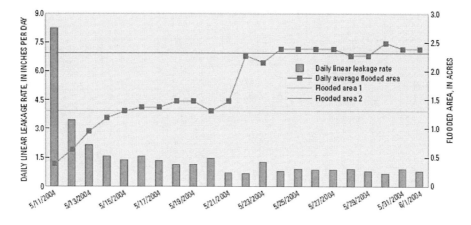

Figure 40. Daily linear leakage rate and flooded area in W-5 Augmented Cypress wetland during the augmentation experiment.

Runoff to Wetlands

Daily water-budget results provided insight into the importance of runoff on the hydrology of isolated wetlands. Runoff here refers to the rainfall that flows off of the surrounding upland and into the wetland, rather than water flowing out of the wetland. At 8 out of the 10 wetlands, some fraction of the water-budget days produced positive residual terms that were representative of runoff. Most, but not all, days with a positive residual term also had rainfall, whereas most days with a negative residual term did not (table 4). At S-68 Natural Cypress, for example, the 331 days that had negative residual values (equated to leakage) experienced a total of only 4.55 in. of rainfall, whereas the 121 days with positive residual values interpreted as runoff experienced 41.08 in. of rainfall (table 4). The positive residual values, which may at times include a small amount of ground-water inflow, represent the daily runoff volumes to the wetland that exceeded the daily leakage loss.

The two augmented cypress wetlands had far fewer days with positive residual values than the unaugmented wetlands. In addition, at augmented wetlands, a "runoff day" was associated with more rainfall than the runoff days computed for natural wetlands (table 4). This result probably reflects the greater amount of rainfall required to generate runoff at wetlands where the water table was both lowered by pumping and lower than the wetland water level. Moreover, at augmented sites, only days with substantial rainfall would generate enough runoff and other inflow to exceed the typically large leakage losses and generate a positive residual term (eq. 2). For example, no positive residual terms occurred at either of the augmented marshes. Days with no rainfall, but with apparent runoff (positive residual term) had an irregular distribution in the record and the associated runoff amounts were small. These small positive residuals are considered to be an artifact of measurement errors.

Table 6. Regression Results Relating the Daily Rainfall Volume to the Daily Change In Wetland Volume at the Unaugmented Wetlands.
[Results Are Limited to Days When Wetland Stage Was Below the Wetland Perimeter. Days with Streamflows Into Wetlands Were Not Included in the Analysis But Would Be Expected to Greatly Increase the Slope Between Rainfall Volume and Change in Wetland Volume. Slope of the Best Fit Line Relating Daily Rainfall Volume to Daily Change in Wetland Volume for the Unaugmented Wetlands. Correlation Coefficient is R^2 Value of a Best Fit Line Through the Data with Non-Zero Intercept]

Wetland group and/or type		Wetland name	Slope[1]	Correlation coefficient
Unaugmented	Marsh	GS Natural Marsh	1.49	0.95
		HRSP Natural Marsh	1.26	0.90
		W-29 Impaired Marsh	1.33	0.94
	Cypress	GS Natural Cypress	1.90	0.80
		S-68 Natural Cypress	1.74	0.89
		W-19 Impaired Cypress	2.45	0.77

[1] Slopes exceed 1.0 due to the contribution of runoff to the wetland volume.

Table 7. The Volume Ratio of Runoff to Rainfall in the Study Wetlands

Wetland group and type		Wetland name	Volume ratio of runoff to rainfall
Augmented		Duck Pond Augmented Marsh	No data
		W-3 Augmented Marsh	No data
		S-63 Augmented Cypress	0.67
		W-5 Augmented Cypress	0.96
Unaugmented	Marsh	GS Natural Marsh	0.80
		HRSP Natural Marsh	0.69
		W-29 Impaired Marsh	0.45
	Cypress	GS Natural Cypress	1.14
		S-68 Natural Cypress	1.05
		W-19 Impaired Cypress	1.82

The contribution of runoff to isolated wetlands also was evident in the relation between daily rainfall volume and the daily change in wetland volume. Absent other effects, the increase in wetland volume on a day with rainfall should equal the daily rainfall volume, creating a 1:1 ratio between the variables. At the six unaugmented wetlands, the slope of the regression line relating these variables was substantially greater than 1 (table 6). For example, at S-68 Natural Cypress, the best-fit line indicated the change in daily wetland volume was 1.74 times the daily rainfall volume. At other wetlands, slopes were 1.26 and 1.33 at HRSP Natural Marsh and W-29 Impaired Marsh, respectively, and 2.45 at W-19 Impaired Cypress (table 6). Slopes were greater in the cypress wetlands than the marshes, probably because the higher rainfall and ground-water levels during the cypress period enhanced runoff. W-19 Impaired Cypress had the highest runoff ratio of all the cypress wetlands, perhaps because its ground-water flow-through setting favored runoff because the water table was above the wetland stage and closer to land surface on one side of the wetland (Hernandez and others, 2003).

Runoff was a substantial part of the hydrologic budget of all of the unaugmented wetlands and at least two of the augmented wetlands. The runoff at each wetland (during runoff days only) was compared to the direct rainfall received on those days to help determine the relative importance of the two processes. At the unaugmented (natural and impaired) marshes, runoff contributed additional water equal to 45 to 80 percent of the rainfall volume entering the wetland (table 7). At the natural and impaired cypress wetlands, the runoff volume exceeded rainfall. The difference between the marsh and cypress wetland volume ratios probably reflects the preferential runoff conditions during the wetter cypress period. Estimates of the runoff contribution to both the marsh and cypress wetlands are conservative, because the positive residual term representing runoff has been reduced by the leakage losses. However, runoff was an important part of the water budget for both wetland types (table 7).

The water budgets of the isolated wetlands provide a conservative estimate of the importance of runoff processes because they quantify runoff only until the wetland stage reaches the wetland perimeter. As wetland stage rises above the perimeter, and water-table elevations in the upland areas approach land surface, less rainfall would be expected to infiltrate in the surrounding basin, and the relative contribution of runoff from rainfall would increase. In this analysis, for example, water-budget calculations for all of the cypress wetlands were interrupted when the wetlands flooded beyond their perimeters. All five cypress wetlands generated an outflow stream during parts of the study, and all except W-5 Augmented Cypress received stream inflow from a neighboring wetland.

The transition from isolated cypress wetlands into a chain of streaming wetlands is the culmination of the wet season response for cypress-pine flatwood wetlands in Florida (Ewel and Odum, 1984). This transition does not occur every year, however, and its frequency as well as the requisite climate and ground-water conditions for it to occur are not well described. When this condition does occur, cumulative runoff from the linked basins can be estimated by gaging streamflow at a downstream location in the watershed (Sun and others, 2002). No instrumentation is in place to gage the periodic outflows from the basins containing the 10 isolated wetlands in this study. Gaging these flows would greatly improve current understanding of runoff processes in wetland basins.

The size of the catchment generating runoff to wetlands varies in different geologic settings (Riekerk and Korhnak, 1992, 2000; O'Driscoll and Parizek, 2003) and for different rainfall and antecedent soil moisture conditions (Gerla, 1992; Hernandez and others, 2003). Riekerk and Korhnak (2000) estimated it to be 2 to 3 times larger than the vegetative wetland area of cypress wetlands in north-central Florida. Typical catchment sizes for isolated wetlands in the mantled karst terrain of Florida are not well understood; however, runoff results of this study were used to infer their minimum sizes. For the runoff and rainfall contributions to an isolated wetland to be equal, for example, the catchment would need to be equivalent in size to the flooded area, and all of the rainfall on the catchment would have to run off. If perfectly efficient at generating runoff, the catchment for a geometrically circular wetland with 2 acres of flooded area would extend into the uplands about 70 ft. If the runoff efficiency were 25 percent, with 75 percent lost to infiltration, the catchment would need to be four times the size of the flooded area, and the catchment radius would extend onshore about 205 ft. These radial distances, or other ones determined using different assumptions, are conceptualized, but emphasize the linkage between wetlands and the surrounding uplands contributing runoff to each wetland (Taylor and others, 2007).

All of the wetlands in this study were surrounded by relatively undisturbed uplands. For wetlands outside well fields, parks, and wildlife management areas, however, land-use changes are common within the distances described here. For example, 30 ft is the recommended setback distance to buffer wetlands from land development in Hillsborough County (Hillsborough County Environmental Protection Commission, 2006), whereas Florida State law requires a buffer with a minimum width of 15 ft and average width of 25 ft (Florida Legislature, 2007). Further research is needed to establish a scientific basis for decisions related to the creation and maintenance of buffer zones. Runoff estimates in this study reinforce the importance of preserving the linkages between wetlands and surrounding uplands to sustain natural wetland hydrology.

Overview of Wetland Water Budgets

The wetland water-budget approach, which is based on a population of daily residual values, permits a comparative analysis of leakage from different types and groups of wetlands. Linear leakage rates were shown to be time dependent upon the climate and hydrogeologic conditions during the water-budget period. Combining wetland leakage rates with the vertical head differences at each wetland was pivotal to understanding leakage losses from these wetlands, and results indicate it may be fundamental to properly interpreting water budgets for other wetlands in the mantled karst terrain of Florida.

Median linear leakage rates for the six unaugmented wetlands ranged from 0.07 to 0.26 in/d, and were similar to the average daily leakage rates calculated for unaugmented lakes in central Florida. Sacks and others (1998) described leakage losses, ranging from 0.046 to 0.23 in/d (17-85 in/yr) in 10 lakes in ridge areas of central Florida, using an approach that combined water and isotope mass-balances. Lake leakage rates toward the lower end of this range, 0.048 to 0.079 in/d (17.5-29 in/yr), were computed for Lake Lucerne and Lake Starr, two lake basins in central Florida analyzed using water budgets and numerical ground-water flow modeling (Lee and Swancar, 1997; Swancar and Lee, 2003).

The four augmented wetlands resembled augmented lakes in central Florida by displaying higher leakage rates and a wider range of leakage rates than their unaugmented counterparts. For example, Round Lake, an augmented 11-acre lake adjacent to a municipal well field in Hillsborough County, had an average daily leakage rate of 0.5 in/d (182 in/yr average, 153-225 in/yr range) (Metz and Sacks, 2002), a rate comparable to the lowest leakage rates in the augmented wetlands. The greatest wetland leakage rate measured in this study at Duck Pond Augmented Marsh was about 5 times greater than the lowest leakage rate. In contrast, leakage from Triangle Lake and Monsee Pond, two augmented lakes located near Cross Bar Ranch Well Field, were 2 and 17 times greater, respectively, than the leakage rate computed for augmented Round Lake (Biological Research Associates, Inc., and SDI Environmental Services, Inc., 2001).

Leakance coefficients derived for the study wetlands indicate that marshes generally were underlain by less conductive geologic material than cypress wetlands. The slower leakage from the unaugmented marshes compared to unaugmented cypress wetlands was consistent with the flooding and geochemical evidence described later for the two wetland types. The result could be an artifact of the small sample size. If not, however, the mechanism responsible for this fundamental difference is unclear. One possibility is that the roots of cypress trees may penetrate and disrupt the lower permeability, clay-rich layers below cypress wetlands making cypress wetlands leakier than marshes.

The distance of the potentiometric surface of the Upper Floridan aquifer below the wetland bottom was indicative of the hydrologic status of the wetland. The potentiometric surface of the Upper Floridan aquifer was generally within 5 ft of the bottom elevation of the two natural marshes in this study, and was higher than the bottom elevation during some period each year. In contrast, the potentiometric surface ranged from about 8 to 30 ft below the impaired and augmented marshes and never approached the bottom elevation of the wetlands. If the proximity of the potentiometric surface to the bottom of the natural marshes is a characteristic of natural conditions in this area, then the two impaired wetlands and one augmented wetland on the Cypress Creek Well Field experienced natural ground-water conditions during the wet 2003-04 study period when well-field pumping was greatly reduced. Ground-water pumping was not reduced at Starkey Well Field during the same period, and probably for this reason the characteristic distance was exceeded at the natural wetland on this well field. The median potentiometric surface was typically within 7 ft of the bottom of S-68 Natural Cypress, and never rose above the wetland bottom.

The water-budget approach used in this study, which quantified the daily change in wetland volume and area, provided a means to evaluate the minimum runoff to the isolated wetlands. At a minimum, runoff contributed from half (45 percent) to twice (182 percent) as much water as direct rainfall at individual wetlands, and indicated the scale of the surrounding catchment. When the isolated wetlands in this study began to connect with neighboring wetlands through outflow streams, however, runoff processes could not be quantified for the expanded watershed. Quantifying these ephemeral stream flows would further the understanding of the hydrology of isolated wetlands as well as the hydrology of downgradient rivers that receive the outflow from these watersheds.

WETLAND WATER QUALITY AND GEOCHEMISTRY OF WETLAND BASINS

Surface water in the isolated wetlands of west-central Florida is composed of rainfall, surface runoff, and ground-water inflow from the surficial aquifer. The hydrologic setting and interactions between ground water and surface water influence water quality in the wetlands, as well as ground-water geochemistry near the wetlands (LaBaugh and others, 1987). When anthropogenic activities such as ground-water withdrawal and wetland augmentation are superimposed on the landscape, the direction and rate of surface- and ground-water movement are altered. Consequently, wetland water quality and the geochemistry of wetland basins may change measurably. These changes affect the biota in wetlands, and they also can be used to describe and predict ground-water flow patterns in wetland basins.

Water-Quality and Geochemical Methods

Surface-water samples (1.3-L subsurface grab samples) were collected at three widely spaced locations in each of the 10 wetlands quarterly if the wetlands were not dry. The grab samples from each wetland were composited into a 4-L container and chilled. Composited water samples were processed using standard USGS methods described in Wilde and others (1998), and sent to the USGS Water Quality Laboratory in Ocala, Florida, for analysis of major ions and nutrients. Quality-assurance samples were collected for about 10 percent of the samples, including duplicate samples and field-blank samples. Field properties (water temperature, pH, specific conductance, and dissolved oxygen concentration) were measured using standard USGS methods at the same three locations on each sampling date with a multiparameter probe and stirring assembly. Ground-water samples were collected in seven wetland basins to describe chemical characteristics in the shallow ground water surrounding the wetlands. These water-quality data were then used to help determine ground-water flow patterns in the basins surrounding the wetlands. Ground water was sampled semiannually (during wet and dry periods) from 6 to 12 selected monitoring wells in the surficial aquifer around each wetland. Marshes were sampled during 2000-02, and cypress wetlands were sampled during 2003-04 (figure 2). In addition, water from the Upper Floridan aquifer used to augment wetlands was sampled concurrently.

Standard USGS protocols were used to collect groundwater and quality-assurance samples (Wilde and others, 1998). Surficial aquifer samples were collected using a peristaltic pump. Three casing volumes were removed from each monitoring well, and after field properties (temperature, pH, dissolved oxygen, and specific conductance) stabilized, the water sample was collected. For low-yield wells, the wells were pumped dry and then sampled the following day. Augmentation water was collected as a grab sample from the augmentation outflow pipe. The USGS laboratory in Ocala, Florida, analyzed ground-water samples for concentrations of major ions and nutrients. Results for surface and ground water are available in the USGS water data reports for southwest Florida (Kane and Fletcher, 2002; Kane and others, 2003; Kane, 2004a,b) and from the USGS National Water Information System (NWIS) database at http://waterdata.usgs.gov/nwis.

Differences between water-quality parameters for different groups and types of wetlands were described statistically using the Wilcoxon-Mann-Whitney two-sided test and visually using box plots. The Wilcoxon-Mann-Whitney test was chosen for statistical analysis because most water-quality parameters were not normally distributed, and this non-parametric test does not assume that the data are drawn from a given probability distribution. For the calculation of median concentrations of the various forms of nitrogen and phosphorus, values below the reporting limits were set to the reporting limit.

Stable isotope samples were used to help determine flow patterns in the wetland basins. In March 2004, all wetland surface waters were sampled for the stable isotopes deuterium (^{2}H or D) and oxygen-18 (^{18}O). Unfiltered water samples were collected in glass bottles with polyseal caps for isotope analysis. Ground-water samples for analysis of the stable isotopes deuterium and ^{18}O were collected at two wetland basins. All isotope samples were analyzed by the USGS Stable Isotope Laboratory in Reston, Virginia (isotope information available at http://isotopes.usgs.gov/). Stable isotope abundance is expressed as the ratio of the two isotopes in the sample (^{2}H/^{1}H or ^{18}O/^{16}O) compared to the same ratio in an international standard, using the delta notation (δ) as the unit of measurement (parts per thousand, or per mil) (Sacks, 2002).

Water-Quality Constituents

In this study, water-quality constituents of interest in the wetlands include pH, specific conductance, major ions, alkalinity, dissolved organic carbon, nutrients, and stable isotopes. These constituents are of interest either because they affect the biotic community, or because they can be used to indicate the direction and magnitude of surface- and ground-water flow in the wetland basins. Radium-226 also was analyzed in water and sediments at the wetlands (^{226}Ra results are summarized in the Wetland Hydrogeologic Setting section of the report). Water-quality comparisons primarily are made between groups of wetlands (natural, impaired, and augmented), although some comparison are made between types of wetlands (marshes and cypress). For some comparisons, natural and impaired wetlands were grouped together as "unaugmented wetlands," and collectively compared to augmented wetlands.

Field Properties and Major Ions

The six natural and impaired marsh and cypress wetlands in this study receive the majority of their hydrologic input from rainfall and runoff from undisturbed uplands. Water in these wetlands is dilute and poorly buffered (figure 41). The median specific conductance in these six wetlands was 45 µS/cm, median acid neutralizing capacity (ANC) was 1.2 mg/L as calcium carbonate, and the pH was relatively low (median 4.5, table 8). The low pH originates, in part, from humic substances released by the slow decomposition of plant material, and wetland water typically is stained by organic compounds. Median concentrations of all major ions were low, typically less than 5 mg/L. Water quality in W-29 Impaired Marsh was similar to that of the four natural wetlands. W-19 Impaired Cypress, however, had a somewhat higher median pH (6.0), calcium concentration (12.0 mg/L) and ANC (18 mg/L as calcium carbonate) than the four natural wetlands. Although rainfall water quality was not assessed in this study, studies in north-central Florida (Riekerk and Korhnak, 1992) indicate that rainfall pH averaged 4.8 over an 11-year period. Therefore, pH at the natural sites and W-29 Impaired Marsh was similar to that of rainfall. The higher pH at W-19 Impaired Cypress may indicate ground-water inflow to the wetland.

The range of water quality in the natural wetlands in this study is similar to water quality reported for natural wetlands in other studies in west-central Florida (Dierberg and Brezonik, 1984; Berryman and Hennigar, Inc., 1995; 2000). Mitsch (1984) and Dierberg and Brezonik (1984) reported consistently low pH, low concentrations of cations, low alkalinity, and low concentrations of nutrients in short- and long-term studies of cypress domes in central Florida.

Augmentation water applied to study wetlands is drawn from the Upper Floridan aquifer, which is composed primarily of calcite and dolomite. As a consequence, augmented marsh and cypress wetlands in this study had a higher median specific conductance (346 µS/cm) and pH (7.5) than natural and impaired wetlands of either type (table 8). Major ions in augmented wetlands were calcium (median 62.8 mg/L) and bicarbonate (median 205 mg/L). Major ion concentrations and ANC (median 172.5 mg/L as calcium carbonate) also were much higher in augmented wetlands than in natural and impaired wetlands (figure 41). These changes in water quality related to augmentation are similar to those reported by Cooney and Allen (2006) for augmented lakes.

Concentrations of all major ions (including calcium, magnesium, potassium, and sulfate), specific conductance, and pH were higher in augmented wetlands than in unaugmented wetlands (figure 42); these differences were statistically significant ($p < 0.01$) based on the Wilcoxon-Mann-Whitney test. The higher values in the augmented wetlands are characteristic of the augmentation source water from the Upper Floridan aquifer. Dissolved oxygen concentrations typically were higher in the augmented wetlands, and this difference also was statistically significant ($p = 0.01$). Higher dissolved oxygen concentrations may be an artifact of water delivery because when augmentation water is added to the wetlands, the position of the augmentation pipe above the water surface and the subsequent turbulence results in mixing of air with the water. In addition, the residence time of water in the augmented wetlands is expected to be less than in unaugmented wetlands, and the resulting flushing effect may allow less time for the accumulation of water rich in organic compounds that can subsequently deplete dissolved oxygen. Dissolved organic carbon, iron, and organic nitrogen concentrations were all lower in augmented wetlands than in unaugmented wetlands (figure 42) by amounts that were statistically significant ($p < 0.01$). This also is likely due to the low residence times of these constituents in the augmented wetlands, as well as low respective concentrations in the augmentation water. Differences in temperature and ammonia, nitrite plus nitrate, and total phosphorous concentrations were not statistically significant (p > 0.10 in all cases) between the augmented and unaugmented wetlands.

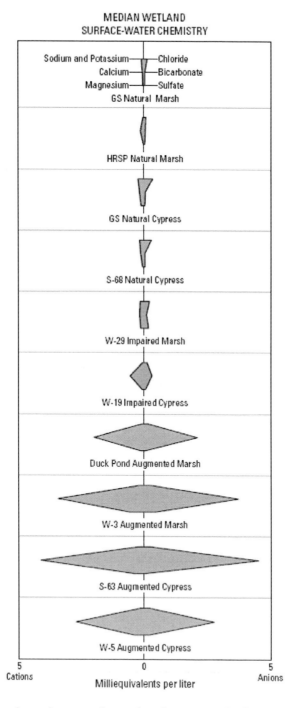

Figure 41. Stiff diagrams for surface water in marsh and cypress wetlands.

Table 8. Range and median water quality for surface water in wetlands. [All units in milligrams per liter unless noted; μS/cm, microsiemens per centimeter at 25 degrees Celsius; Min., minimum value; Max., maximum value; Med., median value; ANC, acid neutralizing capacity; CaCO$_3$, calcium carbonate; N, nitrogen; P, phosphorus; <, less than]

Wetland name and number of samples		Field specific conductance (μS/cm)			Field pH (standard units)			Calcium, dissolved			Magnesium, dissolved			Sodium, dissolved			Potassium, dissolved		
		Min.	Max.	Med.	Min.	Max.	Med.	Min.	Max.	Med.	Min.	Max.	Med.	Min.	Max.	Med.	Min.	Max.	Med.
GS Natural Marsh	7	36.0	85.0	45.0	3.9	5.5	4.5	1.4	3.6	2.1	0.6	1.3	0.9	2.2	5.7	2.8	0.2	2.2	0.4
HRSP Natural Marsh	9	32.0	75.7	37.3	4.4	5.7	4.8	1.4	6.6	3.3	0.7	1.1	0.8	1.3	6.2	2.4	<0.1	2.9	0.3
W-29 Impaired Marsh	3	43.0	67.0	65.0	4.1	5.1	4.4	1.1	5.1	4.1	0.6	2.5	2.1	1.9	3.7	2.0	0.2	1.4	0.2
Duck Pond Augmented Marsh	10	240	346	292	7.0	8.0	7.3	42.0	66.3	54.0	2.0	2.5	2.3	2.8	4.1	3.6	0.3	0.9	0.4
W-3 Augmented Marsh	8	331	499	433	7.1	7.8	7.4	51.8	85.7	73.5	5.0	8.6	7.0	4.5	5.1	4.7	0.6	2.0	0.7
GS Natural Cypress	4	33.3	94.9	51.0	4.1	4.4	4.2	1.3	4.1	1.6	0.6	1.9	0.7	1.3	6.4	2.9	<0.1	0.2	0.2
S-68 Natural Cypress	7	29.8	69.8	53.0	4.2	4.8	4.5	0.8	3.7	1.6	0.4	1.1	0.8	<0.1	0.8	0.3	1.4	5.3	4.3
W-19 Impaired Cypress	6	45.8	101	59.2	5.7	6.5	6.0	8.6	15.0	12.0	0.8	1.5	0.9	0.9	3.9	1.4	0.2	1.1	0.3
S-63 Augmented Cypress	8	47.9	473	464	6.7	7.7	7.5	8.0	86.0	83.0	0.7	5.5	5.3	1.0	5.9	5.8	0.4	1.8	0.9
W-5 Augmented Cypress	5	109	494	325	6.5	7.6	7.4	20.0	85.0	57.0	2.0	8.3	5.3	1.6	4.8	3.6	0.6	0.8	0.6

Wetland name and number of samples		Chloride, Dissolved			Sulfate, Dissolved			ANC, total, as CaCO$_3$			Total nitrogen, dissolved as N			Total phosphorus, dissolved as P			Dissolved organic carbon		
		Min.	Max.	Med.	Min.	Max.	Med.	Min.	Max.	Med.	Min.	Max.	Med.	Min.	Max.	Med.	Min.	Max.	Med.
GS Natural Marsh	7	3.1	9.3	4.2	<0.2	1.0	0.3	0.2	3.8	1.5	1.7	3.5	2.2	<0.008	0.014	0.008	24.7	50.3	37.0
HRSP Natural Marsh	9	1.8	9.0	3.3	<0.2	1.0	0.4	0.0	5.3	2.0	1.1	2.9	1.8	<0.008	0.023	0.011	23.0	45.0	38.0
W-29 Impaired Marsh	3	2.9	6.9	3.2	0.3	9.4	7.1	0.0	3.0	0.0	2.1	3.9	2.8	<0.008	0.022	0.012	30.0	41.0	39.0
Duck Pond Augmented Marsh	10	5.0	7.1	6.2	0.8	2.4	1.4	111.0	173.8	138.5	0.2	0.5	0.3	<0.008	0.020	0.005	2.3	6.8	4.4
W-3 Augmented Marsh	8	7.9	10.0	8.2	4.6	31.0	7.7	152.8	212.3	201.0	0.2	0.5	0.2	0.017	0.030	0.026	2.2	7.2	3.8
GS Natural Cypress	4	1.8	12.0	4.1	<0.2	0.6	0.3	0.0	1.5	0.0	1.0	2.2	1.2	<0.008	0.018	0.012	28.0	71.0	39.0
S-68 Natural Cypress	7	3.0	13.0	8.8	0.3	2.1	0.6	0.0	2.7	0.0	0.5	2.8	0.9	<0.008	0.020	0.004	14.0	49.0	24.0
W-19 Impaired Cypress	6	1.8	11.0	3.1	0.7	1.3	0.9	13.5	23.8	18.0	0.7	3.0	1.2	0.011	0.112	0.020	24.0	49.0	31.0
S-63 Augmented Cypress	8	1.4	8.6	8.5	1.3	4.3	2.0	6.9	237.5	214.5	0.2	0.5	0.3	<0.008	0.026	0.012	3.8	11.0	4.6
W-5 Augmented Cypress	5	2.2	8.3	6.9	3.6	34.0	9.4	24.7	196.8	144.8	0.2	1.0	0.5	<0.008	0.037	0.020	2.3	32.0	12.0

There were no significant differences ($p > 0.20$ in all cases) in major ion concentrations or most field properties between wetland types; specifically, between unaugmented marsh and cypress wetlands, or between augmented marsh and cypress wetlands. These results indicate that the water source, rather than the vegetation type, may be the most important factor influencing these aspects of wetland water quality.

Average surface-water temperatures were significantly different ($p = 0.007$) between marshes and cypress wetlands. Marsh temperatures typically were higher, most likely because marshes are open to sunlight with no tree canopy. Light penetration in forested (cypress) wetlands is much lower (Dierberg and Brezonik, 1984). Although field properties in marsh wetlands were collected during different years (2000-02) than the field properties in cypress wetlands (2002-04), the mean sample collection time in marsh wetlands (12:29 p.m.) was close to the mean sample collection time in cypress wetlands (12:32 p.m.), indicating that time of day was not the cause of different average temperatures. Battle and Golladay (2001) also reported lower water temperatures in cypress wetlands compared to marsh wetlands.

Specific conductance, chloride, and sodium concentrations were higher in unaugmented wetlands in the dry season compared to the wet season (data available at http://waterdata.usgs.gov/nwis). This pattern indicates evaporative concentration in the dry season and dilution by rainwater in the wet season. Augmented wetlands generally showed little seasonal variation in chemical composition. However, during one wet period (June 2003), the augmented cypress wetlands were diluted considerably by rainwater and concentrations of many constituents were similar to those in the unaugmented wetlands.

Greater concentrations of iron in unaugmented cypress (254-724 mg/L) and marsh (456-536 mg/L) wetlands compared to those in augmented wetlands (6-33 mg/L) were evident in this study (figure 42). The higher iron concentrations in the unaugmented wetlands are attributed to low pH and the abundance of humic materials, both of which are known to increase the solubility of iron (Dierberg and Brezonik, 1984).

Nutrients and Dissolved Organic Carbon

Nutrients, including the various forms of nitrogen and phosphorus as well as dissolved organic carbon, are important constituents in freshwater wetlands because they can influence the growth of algae and aquatic plants. Concentrations of several nutrients were significantly different ($p < 0.05$) when natural and impaired marsh and cypress wetlands were compared. Organic nitrogen concentrations were higher in marshes than in cypress wetlands, whereas orthophosphate concentrations were significantly lower in marshes than cypress wetlands.

Differences in nutrient concentrations among the groups of wetlands in this study were smaller than differences in concentrations of some of the major ions, such as calcium or bicarbonate. In natural wetlands, the median concentration of total nitrogen was 0.9-2.2 mg/L, whereas the median concentration for augmented wetlands was 0.2-0.5 mg/L (table 8). Median concentrations of total nitrogen in the impaired wetlands ranged from 1.2 mg/L in W-19 Impaired Cypress to 2.8 mg/L in W-29 Impaired Marsh (table 8). Organic nitrogen was the predominant form of nitrogen in all three groups of wetlands, and was present in higher concentrations in natural and impaired wetlands than in augmented wetlands (figure 42). Nitrate and nitrite concentrations were minimal in all wetlands (less than 0.1 mg/L) (figure 42). Median ammonia nitrogen concentrations were similar in natural (0.019 mg/L) and augmented (0.022 mg/L) wetlands, and W-29 Impaired Marsh had the highest ammonia nitrogen concentrations in the study (0.1 mg/L). Median total phosphorus concentrations were highest at W-3 Augmented Marsh (0.026 mg/L), and concentrations ranged from less than 0.008-0.020 mg/L at the other augmented wetlands. Median total phosphorus concentrations were generally lower at the natural wetlands (less than 0.008-0.012 mg/L) (table 8). Median orthophosphate concentrations were lower at the unaugmented wetlands than at the augmented wetlands (figure 42). Median dissolved organic carbon (DOC) concentrations were substantially higher in natural (24.0-39.0 mg/L) and impaired (31.0-39.0 mg/L) wetlands of both types than in augmented wetlands (3.8-12.0 mg/L), reflecting the typically low DOC concentrations in augmentation water from the Upper Floridan aquifer (figure 43).

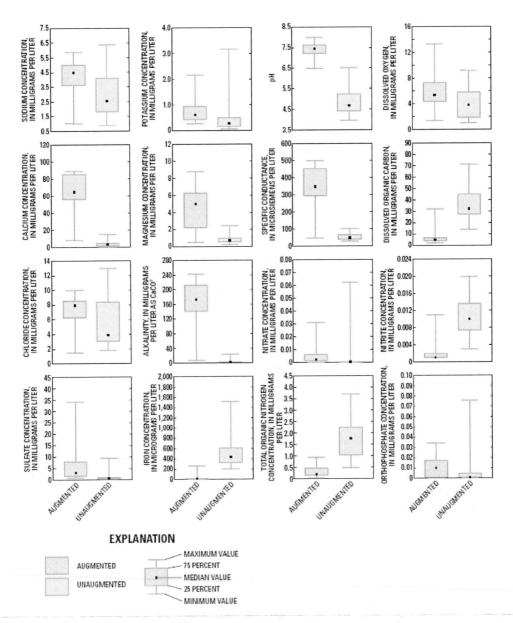

Figure 42. Box plots of field properties and chemical constituents in surface waters of augmented and unaugmented (natural and impaired) wetlands.

Differences in concentrations of most nutrients were statistically significant between unaugmented and augmented wetlands. Organic nitrogen, nitrite, and dissolved organic carbon concentrations were all significantly higher in unaugmented wetlands compared to augmented wetlands ($p < 0.05$) (figure 42). If natural and impaired wetlands were grouped together as unaugmented wetlands, then the total phosphorus concentration in these wetlands was not significantly different from augmented wetlands. However, when only natural and augmented wetlands are compared, total phosphorus concentrations were significantly different between these two groups of wetlands (table 8). Nitrate, orthophosphate, and total phosphorus concentrations were significantly higher in augmented wetlands than in unaugmented wetlands. Cooney and Allen (2006) also reported higher total phosphorus concentrations in augmented lakes compared to natural lakes. Higher orthophosphate concentrations in augmented wetlands are likely due to augmentation with water from the Upper Floridan aquifer that has been in contact with overlying Hawthorn Group deposits. Higher concentrations of organic nitrogen, DOC, and nitrite in natural wetlands may be due to accumulation from longer residence times and the absence of flushing found in augmented wetlands. Higher concentrations of nitrate in augmented wetlands could be attributable to shorter residence times and less time for denitrification to occur.

Figure 43. Decomposing leaves and other plant material contribute humic substances to wetlands

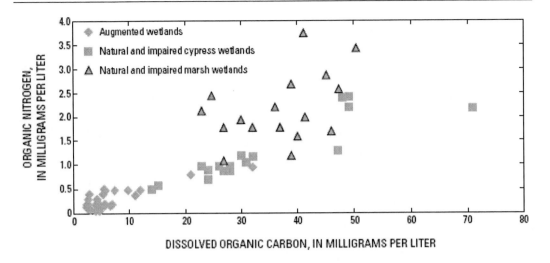

Figure 43. Organic nitrogen and dissolved organic carbon in wetland surface water.

The nitrogen to phosphorus (N/P) ratio is often used to characterize aquatic ecosystems. The N/P ratio in most natural and impaired wetlands in this study (median 74) was significantly higher than the N/P ratio in augmented wetlands (median 19) (figure 44). The high N/P ratios at W-29 Impaired Cypress are due to the high ammonia nitrogen concentrations (>0.5 mg/L as nitrogen) measured in water samples collected in the wetland. Plant communities in the natural wetlands may be phosphorus limited, a pattern reported by Bedford and others (1999) for a large proportion of North American wetlands. The lower N/P ratios in augmented wetlands are probably due to the higher concentrations of available phosphate in augmentation water.

Stable Isotopes

The stable isotopes deuterium and [18]O can be used to develop an understanding of residence times of surface water in wetlands. When deuterium and [18]O are part of a water molecule, it takes additional energy to break the bonds in that molecule as it moves through the water cycle. Thus, in the process of evaporation, the heavier isotopes become enriched in the residual wetland water. To qualitatively compare stable isotope data from the wetlands in this study, the assumption was made that all the wetlands were influenced by similar regional hydrologic conditions (for example, rainfall and evaporation rate). Using this simplification, an increased proportion of these heavy molecules in wetland water indicates an increased evaporation effect, and hence, longer residence time. The ratios of deuterium and [18]O in rainwater in west-central Florida can be plotted and used to describe a local meteoric water line, which is similar to the global meteoric water line (figure 45) (Craig, 1961; Sacks, 2002). As wetland water evaporates, the relative proportions of deuterium and [18]O shift away from the meteoric water line because of differences in the vapor pressures of the isotopes (Clark and Fritz, 1997). The farther along the evaporation trend line a water sample plots away from the meteoric line, the more extensive evaporation is relative to the water body volume. With this technique, isotopic evidence can be used to estimate how much of the surface water and shallow ground water in and around wetlands is of meteoric origin and how much is derived from deep ground water (Matheney and Gerla, 1996).

All wetland surface waters were sampled for deuterium and ^{18}O in March 2004. The results describe a local evaporation trend line (figure 45), and can be grouped according to wetland type (marsh or cypress). The natural marsh wetlands were the most isotopically enriched and, therefore, the farthest from the intercept of the evaporation trend line with the local meteoric water line. Deuterium and ^{18}O values in natural cypress wetlands were closer to this intercept, indicating less evaporation relative to wetland volume and a shorter residence time than in the marshes. Marshes generally undergo more evaporation relative to their volume than cypress wetlands because they are more open and the evaporation rate is higher. Some marshes in this part of central Florida (particularly the deeper marshes) appear to be inundated a greater proportion of time than cypress wetlands; that is, their hydroperiod is longer than that of nearby cypress wetlands (CH$_2$M Hill, 1996). Those marshes may have a greater potential for evaporation and isotope enrichment than the nearby cypress wetlands.

Augmentation water is a substantial input to the water budget of augmented marsh and cypress wetlands because these wetlands would typically dry up without it. Augmentation waters were isotopically depleted compared to surface water in the wetlands (figure 45). W-3 Augmented Marsh was the most isotopically enriched augmented wetland, and plots far from its augmentation water (figure 45). This indicates that either surface water in W-3 Augmented Marsh has a longer residence time, or the marsh may leak less than the other augmented wetlands. The other augmented wetlands do not plot as far along the evaporation trend line (figure 45). S-63 Augmented Cypress and Duck Pond Augmented Marsh were the most isotopically depleted, indicating short residence times for water in these wetlands. Duck Pond Augmented Marsh was closest in isotopic composition to its augmentation source water (figure 45), implying a minimal residence time because wetland water has little opportunity to become isotopically enriched through evaporation.

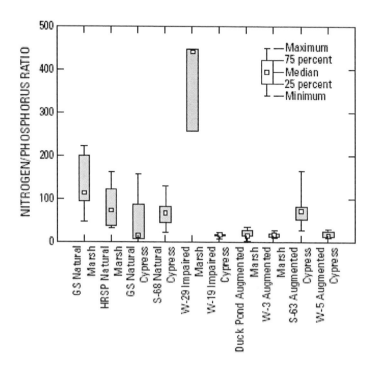

Figure 44. Box plot of nitrogen to phosphorus ratio in wetland surface water.

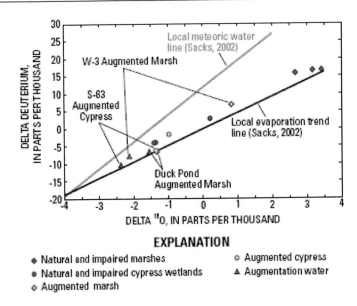

Figure 45. Delta deuterium and delta ^{18}O in wetland surface water and augmentation water.

Basin Geochemistry

The difference in water chemistry between the surficial aquifer, Upper Floridan aquifer, and wetland surface water was useful for determining ground-water flow patterns and the influence of augmentation on basin water quality. For example, the surficial aquifer consists mostly of quartz, which is relatively insoluble and is recharged by dilute rainwater and wetland leakage; therefore, water in this aquifer is not highly mineralized. The Upper Floridan aquifer is more mineralized than the surficial aquifer because of the dissolution of calcite and a longer residence time, which enriches the water in calcium bicarbonate. The surface-water chemistry of the natural and impaired wetlands is dilute, indicating recharge by rainwater, whereas the water chemistry of the augmented wetlands reflects the calcium-bicarbonate waters of the Upper Floridan aquifer. These variations in water chemistry between the two aquifers and the natural, impaired, and augmented wetlands provide insight into the multiple flow processes occurring around the wetlands.

Field Properties and Major Ions

Stiff diagrams were used to compare the wetland surface- water chemistry with the surrounding shallow ground-water chemistry, as well as to compare ground-water chemistry among wetland types (figure 46). Ground-water samples from wells that had the lowest and highest ionic strength were used to show the variability of surficial aquifer water chemistry around each of the seven study wetlands where wells were located. Because the seasonal variability of wetland surface-water chemistry was minimal, median values were used to compare surface-water chemistry with the high and low ionic strength ground-water chemistry.

S-68 Natural Cypress and W-29 Impaired Marsh had the lowest ionic strength ground water surrounding the wetlands (figure 46B and C, respectively). The ions that typically dominated the shallow ground water at these sites were dilute concentrations of sodium, chloride, and sulfate. Median values for field properties such as pH (4.3-4.5), specific conductance (77-144 µS/cm), and alkalinity (1-4.4 mg/L ANC, total, as calcium carbonate) were all relatively low (table 9). Ground water in these areas is influenced by the low ionic strength input from wetland leakage and by recharge from overland flow and rainwater.

HRSP Natural Marsh and W-19 Impaired Cypress had the most variable water quality in shallow ground water surrounding the wetlands, as indicated by minimum and maximum values for pH (4.9-7.7), specific conductance (101-8 14 µS/cm), and alkalinity (6.8-401 mg/L ANC, total, as calcium carbonate) (table 9). Shallow ground-water chemistry for these two sites ranged from low to high ionic strength, and reflects the influence of different source waters. The near-shore well HRSP LSE has the lowest conductivity, because it is influenced by leakage from wetland surface water that has low ionic strength (figure 46A). The higher conductivity ground water in wells HRSP USW and W1 9 L is influenced by the upwelling of calcium-bicarbonate enriched water from the Upper Floridan aquifer (figure 46A and D, respectively).

Augmentation altered the shallow ground-water chemistry around the augmented wetlands. Shallow ground water surrounding S-63 Augmented Cypress, Duck Pond Augmented Marsh, and W-5 Augmented Cypress is dominated by relatively high ionic strength water enriched in calcium and bicarbonate ions. In nearshore wells surrounding these augmented wetlands, the following field property maximums indicate the influence of the augmentation water: pH (6.5-7.5), specific conductance (431-765 µS/cm), and alkalinity (220-407 mg/L ANC, total, as calcium carbonate) (table 9). Because the augmented water levels are typically higher than the adjacent water table, lateral leakage results in elevated calcium and bicarbonate concentrations in the surficial aquifer. Calcium and bicarbonate concentrations in the ground water, however, progressively decreased with distance away from the augmented wetlands (figure 46). Similar patterns in water chemistry were observed in the surficial aquifer in northwest Hillsborough County near Round Lake, which also was augmented with water from the Upper Floridan aquifer (Metz and Sacks, 2002).

Calcium and bicarbonate concentrations in the surficial aquifer decreased more rapidly with increasing distance from the wetland at S-63 Augmented Cypress compared to at Duck Pond Augmented Marsh. For example, a decrease in calcium and bicarbonate concentrations of similar magnitude was apparent in water taken from the S-63 MNW and Duck Pond UNW wells, which are about 125 and 250 ft from the wetland perimeter, respectively (figure 46E and F). The more abrupt decrease at S-63 Augmented Cypress may be related to subsurface geologic features that create more direct downward ground-water flow at that site, and, by comparison, more lateral movement of ground water at Duck Pond Augmented Marsh.

Nutrients and Dissolved Organic Carbon

Dissolved nitrogen occurs in various forms in ground water such as organic nitrogen, ammonium cations (NH_4^+), and nitrite and nitrate anions (NO_2^- and NO_3^-) (Hem, 1985). The extent and type of nitrogen cycling reactions can determine which form of nitrogen is most prevalent in ground water surrounding the wetlands. For example, under aerobic conditions, oxidation of organic nitrogen (nitrification) by soil bacteria results in the successive conversion to ammonium, followed by nitrite, then nitrate anions. Nitrification processes typically occur above the water table in the soil zone where oxygen and organic matter are abundant (Freeze and Cherry, 1979).

Table 9. Range and median water quality for ground water in wetland basins.[All units in milligrams per liter unless noted; µS/cm, microsiemens per centimeter at 25 degrees Celsius; E, estimated; Min., minimum value; Max., maximum value; Med., median value;ANC, acid neutralizing capacity; CaCO$_3$, calcium carbonate; N, nitrogen; NH$_4^+$, ammonium; NO$_2^-$, nitrite; NO$_3^-$, Nitrate; <, less than]

Wetland name and number of samples		Field specific conductance (µS/cm)			Field pH (standard units)			Dissolved oxygen			Calcium, dissolved			Magnesium, dissolved		
		Min.	Max.	Med.	Min.	Max.	Med.	Min.	Max.	Med.	Min.	Max.	Med.	Min.	Max.	Med.
HRSP Natural Marsh	30	101	837	433	4.9	7.7	6.7	0.3	6.0	1.5	8.4	147	81	0.5	4.3	1.2
W-29 Impaired Marsh	16	60	279	144	4.0	5.5	4.3	0.5	4.0	1.0	2.7	30	9.5	0.55	9.4	1.4
Duck Pond Augmented Marsh	34	55	431	156	4.5	7.0	6.1	0.7	6.0	1.7	0.57	83	20	1.1	3.4	2.2
S-68 Natural Cypress	29	51	633	77	4.2	7.2	4.5	0.7	3.6	1.1	1.2	116	2.4	0.29	6.4	1.2
W-19 Impaired Cypress	10	145	763	372	5.0	7.2	6.4	0.6	4.4	0.9	7.0	148	66	1.4	9.5	4.0
S-63 Augmented Cypress	30	58	671	116	4.5	7.1	5.6	0.3	1.9	0.9	2.3	122	11	0.61	8.9	1.3
W-5 Augmented Cypress[1]	6	207	767	564	5.8	6.5	6.4	0.53	2.0	1.3	36	164	94	3.3	13	7.3
W-5 Augmented Cypress[2]	6	283	765	474	5.9	7.5	6.3	0.7	3.6	1.0	49	140	83	4.1	15	6.5

Wetland name and number of samples		Sodium, dissolved			Potassium, dissolved			Chloride, dissolved			Sulfate, dissolved			ANC, total, as CaCO$_3$		
		Min.	Max.	Med.	Min.	Max.	Med.	Min.	Max.	Med.	Min.	Max.	Med.	Min.	Max.	Med.
HRSP Natural Marsh	30	1.1	26	7.8	<0.1	1.2	0.1	0.2	43	13	0.2	60	18	12.7	299	179
W-29 Impaired Marsh	16	0.7	3.9	2.0	0.3	0.7	0.6	1.4	8.0	3.9	8.4	93	18	0.1	18	4.3
Duck Pond Augmented Marsh	34	1.6	4.4	3.5	<0.1	3.6	0.4	2.7	9.0	6.1	0.2	8.8	1.6	0	220	85
S-68 Natural Cypress	29	1.5	12	5.3	<0.1	1.1	0.1	3.5	18	8.7	0.3	27	7.3	0	328	1
W-19 Impaired Cypress	10	1.0	15	9.2	<0.1	0.5	0.2	1.3	40	11	0.2	40	3.2	6.8	401	197
S-63 Augmented Cypress	30	2.8	19	5.9	<0.1	1.1	0.3	3.2	21	8.5	0.2	14	3.4	0	316	23
W-5 Augmented Cypress[1]	6	2.4	14	4.3	<0.1	0.4	0.3	0.5	17	6.6	1.5	6.1	2.4	95	407	236
W-5 Augmented Cypress[2]	6	2.4	14	5.3	<0.1	0.4	0.2	0.5	20	7.2	1.0	53	4.2	137	392	208

Wetland name and number of samples		Organic Nitrogen, dissolved as N			Ammonium (NH$_4^+$), dissolved as N			Nitrite (NO$_2^-$), dissolved as N			Nitrate (NO$_3^-$), dissolved as N			Dissolved organic carbon		
		Min.	Max.	Med.	Min.	Max.	Med.	Min.	Max.	Med.	Min.	Max.	Med.	Min.	Max.	Med.
HRSP Natural Marsh	30	0.10	2.7	0.19	<0.002	0.11	0.01	<0.001	0.01	0.001	<0.001	2.3	0.001	1.3	40	3.0
W-29 Impaired Marsh	16	0.30	1.61	0.74	0.007	0.89	0.08	E0.001	0.011	0.006	0.01	17.9	4.29	5.7	23	8.6
Duck Pond Augmented Marsh	34	0.18	1.26	0.40	<0.002	2.0	0.12	<0.001	0.01	0.001	<0.001	7.54	0.002	1.2	29	8.6
S-68 Natural Cypress	29	0.11	0.90	0.30	0.006	1.1	0.19	<0.001	0.006	0.002	<0.001	0.005	0.002	3.1	29	12
W-19 Impaired Cypress	10	0.11	0.64	0.22	0.005	1.7	0.04	<0.001	0.004	0.001	<0.001	0.007	0.002	0.9	23	5.2
S-63 Augmented Cypress	30	0.13	1.21	0.32	0.01	0.40	0.06	<0.001	0.004	0.001	<0.001	0.008	0.001	5.2	47	15
W-5 Augmented Cypress[1]	6	0.16	1.51	0.66	0.01	0.32	0.05	<0.001	0.005	0.003	<0.001	0.001	0.001	5.3	44	22
W-5 Augmented Cypress[2]	6	0.16	1.37	0.57	0.01	0.16	0.03	<0.001	0.005	0.003	<0.001	0.055	0.001	5.4	34	17

[1]Before augmentation. [2]After augmentation.

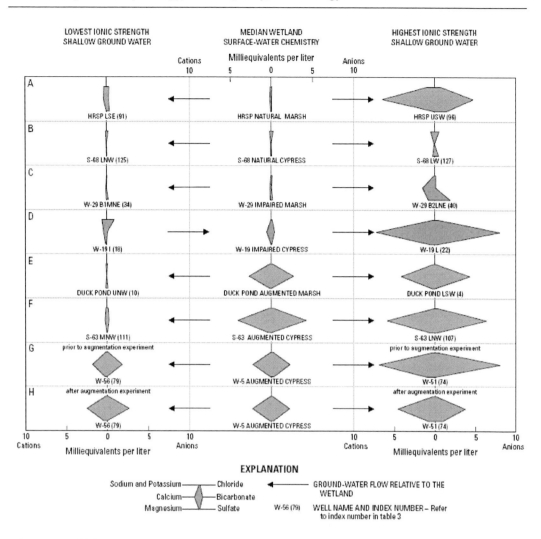

Figure 46. Stiff diagrams for surface water and shallow ground water at selected wetlands.

The organic-rich soils surrounding the wetlands are reflected in the dominance of organic nitrogen over other nitrogen species in ground water (table 9). Organic nitrogen was the dominant form of nitrogen present in 71 percent of the shallow ground-water samples. Concentrations of organic nitrogen ranged from 0.10 to 2.7 mg/L, with a median of 0.31 mg/L (table 9). When ammonium ion was the dominant form of nitrogen (17 percent of samples), concentrations ranged from 0.17 to 2 mg/L, with a median value of 0.54 mg/L. When nitrate was the dominant form of nitrogen (12 percent of samples), concentrations ranged from 0.49 to 18 mg/L, with a median value of 10 mg/L.

The ground water underlying W-29 Impaired Marsh had the highest nitrate concentration of all the wetlands sampled. During the winter of 2001 at W-29 Impaired Marsh, nitrate concentration ranged from 1 to 18 mg/L and the median value was 9 mg/L. A reduction in the nitrate concentration was observed in subsequent sampling during the spring of 2002 when nitrate concentrations ranged from 0.01 to 7 mg/L, with a median value of 4 mg/L. Unlike the other wetlands, W-29 Impaired Marsh was the only wetland where the majority of wells were located within the wetland rather than outside the wetland perimeter. Specifically, these wells were situated where partially decomposed plant material accumulates, resulting in a high organic content in the wetland bottom.

The DOC data also were used to determine groundwater/surface-water interactions between wetlands and the surrounding aquifer (table 9). Decomposition of plant material produces organic matter that is rich in carbon and is soluble in ground water. The most common category of soil-derived organic matter is humic matter, which imparts a dark color to the soil and wetland water. The typical range of DOC in ground water is <0.2 to 10 mg/L, although in certain environments such as wetlands, DOC concentrations can be much higher (Wassenaar, 1990).

A total of 60 percent of the shallow ground-water samples from the wetland basins had DOC concentrations less than 10 mg/L, and 40 percent ranged from 11 to 47 mg/L. These higher DOC concentrations in ground water were associated with samples obtained from all wetland types (augmented, natural, impaired marsh, and cypress wetlands). However, S-63 Augmented Cypress, S-68 Natural Cypress, and W-5 Augmented Cypress had the greatest number of wells surrounding the wetlands with elevated DOC concentrations. These elevated concentrations may be related to the relatively high tannin content of soils associated with cypress wetlands.

Stable Isotopes

The naturally occurring stable isotopes deuterium and ^{18}O were used to help understand ground-water flow paths around the two augmented cypress wetlands and the S-68 Natural Cypress wetland. As residence time increases, evaporation causes wetland water to become enriched in heavier isotopes, leaving the water with a higher δ value (the isotopic composition in delta notation) than rainwater. In the shallow ground water, however, less evaporation occurs and isotopes are relatively less enriched, or have a lower δ value. The relative enrichment (in surface water) or lack of enrichment (in ground water) of these isotopes can be used to help determine flow paths between the wetlands and the surrounding ground-water flow system. For example, isotopically enriched ground water (with a higher δ value) near a wetland can indicate areas of wetland leakage, because of the enrichment in isotopes from the surface water.

Isotopes were sampled in the ground water surrounding W-5 Augmented Cypress during a period when the wetland was not augmented for 79 days. The wetland was dry when the samples were collected, although a ground-water mound existed underneath the wetland. Analysis results indicate that some of the wells sampled (W-5 wells 2, 3, and 6) plot near the lower end of evaporation trend line, which indicates minimal wetland leakage to the ground-water system (figure 47A). Two wells (W-5 wells 4 and 5) west of the wetland, however, did show evidence of wetland leakage, as indicated by the enrichment in heavier isotopes. Based on the isotopic analysis, the direction of ground-water flow was inferred to be westward, toward nearby Cypress Creek.

The wells were sampled again for isotopes about 1 month after augmentation had resumed at W-5 Augmented Cypress. Sample analyses indicate that ground-water flow paths were altered by the augmentation. Most of the ground water sampled showed isotopic signatures similar to those of the augmentation water. This is especially true for W-5 Augmented Cypress wells 1 and 2 (index wells 74 and 75) southeast of the wetland (figure 47B). A karst subsidence feature may lower the water table and increase wetland leakage toward this area (figure 37).

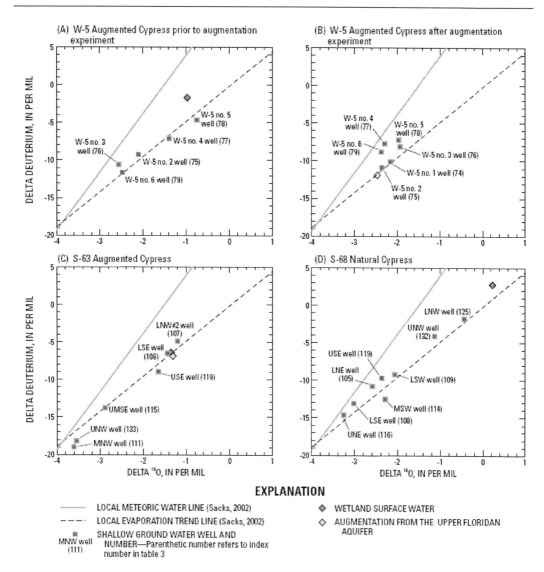

Figure 47. Delta deuterium and delta ^{18}O in wetland surface water, shallow ground water, and augmentation water from the Upper Floridan aquifer at W-5 Augmented Cypress, S-63 Augmented Cypress, and S-68 Natural Cypress.

Isotopic data also were compared between an augmented wetland (S-63 Augmented Cypress) and a nearby natural wetland (S-68 Natural Cypress) to understand the differences between ground-water flow patterns around the two wetlands. For S-63 Augmented Cypress, the isotopic signatures for surface water, augmentation water, and the S-63 LSE well were similar (figure 47C). The wetland leakage is directed to the east toward this well, which is located near areas of karst subsidence. The similarity in the isotopic signatures of surface water, augmentation water, and shallow ground water also may indicate the wetland is augmented, in part, by recirculated wetland water that has returned to the Upper Floridan aquifer. This recirculation pattern also was evident in isotopic data from lakes augmented with ground water from the Upper Floridan aquifer (Metz and Sacks, 2002). Two other wells

(S-63 LNW 2 and S-63 USE) also show the influence of wetland leakage but not as clearly as the LSE well (figure 47C).

Isotopic data for six out of eight S-68 Natural Cypress wells plot near the lower end of the evaporation trend line, which indicates minimal wetland leakage to the groundwater system (figure 47D). Samples were collected during the dry season when water levels were low in the wetland and the surrounding ground-water system. Two wells (LNW and UNW) northwest of S-68 Natural Cypress did show evidence of wetland leakage as indicated by the enrichment in heavier isotopes. This result implied that ground water was flowing to the northwest and generally toward nearby Cross Cypress Branch.

Overview of Water Quality and Geochemistry

Water quality in the unaugmented wetlands is similar to that of the rainwater from which it is primarily derived— dilute, acidic, poorly buffered, and lacking in nutrients. Augmented wetlands had higher major ion concentrations, specific conductance, pH, and alkalinity, reflecting the chemistry of the Upper Floridan aquifer, which is the source of the augmentation water. Dissolved organic carbon, iron, and organic nitrogen concentrations were lower in augmented than in unaugmented wetlands, most likely due to the low residence time as well as the low concentrations in augmentation water. Differences in temperature, and ammonia, nitrite plus nitrate, and total phosphorus concentrations were not significantly different between augmented and unaugmented wetlands. Specific conductance, chloride, and sodium concentrations were higher in unaugmented wetlands in the dry season than in the wet season, because they are influenced by evaporative concentration and dilution, respectively, but augmented wetlands generally showed little seasonal variation in chemical composition.

Major ion concentrations and most field properties were similar between marsh and cypress wetlands of the same type; that is, between unaugmented marsh and cypress wetlands, or between augmented marsh and cypress wetlands. These results indicate that the water source, and not the vegetation type, may be the most important factor influencing these aspects of wetland water quality. However, water temperatures in marshes of all types tended to be higher than water temperatures in cypress wetlands, because tree cover in cypress wetlands limits light penetration. Because they are more open systems, marshes undergo more evaporation relative to their volume than cypress wetlands, as indicated by analysis of stable isotopes. Stable isotope ratios indicate that cypress wetlands may have shorter residence times compared to marsh wetlands. The two augmented cypress wetlands had the shortest residence times of all the wetlands in the study, based on analysis of stable isotopes.

Wetland leakage influenced the shallow ground-water quality near the augmented and unaugmented wetlands. Unaugmented wetlands S-68 Natural Cypress and W-29 Impaired Marsh had low ionic strength ground water surrounding the wetlands, because the surficial aquifer in their basins is influenced primarily by wetland leakage and recharge from rainwater. In contrast, leakage from HRSP Natural Marsh diluted the carbonate-rich ground water that characterizes the surficial aquifer in this area. In W-19 Impaired Cypress basin, the influence of shallow ground water with a relatively high ionic strength periodically dominated the low ionic strength wetland surface water that leaked into the surrounding basin.

When wetlands are augmented with calcium-bicarbonate enriched water from the Upper Floridan aquifer, the surrounding ground-water chemistry is altered. Shallow ground water surrounding the augmented marsh and cypress wetlands was dominated by high ionic strength water derived from lateral outflow and downward leakage from the augmented wetlands. However, calcium and bicarbonate concentrations in shallow ground water progressively decreased with distance away from augmented wetlands, and the rates of decrease are related to subsurface geologic features.

The influence of wetland water chemistry on the shallow ground water in wetland basins is also evident in other constituents. The organic rich soils surrounding the wetlands and covering the wetland bottom are reflected by the dominance of organic nitrogen over other nitrogen species in the shallow ground water. Higher DOC concentrations in shallow ground water near the wetlands are derived from the decomposition of wetland vegetation, and are associated with all wetland types and groups.

WETLAND FLOODING CHARACTERISTICS

The flooding patterns of wetlands over time can provide a more informative and useful indication of their hydrologic and ecological condition than water levels alone (Haag and others, 2005; Lee and Haag, 2006). In the northern Tampa Bay area, for example, wetland water levels are routinely monitored in several hundred wetlands. The hydrologic condition and regulatory status of a subset of these wetlands is determined by comparing their measured water levels to a minimum target water level established for each wetland (Southwest Florida Water Management District, 1 999b). The benefit of this approach can be increased by combining wetland water levels with bathymetric mapping results to determine how much of the total wetland area is being flooded over time. The size of the flooded area, when expressed as a percentage of a total wetland area, is a quantitative measure that is independent of the size of the wetland and is directly comparable to other wetlands. Describing the size of the flooded areas of wetlands provides a "landscape perspective" to wetland assessment and allows wetlands to be described collectively as a regional surface-water resource (Lee and Haag, 2006).

The flooded areas of 10 wetlands were examined in detail over the data-collection period, and then over a longer "historical" period of up to 16 years using historical stage data. Short-term variability in the size of the flooded area is examined by describing and comparing the weekly average flooded areas in the 10 wetlands over several years. Stage data routinely collected over the past 8-16 years are then used with bathymetric data to describe the historical average flooding characteristics of the 10 wetlands. Finally, the seasonal flooding regime of each wetland is characterized using the historical monthly average flooded area. The results of each approach are compared for the natural, augmented, and impaired groups of wetlands, and for the marsh and cypress wetland types.

Methods of Flooded Area Determination

Bathymetric maps of the 10 wetlands were used to determine the size of the inundated area and the water volume stored in the study wetlands over a range of stage values. The elevation of land surface was surveyed at numerous locations across the wetland, and digital interpolation and contouring routines were used to delineate the outline of the flooded area at different values of wetland stage. Bathymetric maps and curves defining the relation between stage and area, and stage and volume, were published in Haag and others (2005). The wetland perimeter was delineated using biological indicators or hydric soil indicators.

With the exception of W-3 Augmented Marsh, stage in each wetland (reported in feet above NGVD 29) was continuously monitored at a center well located in the deepest part of the wetland (table 3). The well casing was slotted above and below the ground surface. Consequently, the pressure transducer measured stage or ground-water level if the water level was above or below the wetland bottom, respectively.

Bathymetry data and hourly values of wetland stage were used to compute the daily and weekly average flooded areas in the wetlands. Flooded areas for each wetland were expressed as a percentage of the total area of the wetland. Daily stage equaled the 12 a.m. stage reading at each site. Continuously recorded measurements were checked in the field every 2 weeks for quality assurance. During site visits, a staff gage was read by USGS personnel when wetlands were flooded, and the water level was measured in the center well whether the wetland was flooded or not. Wetland water-level data for this study are available online from the USGS National Water Information System database at http://waterdata.usgs.gov/fl/nwis (U.S. Geological Survey, 2007).

At W-3 Augmented Marsh, wetland stage was not monitored in the deepest part of the wetland, but instead, closer to the perimeter near the historical staff gage. As a result, continuous water levels measured in the center well fell slightly below land surface when deeper areas of the wetland were still inundated. When this occurred, wetland stage was estimated from the ground-water levels in the center well. Because the water table sloped away from the flooded area of W-3 Augmented Marsh, using the ground-water levels probably slightly underestimates wetland stage and, therefore, the size of the flooded area, particularly during the driest periods. This approximation however, was considered to have a small affect on the interpretation of the percentage of total wetland area flooded weekly.

The historical stage data used to analyze the flooded area in three of the four natural wetlands (GS Natural Marsh, GS Natural Cypress, and HRSP Natural Marsh) were collected by the Southwest Florida Water Management District (Michael Hancock, Southwest Florida Water Management District, written commun., 2003). The earliest water-level readings were made once or twice a month from staff gages. More recent daily readings were collected by continuous recorders. Historical data at the remaining seven wetlands were collected by Tampa Bay Water, typically every 2 weeks (Tampa Bay Water, 2000) (table 10).

The saturated soil moisture content in the uppermost foot of soil was monitored in the deepest areas of W-29 Impaired Marsh and HRSP Natural Marsh for about 9 months using a variant of the time-domain reflectometry approach developed by Topp and others (1980). Measurements were made using CS 615 water content reflectometers with 1 5-min output to CR1 0X data loggers (Campbell Scientific, Inc., 1996).

Table 10. Description of stage data used for the historical flooding analyses. [SWFWMD, Southwest Florida Water Management District; HRSP, Hillsborough River State Park; GS, Green Swamp Wildlife Management Area]

Group	Wetland	Starting year	Historical period (years)	Measurement frequency	Data source
Natural	GS Natural Cypress	1988	16	Daily (Jan 1988–Dec 2003)	SWFWMD
	S-68 Natural Cypress	1989	15	Monthly (Jan 1989–Jun 2003) Biweekly (Jul 2003–Dec 2003)	Tampa Bay Water
	HRSP Natural Marsh	1988	16	Monthly (Jan 1988–Oct 1994) Daily (Sep 1994–Dec 2003)	SWFWMD
	GS Natural Marsh	1996	8	Daily (Jan 1996–Dec 2003)	SWFWMD
Augmented	Duck Pond Augmented Marsh	1988	16	Monthly (Jan 1988–Sep 1996) Biweekly (Oct 1996–Dec 2003)	Tampa Bay Water
	W-5 Augmented Cypress	1988	16	Monthly (Jan 1988–May 1994) Biweekly (Jun 1994–Dec 2003)	Tampa Bay Water
	W-3 Augmented Marsh	1995	9	Biweekly (Jan 1995–Dec 2003)	Tampa Bay Water
	S-63 Augmented Cypress	1991	13	Monthly (Jan 1991–Oct 1994) Biweekly (Nov 1994–Dec 2003)	Tampa Bay Water
Impaired	W-29 Impaired Marsh	1989	15	Monthly (Jan 1989–Oct 1994) Biweekly (Nov 1994–Dec 2003)	Tampa Bay Water
	W-19 Impaired Cypress	1989	15	Monthly (Jan 1989–Oct 1994) Biweekly (Nov 1994–Dec 2003)	Tampa Bay Water

Changes in Extent of Flooded Area

Because most isolated freshwater wetlands are shallow, the size of their flooded areas changes rapidly when surface- water levels change. The timing and extent of these changes on a yearly or daily basis are not well described in the wetland literature, yet understanding the rate of change is informa tive for studies of both wetland ecology and hydrology. For example, monthly measurements of stage may be adequate to describe the average annual stage and flooded area in a wetland over a long-term period (Shaffer and others, 2000). However, monthly measurements of wetland stage can introduce sizeable errors in estimates of monthly average flooded areas, and under-represent extremes, such as dry or bank-full conditions, that can exist briefly and be missed in monthly or biweekly sampling. Accurately documenting extremes, especially the length of time that a target water level is exceeded, can require more frequent (daily) data collection (Shaffer and others, 2000). The weekly flooding regime, based on daily measurements, is described herein and compared in natural, augmented, and impaired wetland groups. Marshes and cypress wetlands types are discussed separately because the two types of wetlands were studied sequentially, not concurrently, and rainfall conditions differed substantially between the two data-collection periods.

Marshes

The flooded areas of the natural marshes changed similarly despite the approximately 20-mi distance between their locations within the northern Tampa Bay area (figure 48A-B). The size of the flooded areas at both sites changed substantially on a week-to-week basis, and ranged from 0 percent (dry) to greater than 100 percent of the total wetland area. Flooded area size was relatively constant at each marsh for only a small part of the 21-month study period. If surface-area fluctuations within a ±10 percent range are considered constant, then the weekly average flooded area was nearly constant at HRSP Natural Marsh for about 17 weeks in the winter and early spring of 2002 (figure 48A-B). Although flooding beyond the wetland perimeter inundated 100 percent of the marsh area, the condition was not static because the size of the flooded area beyond the perimeter changed.

Periodic water-level readings are made from staff gages

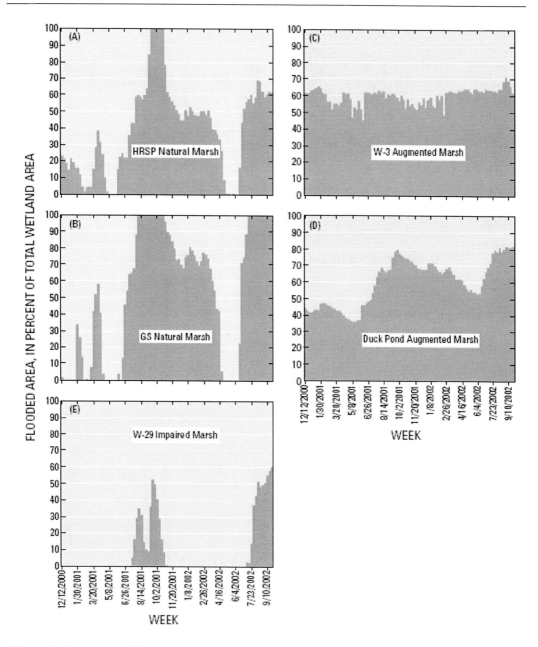

Figure 48. Percentage of the total wetland area flooded on average each week in the natural, augmented, and impaired marshes from December 12, 2000 to September 30, 2002. Flooded areas beyond 100 percent are not shown.

The flooded areas of the two augmented marshes were relatively constant compared to the natural marshes, with less weekly variation and less overall range in flooded area (figure 48C-D). The augmented marshes remained flooded during both dry seasons (roughly April and May of 2002 and 2003), while the natural marshes dried out. Water levels in W-3 Augmented Marsh varied the least of all marshes because the switch controlling the flow of augmentation water operated within a narrow range of stage. When the wetland water level dropped below a fixed level, a float switch opened a pipeline valve, adding augmentation water until the stage recovered and the switch turned off flow. Flow rates into W-3 Augmented Marsh were always sufficiently large to replace the daily water losses due to evapotranspiration and leakage. As a result, the effects of seasonal differences in climate and leakage were not evident in the wetland water levels, and 50 to 70 percent of the total wetland surface area stayed inundated throughout the 21-month study period (figure 48C).

The flooded area of Duck Pond Augmented Marsh contracted and expanded more than W-3 Augmented Marsh during the study (figure 48D). The daily augmentation flow to Duck Pond Augmented Marsh was relatively constant for nearly 2 years (mean = 23,420 ft^3/d, standard deviation = 1,912 ft^3/d). During the drier spring months, augmentation did not offset the daily losses due to evaporation and leakage, and flooded area became smaller. During the wetter summers, stage and flooded area increased because of greater rainfall and slower leakage as a result of rising groundwater levels (figure 48D).

During the same 21-month time period, W-29 Impaired Marsh was usually dry, and periodic flooding inundated substantially less area than in the natural marshes (figure 48E). The flooded area inundated 50 percent of the marsh vegetated area for 2 weeks during the rainy summer season of 2001 (July–September). The marsh dried up over the next 5 weeks and remained dry until the following summer when flooding covered 60 percent of the total wetland area. W-29 Impaired Marsh flooded less than the natural marshes, in part because it received about 7.5 to 10 in/yr less rainfall during 2001 than the two natural marshes (figure 5). However, it probably flooded less than the natural marshes would have with the same amount of rainfall because the drier soil conditions at W-29 Impaired Marsh favored infiltration over runoff.

W-29 Impaired Marsh experienced drier soil conditions than HRSP Natural Marsh because the water table of the impaired marsh was lower than that of the natural marsh (figure 49). The soils were composed of similar organic-rich sands in both locations. During the first 6 months of the study period (prior to May 2002) HRSP Natural Marsh was flooded and W-29 Impaired Marsh was dry. The two sites could be directly compared when they both dried out for 2 months starting in May 2002 (figure 49).

At W-29 Impaired Marsh, the soil moisture content in the uppermost foot of soil dropped steeply when the water table fell from 1 to 2 ft below the wetland bottom, and then dropped steadily with increasing depth (figure 50). When the water-table depth was between 1 and 2 ft, soil moisture remained between 0.8 and 0.4 cm^3/cm^3. A similar relation was observed between the water-table depth and soil moisture content at HRSP Natural Marsh. Because the water table was never more than 1.75 ft below HRSP Natural Marsh, however, soil moisture content remained above 0.4 cm3/cm3 (figure 49). During this same time, the water table dropped to about 5 ft below the deepest part of W--29 Impaired Marsh, and soil moisture fell below 0.2 cm3/cm3. Because the water table slopes away from W--29 Impaired Marsh, the higher areas of the wetland bottom are farther above the water table and presumably were even drier.

Cypress Wetlands

Weekly flooding patterns in the natural cypress wetlands resembled those of the natural marshes in several respects (figs. 48A-B and 5 1A-B). The natural cypress wetlands were nearly full a greater percentage of time than the natural marshes because of the wetter climate conditions during the cypress monitoring period, particularly in December 2002. Both natural cypress wetlands remained flooded in 2003 during late spring, which is usually dry. Following what is probably more typical behavior, both wetlands dried out during late spring in 2004, and within a few months were 100 percent flooded by summer rainfall. Because of the above-average rainfall and reduced ground-water pumping on Cypress Creek Well Field, flooding in W-19 Impaired Cypress was not diminished, but instead resembled flooding in the natural cypress wetlands.

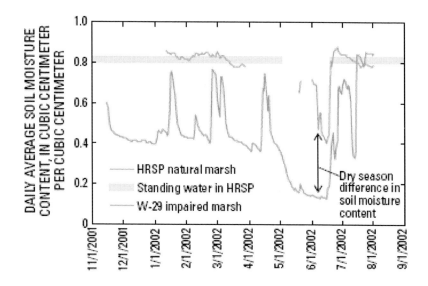

Figure 49. Soil moisture content in HRSP Natural Marsh and W-29 Impaired Marsh during the same time period. Soil moisture values of 0.8 or greater indicate water is at or above land surface.

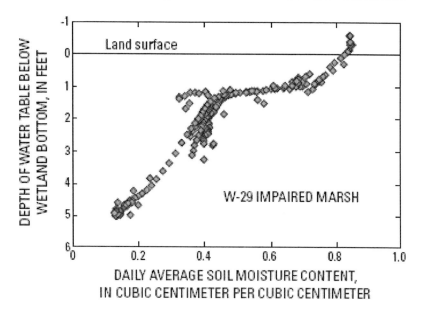

Figure 50. The relation between daily average soil moisture in the top one foot of soil and the daily average water-table depth below W-29 Impaired Marsh.

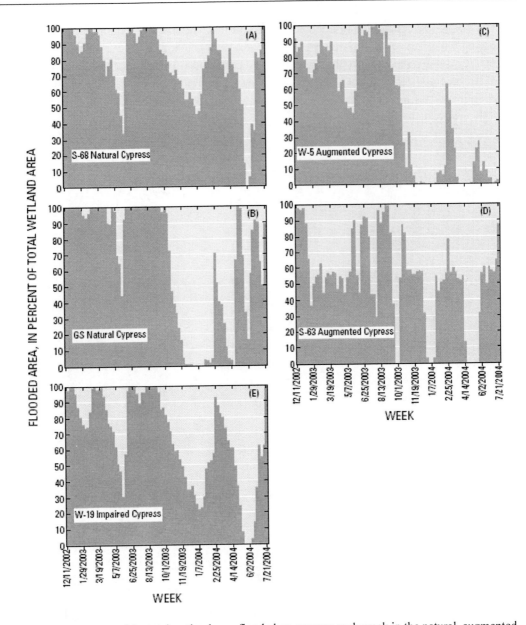

Figure 51. Percentage of the total wetland area flooded on average each week in the natural, augmented, and impaired cypress wetlands from December 11, 2002 to July 27, 2004. Flooded areas beyond 100 percent of the total wetland area are not shown.

The two augmented cypress wetlands did not maintain stable flooded areas like the augmented marshes, mostly because of changes in the augmentation regimes (figs. 48C-D and 51C-D). Instead, flooded area changed substantially on a weekly basis at the augmented cypress wetlands, which ranged from 0 to 100 percent full. The typical augmentation regime in both wetlands called for stage to be augmented to a minimum level in both wetlands, and augmentation to be shut off if stage rose above a maximum target level. However, unplanned extremes in the flooded area occurred at both sites.

Most of W-5 Augmented Cypress flooded in December 2002 and again in June 2003 because rainfall was well above average and augmentation never shut off due to an open flow valve. The resulting augmentation rate of about 5,270 ft^3/d combined with above-average rainfall raised the water level above the elevation of a roadside ditch intersecting the wetland perimeter (Haag and others, 2005). As a consequence, flooding in W-5 Augmented Cypress resembled the natural cypress sites until August 2003, when the augmentation pipeline was manually shut off. With no augmentation, the flooded area declined quickly and W-5 Augmented Cypress dried out in 3 months, remaining dry except during two short episodes of augmentation (January to March of 2004 and mid-May to early June 2004) (figure 51C). Flooding between May and June 2004 resulted from the controlled augmentation experiment discussed earlier.

At S-63 Augmented Cypress, the augmentation was designed to follow a regime of target stages that would be lowered step-wise during the drier months and raised during the wet season (with a total stage range of 0.85 ft) in an effort to resemble natural seasonal variation. The actual regime was more variable. The weekly flooded area at S-63 Augmented Cypress wetland changed more abruptly than any other wetland studied, generally existing in one of three conditions: 0 percent flooded, about 50 percent flooded, or 80 to 100 percent flooded (figure 51D). Dry conditions occurred when augmentation stopped due to mechanical problems, or when the daily augmentation flow was too low to maintain flooding. In contrast, large daily rainfall events combined with augmentation flooded an area between 80 to 100 percent. Augmentation in the absence of substantial rainfall resulted in flooding of about 50 percent of the total wetland area.

During certain times of the year, the flooded area at S-63 Augmented Cypress changed on an hourly basis. The daily 12 a.m. stage readings indicated that the wetland was completely dry for several weeks in late December 2003 (and April-May 2004). Hourly readings, however, showed that augmentation inundated as much as 45 percent of the total area during the day, but the water quickly leaked out when augmentation stopped, generally leaving the wetland dry by midnight (figure 52). This hourly variation in flooded area occurred on repeated occasions during the relatively wet study years, and thus, has probably also occurred in other years.

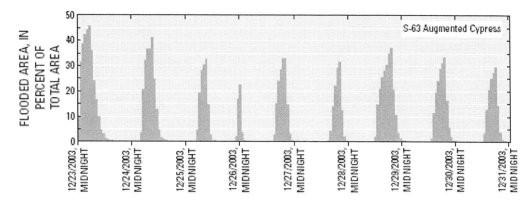

Figure 52. Hourly variation in flooded area at S-63 Augmented Cypress from December 24, 2003 to December 31, 2003.

Comparison of Recent and Historical Flooded Area Duration Distributions

Tracking wetland flooded area through time yields a time series that can be summarized statistically and compared to other wetlands. Alternatively, flooding statistics for an individual wetland can be compared for different time periods. Statistically derived flooded-area duration distributions, referred to as flooded-area frequency distributions in Haag and others (2005), are used to compare the overall character of flooding at the different wetlands. Flooded-area duration distributions show the percentages of time that the boundary of the flooded area was within different 20-percent intervals of the total wetland area (figure 53). The amount of time spent with the boundary of the flooded area in each 20-percent interval can be summed to compute the cumulative duration of flooding for different areas in the wetland, and can provide hydrologic evidence to support observed changes in the vegetation (Haag and Lee, 2006).

Flooded-area duration distributions were used to characterize the wetland flooding behavior over two time periods. For each wetland, the "recent" period covers the study period, which ranged in length from 1.7 years to 4 years at the 10 wetlands (table 4). The "historical" period for each wetland begins earlier and extends through the study period (table 10). For seven of the wetlands, 15 or 16 years of stage data were used. For the other three wetlands, between 8 and 13 years of stage data were available. A modified bathymetric map of each wetland indicates the shape and size of the flooded area for each 20-percent increment of the total wetland area. The flooded-area contours were derived from the original wetland bathymetric data (app. 5).

The interpretation of long-term average flooding behavior can be affected by the length of the historical time period used. In this analysis, the annual average rainfall and well-field pumping were similar over the 8- and 16-year historical periods considered. Except during 2003, ground-water withdrawals from the well fields were relatively consistent over the shortest and longest historical time periods. From 1988 to 2002, the monthly average ground-water pumping from the 11 municipal well fields ranged from 131 to 165 Mgal/d and averaged 145 Mgal/d (figure 6); from 1996 to 2002, it averaged 149 Mgal/d. In 2003, the final year of the "historical" analysis, ground-water withdrawals dropped steeply to 79 Mgal/d. Although annual rainfall fluctuated widely over the 16-year period, the regional average annual rainfall for the period from 1988 to 2003 was about average (52.56 in., as noted earlier), and was similar to the average rainfall of the first and second halves of this period (52.62 in. for 1988-95, and 52.50 in. for 1996-2003).

For the recent time period, the flooded-area duration distributions were computed from USGS daily values of stage, yielding 365 observations of wetland area per year. Historical flooded-area duration distributions were based on monthly average estimates of wetland area, or 12 observations per year, for 8 to 16 years. Monthly averages, in turn, were based on the number of evenly spaced observations of stage available each month from agency databases. Stage data collected by other agencies were adjusted with small offsets where necessary to coincide with USGS elevations (table 2, Haag and others, 2005).

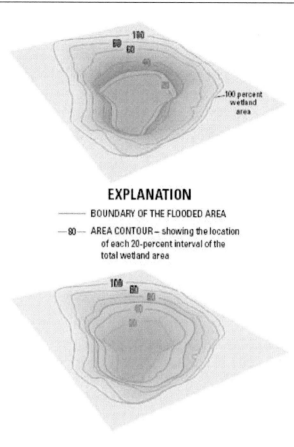

Figure 53. Conceptualized wetland showing the boundary of the flooded area located in different 20-percent intervals of the total wetland area.

Natural Wetlands

The historical flooded-area duration of the four natural wetlands provided preliminary insights into the flooding characteristics of natural wetlands in this region of Florida. Either 15 or 16 years of data were analyzed for three of the natural wetlands. The fourth natural wetland, GS Natural Marsh, had the shortest record, with only 8 years of data available (table 10).

The historical flooded-area duration distributions for the two natural cypress wetlands had two discernible features. In GS Natural Cypress wetland, the largest percentages of time were spent with the boundary of the flooded area in two contrasting flooded area intervals—one in which 81 to 100 percent of the wetland area was flooded, and the other in which 0 to 20 percent was flooded (figure 54A). These contrasting conditions could reflect the wetland response to the annually occurring wet and dry seasons. GS Natural Cypress was mostly dry more often than mostly wet, with 0 to 20 percent flooded about 52 percent of the time, and more than 81 percent flooded about 29 percent of the time (figure 54A). The pattern was similar but less pronounced at S-68 Natural Cypress, which was 21 to 40 percent flooded during the greatest percentage of the historical period (37 percent), and 81 to 100 percent flooded during the second greatest percentage of the period (29 percent) (figure 54B, table 11).

The natural cypress wetlands were 81 to 100 percent flooded more often during the recent period than the historical period. Specifically, the natural cypress wetlands were between 81 and 100 percent flooded during more than half of the recent period (figure 54A-B).

The HRSP Natural Marsh wetland had the same 16-year historical period as the natural cypress wetlands. Unlike its cypress counterparts, however, HRSP Natural Marsh was 0 to 20 percent flooded during the smallest percentage of the period (figure 55A). The duration of flooding at this wetland for the historical period was relatively evenly divided over the other 20-percent increments of the total area.

The HRSP Natural Marsh wetland was drier during the recent period than the historical period. Compared to the historical period, a smaller percentage of time was spent 61 to 100 percent flooded during the recent period, and a substantially larger percentage of time was spent 0 to 20 percent flooded (figure 55A).

The 8-year historical data period for GS Natural Marsh was about half as long as the historical period for HRSP Natural Marsh. GS Natural Marsh was 81 to 100 percent flooded the greatest percentage of the historical period (about 45 percent), and was 0 to 20 percent flooded less than 20 percent of the period (figure 55B).

Augmented Wetlands

During the historical period, between 41 to 80 percent of the total area of three of the four augmented wetlands typically was flooded, and relatively little time was spent with the flooded extent in either the driest or wettest area intervals (figs. 56 and 57A). For example, Duck Pond Augmented Marsh was 41 to 100 percent flooded over 95 percent of the historical period (figure 56A). Similarly, W-3 Augmented Marsh was 61 to 80 percent flooded over 60 percent of the historical period (figure 56B). The wetland was 81 to 100 percent flooded only 7 percent of the historical period, and less than 61 percent flooded only 30 percent of the period. The staff gage location at this wetland required consolidating all observations in the interval between 0 and 60 percent of the total area; however, many of these observations were probably just less than 60 percent. W-5 Augmented Cypress was rarely more than 60 percent flooded during the historical period (figure 57A).

A cypress wetland when the flooded area is small

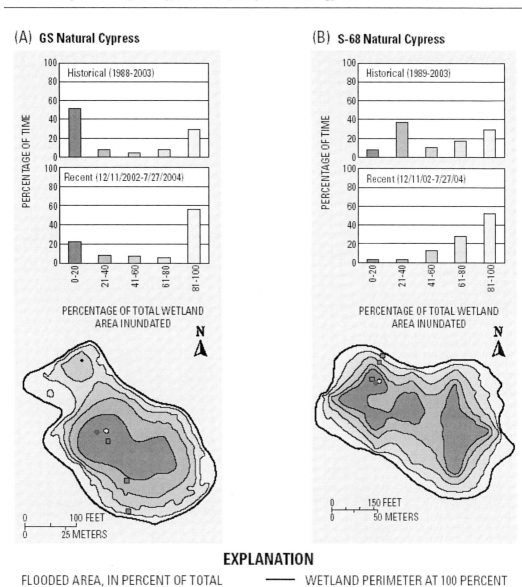

Figure 54. The recent and historical flooded-area duration distributions and maps showing the shapes of these flooded areas in (A) GS Natural Cypress and (B) S-68 Natural Cypress.

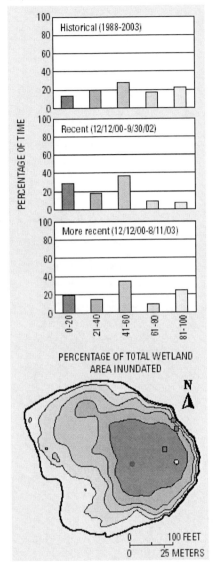

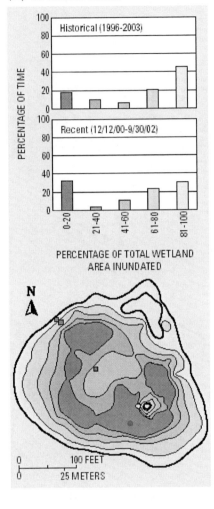

Figure 55. The recent and historical flooded-area duration distributions and maps showing the shapes of these flooded areas in (A) HRSP Natural Marsh and (B) GS Natural Marsh.

**Table 11. Percentage of the Historical Time Each Wetland Area Interval was Flooded.
[Outlined Cells Are Combined Area Intervals]**

Wetland	Area interval (percentage of total area)				
	0-20	21-40	41-60	61-80	81-100
GS Natural Cypress	52	7	4	8	29
S-68 Natural Cypress	7	37	10	17	29
HRSP Natural Marsh	13	20	28	17	22
GS Natural Marsh	18	6	6	22	48
W-5 Augmented Cypress	19	27	42	6	6
S-63 Augmented Cypress	37	17	21	14	11
Duck Pond Augmented Marsh	0	2	23	39	35
W-3 Augmented Marsh	31			62	7
W-19 Impaired Cypress	60	7	10	8	15
W-29 Impaired Marsh	71		8	11	10

In contrast, S-63 Augmented Cypress wetland showed a historical flooded-area duration distribution with flooding in each of the area intervals, with the greatest percentage in the 0 to 20 percent interval (figure 57B). The flooded area of S-63 Augmented Cypress was more variable over time than any other wetland studied, potentially making the historical biweekly staff gage readings less representative of monthly average conditions than at other sites. Nevertheless, the historical flooded-area duration distribution for S-63 Augmented Cypress shared characteristics observed at the natural and impaired cypress wetlands. S-63 Augmented Cypress resembled the natural cypress wetlands because it was 0 to 20 percent flooded about 40 percent of the historical period. However, it resembled the impaired sites by spending a relatively small percentage of the period with flooding over 61 to 100 percent of the total area (figure 57B and table 11).

The flooded-area duration distributions in the augmented cypress wetlands were wetter for the recent period than the historical period. S-63 Augmented Cypress was 41 to 60 percent flooded during nearly half of the recent period, and 80 to 100 percent flooded about twice as often as it was historically (figure 57B). Similarly, W-5 Augmented Cypress was 61 to 100 percent flooded a greater percentage of time in the recent period than the historical period.

Intentionally drying out W-5 Augmented Cypress for a rewetting experiment increased the percentage of time it was 0 to 20 percent flooded during the recent period (figure 57A).

Impaired Wetlands

W-29 Impaired Marsh was largely dry more often during the historical period than both of the natural marshes (figs. 55 and 58A). W-29 Impaired Marsh was 0 to 40 percent flooded 71 percent of the historical period (table 11), and was probably dry during much of this time. Because of its relatively high position, however, the historical staff gage could not be used to determine flooding extent when the wetland was less than 40 percent flooded (figure 58A). W-29 Impaired Marsh was 81 to 100 percent full about 10 percent of the historical period compared to 22 percent for HRSP Natural Marsh, and nearly 50 percent of the time in GS Natural Marsh (compare figure 58A with figure 55A-B).

Two flooded-area duration graphs are used to reflect the recent conditions at W-29 Impaired Marsh because data were collected at the site during the marsh and cypress data-collection periods. Flooding conditions during the marsh period resembled the historical conditions, with 0 to 20 percent flooding over 80 percent of the time (figure 58A). Much of this time, the wetland was dry; moreover, the recent conditions were drier than the historical conditions, with no flooding occurring in the area intervals above 60 percent.

During the wetter cypress period when well-field pumping was reduced, the hydrologic conditions at W-29 Impaired Marsh were nearly the opposite of conditions during the historical and marsh periods. The wetland was 80 to 100 percent full over 70 percent of the time, and never less than 21 percent full. The flooded-area duration distribution of W-29 Impaired Marsh during the later recent period did not indicate impairment, but resembled the recent flooding conditions in the two natural cypress wetlands.

Recent flooding at W-19 Impaired Cypress also resembled recent flooding at the natural cypress wetlands. However, the impaired condition of the wetland was evident in the 16-year historical flooded-area duration distribution. W-19 Impaired Cypress was 0 to 20 percent flooded 60 percent of the historical period (figure 58B), and was completely dry (0 percent flooding over a monthly averaged time period) almost 50 percent of that time. By comparison, GS Natural Cypress was 0 to 20 percent flooded during 52 percent of the same period (figure 54A), but was completely dry only 30 percent of the time. S-68 Natural Cypress, in contrast, was 21 to 40 percent flooded nearly 40 percent of its historical period (figure 54B), but was completely dry only 5 percent of that time. In addition to being completely dry substantially more often than the natural cypress wetlands, W-19 Impaired Cypress was 81 to 100 percent flooded only about half as often (table 11).

Seasonal Average Flooding Patterns

To assess seasonal flooding patterns, historical stage data from each wetland were used to reconstruct their monthly average flooded areas during an average year. The historical, monthly average flooded area, expressed as a percentage of the total wetland area, was computed by averaging all available values of the monthly mean flooded areas for a chosen month. Averaging emphasizes the central tendency of the data and deemphasizes the extremes.

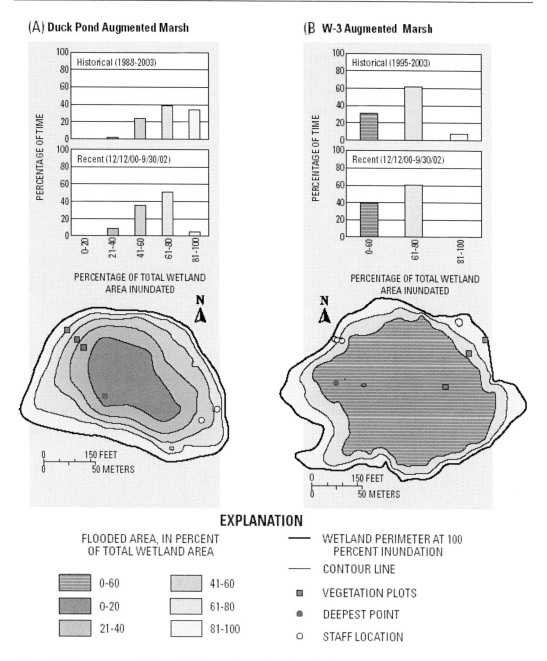

Figure 56. The recent and historical flooded-area duration distributions and maps showing the shapes of these flooded areas in (A) Duck Pond Augmented Marsh and (B) W-3 Augmented Marsh.

The monthly average flooded area patterns for the natural, augmented, and impaired wetlands show characteristic traits by group (figure 59A-I). The natural wetlands show the greatest variation in monthly average flooded area. The smallest monthly average flooded area consistently occurred in June and the largest in September or October (figure 59 A-D). The greatest monthly average flooded area percentage was typically 40 to 60 percent greater than the smallest flooded area percentage. The minimum monthly average flooded area was about 15 percent of the total wetland area at GS Natural Cypress wetland and around 30 percent of the total wetland area in the three other natural wetlands. The maximum monthly average flooded area in the natural sites ranged from about 60 percent of the total wetland area in GS Natural Cypress wetland to about 75 percent of the total wetland area for the two other natural wetlands that shared the same historical time period. The natural marsh with the shorter period of record (GS Natural Marsh) had a maximum monthly flooded area that averaged just over 90 percent of the total wetland area during August, September, and October (figure 59B).

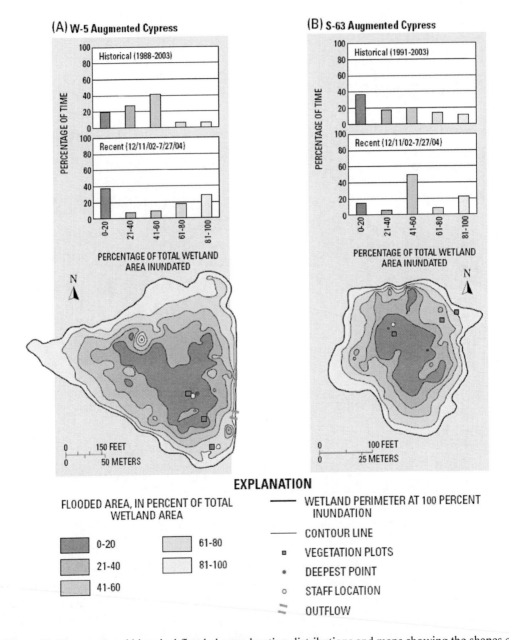

Figure 57. The recent and historical flooded-area duration distributions and maps showing the shapes of these flooded areas in (A) W-5 Augmented Cypress and (B) S-63 Augmented Cypress.

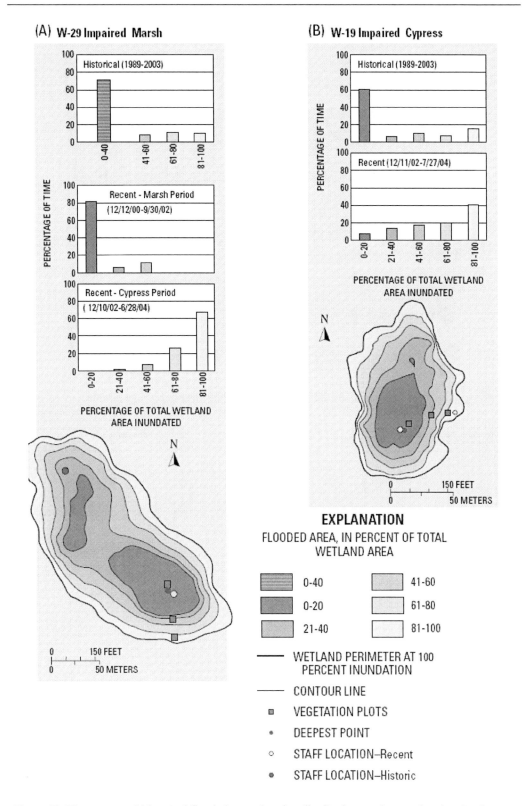

Figure 58. The recent and historical flooded- area duration distributions and maps showing the shapes of these flooded areas in (A) W-29 Impaired Marsh and (B) W-19 Impaired Cypress.

The monthly average flooded area in the impaired wetlands showed a seasonal pattern similar to the natural wetland patterns, but with substantially less area flooded during each month of the year, and a smaller range between the minimum and maximum flooded areas (figure 59E-F).

Seasonal changes in flooding patterns affect habitat for sandhill cranes and other wildlife

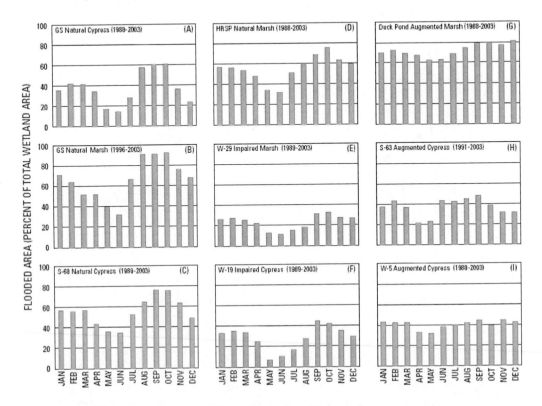

Figure 59. Historical monthly average flooded area in the study wetlands.

For example, at W-19 Impaired Cypress the minimum monthly average flooded area was 7 percent of the total wetland area and the maximum was 45 percent (figure 59F). At W-29 Impaired Marsh, the monthly average flooded area over the historical period was always less than 40 percent of the total area (figure 59E). For this reason, the monthly average flooded areas at this site were inferred using ground-water levels measured by Tampa Bay Water in a well next to the historical staff gage.

The monthly average flooded areas in the augmented wetlands varied less than those in the natural wetlands (figure 59G-I). The augmented wetlands did have a minimum monthly average flooded area, typically in April or May, and a maximum between September and December; however, the average difference between the annual minimums and maximums was the smallest of all three wetland groups. Of the augmented wetlands, the most evident seasonality in flooded area occurred in S-63 Augmented Cypress, where augmentation rates were designed to target different water levels during the year in an effort to impose a more natural cycle. The resulting pattern shows slightly more seasonality than W-5 Augmented Cypress (figure 59H-I). However, the minimum monthly average flooded area occurred in April at S-63 Augmented Cypress, as opposed to June in the natural wetlands. Both augmented cypress wetlands maintained smaller monthly average flooded areas compared to the natural wetlands. The minimum monthly average flooded areas for the two augmented cypress wetlands were similar to those of the natural wetlands, averaging 20 to 30 percent of the total wetland area, although the maximum monthly average flooded areas were substantially less.

The monthly average flooding pattern at Duck Pond Augmented Marsh was the least similar to the flooding patterns of the natural wetland sites. At Duck Pond Augmented Marsh, the minimum monthly average flooded area was about 60 percent of the total wetland area and the maximum was about 80 percent. A similar seasonal analysis was not possible for W-3 Augmented Marsh because areas below 60 percent of the total wetland area could not be differentiated in the historical data. However, a consistently large flooded area probably was maintained throughout the year at W-3 Augmented Marsh, as suggested by flooding results for the recent time period.

Overview of Flooding Characteristics

Flooded area, when expressed as a percentage of total area, is an informative measure for describing and comparing the hydrologic condition of isolated wetlands in a region regardless of their size. Wetland conditions can be compared concurrently, and abundant historical stage data for wetlands can be synthesized into a comparable hydrologic indicator. The flooding patterns in the study wetlands were examined over three different timeframes. Although a relatively small number of wetlands were used in this study, results revealed similarities within the three hydrologic groups associated with the wetlands, and to a lesser extent, the two wetland types.

In the natural wetlands, the weekly average size of the flooded areas changed relatively rapidly and displayed short-lived extremes. Stage observations are currently made once every 2 weeks in about 480 wetlands in west-central Florida (Tampa Bay Water, 2000). Results from this study indicate that biweekly measurements would miss much of the variability captured by averaging daily values. Biweekly observations may provide sufficient measurement frequency for some regulatory purposes, however, such as estimating the annual and monthly average water levels over multiple years. Daily stage data collected at natural wetlands in west-central Florida by the SWFWMD could be used to check this conclusion.

The flooding behaviors in natural wetlands were sufficiently similar to characterize them as a group. For example, natural wetlands showed similar patterns in the percentages of their total areas that were flooded over similar time periods. Although there were differences for individual weeks, overall, the natural wetlands were similar to one another in the timing and magnitude of total wetland area inundated during a given year. These similarities may indicate that shared rainfall conditions determined the weekly flooding patterns in the four natural wetlands as much, or more than, differences in their physical settings. For this reason, the "natural" flooding pattern observed for the first 2 years of the study, when rainfall was about average, was distinctly different than the "natural" pattern observed for the next 2 years when rainfall was above average.

Natural wetlands also showed certain characteristic flooding patterns over the historical period that contrasted with the impaired and augmented wetlands. Comparing all of the wetlands for the same 8-year period, the two natural cypress wetlands had about half of their total areas flooded about 45 percent of the time (41 and 51 percent, table 12). During the same period, water covered more than half of the two natural marshes about 70 percent of the time. Therefore, the upper halves of the marsh wetland areas were flooded more often than the upper halves of the cypress wetlands. Some marshes are recognized as having, on average, longer periods of inundation than cypress wetlands (CH$_2$M HILL, 1996). The average duration of inundation, however, is defined at the location of the staff gage, typically in the deepest part of the wetland. In the current study, the duration of flooding in the deepest part of the natural marsh and cypress wetlands was fairly similar, averaging about 11.4 and 9.4 months per year, respectively (table 13).

Comparing the flooding duration that occurs nearer the wetland margins, in addition to the deepest part of the wetland, may provide a more telling hydrologic difference. Ultimately, describing historic flooding patterns in a larger population of natural marsh and cypress wetlands will help clarify differences between these two types of wetlands.

Table 12. The Percentage of Time That More than Half of the Total Wetland Area was Flooded, Based on Stage Data from 1996 to 2003

Wetland	Percentage of time
GS Natural Cypress	41
S-68 Natural Cypress	51
HRSP Natural Marsh	67
GS Natural Marsh	71
W-5 Augmented Cypress	31
S-63 Augmented Cypress	33
Duck Pond Augmented Marsh	81
W-3 Augmented Marsh[1]	69
W-19 Impaired Cypress	32
W-29 Impaired Marsh	33

[1] Percentage of time more than 60 percent of the wetland area was flooded.

Table 13. Average Duration of Flooding at Deepest Point in Wetland, in Months Per Year, Based on Stage Data from 1996 to 2003

Wetland	Duration, in months per year
GS Natural Cypress	7.9
S-68 Natural Cypress	10.8
HRSP Natural Marsh	11.9
GS Natural Marsh	10.9
W-5 Augmented Cypress	12
S-63 Augmented Cypress	10.9
Duck Pond Augmented Marsh	12
W-3 Augmented Marsh	12
W-19 Impaired Cypress	6.5
W-29 Impaired Marsh	5.1

Differences in flooding characteristics between the natural, augmented, and impaired wetlands are consequences of external factors such as rainfall, physical and geologic settings, augmentation, changes in runoff, and ground-water withdrawals. Flooding in the natural wetlands can be used as an indicator of typical hydrologic conditions to help determine (1) what percentage of the total area of an impaired wetland is no longer flooded like a natural wetland, (2) what percentage of the augmented wetland continues to be flooded like a natural wetland, and (3) how long altered conditions have existed.

Only the inner 40 to 60 percent of the total area of impaired wetlands was flooded with a frequency comparable to that of the natural wetlands. The outer 40 to 60 percent of the total wetland area, nearer the wetland perimeter, flooded much less frequently, and approached a hydrologic status comparable to the adjacent upland area. The effects of the altered hydrology on the vegetation at the impaired wetlands are well documented, and include the encroachment of pine trees into W-29 Impaired Marsh (Berryman and Hennigar Inc., 2000; Haag and others, 2005) and cypress tree mortality in W-19 Impaired Cypress (Reynolds, Smith & Hills, Inc., 2001; Haag and others, 2005).

Neither of the impaired wetlands is considered to be as severely affected by ground-water withdrawals as the augmented wetlands were prior to mitigation. Three of the four augmented wetlands were considered affected as early as the late 1970s. Ground-water withdrawals at Cross Bar Well Field began in 1980, and effects were reported at Duck Pond Marsh soon thereafter. Three of the four augmented wetlands in this study are within several hundred feet of production wells (W-3 Augmented Marsh, Duck Pond Augmented Marsh, and S-63 Augmented Cypress), and all four are subject to ground-water drawdown effects that lower the elevation of the surrounding water table several feet below the wetland bottom. Therefore, without augmentation, the four augmented wetlands probably would have had little or no area with flooding comparable to that of a natural wetland.

Augmentation has most likely prevented a complete loss of flooded area at the four augmented wetlands, both for the historical time period used in these analyses, and for the entire period for which augmentation has been practiced, namely: 1978-present at W-5 Augmented Cypress, 1979-present at W-3 Augmented Marsh, 1987-present at Duck Pond Augmented Marsh, and 1990-present at S-63 Augmented Cypress. Augmentation has imposed routine inundation (defined as inundation for at least 30 percent of the time) over a substantial area of each of these wetlands. For the historical periods given in table 10, augmentation of Duck Pond Augmented Marsh increased the routinely inundated area from perhaps as little as 0 percent to between 81 and 100 percent of the total wetland area. It maintained a permanent pond over 40 to 60 percent of the total area, and a viable marsh fringe in the remaining 40 percent of the area. At W-5 Augmented Cypress, augmentation sustained routine inundation of 40 to 60 percent of the total wetland area. The remaining 40 percent of the area of W-5 Augmented Cypress flooded less frequently than either of the impaired wetlands. Augmentation increased the routinely inundated area in W-3 Augmented Marsh from perhaps 0 to 20 percent of the total wetland area to 61 to 80 percent of the total area. The remaining 20 percent of the wetland area (81-100 percent interval) flooded much less often than the natural wetlands.

At S-63 Augmented Cypress, the wetland surface area routinely inundated by augmentation is more difficult to characterize. Historically, the 0 to 20 percent area interval of S-63 Augmented Cypress was flooded much more often than any other interval. The 81 to 100 percent interval was flooded only 11 percent of the historical time compared to about 30 percent in both natural cypress wetlands. At S-63 Augmented Cypress, the cumulative duration of flooding approached the natural level in the area interval between either 61 to 80 percent of the total area (cumulative flooding 25 percent of the time) or 41 to 60 percent of the total area (cumulative flooding 46 percent of the time) (table 11). In the area of S-63 Augmented Cypress that was routinely inundated, the timing of dry and flooded periods may have differed widely from that of natural wetlands. Based on the weekly flooded area estimates, S-63 Augmented Cypress displayed the least seasonality and continuity in size of the flooded area during successive weeks of any of the study wetlands.

The duration of dry conditions also differed substantially in the three wetland groups. For the 8 years from 1996 to 2003, the natural wetlands all dried out at their deepest points. On average, dry conditions in the natural wetlands lasted 3 days per year at HRSP Natural Marsh, about 1 month per year at S-68 Natural Cypress and GS Natural Marsh, and 4 months per year at GS Natural Cypress. In contrast, the impaired wetlands were dry 5.5 to almost 7 months per year at the deepest point (table 13). Except for S-63 Augmented Cypress, the augmented wetlands never dried out at their deepest points over this time period.

Wetland flooding characteristics relate in various ways to all of the other sections of the report. Differences in flooding behavior have a pronounced and immediate effect on wetland water quality, vegetation, and ecology, and can be interpreted along with measurements of ecosystem function. Moreover, flooding characteristics have a direct and substantial affect on ground-water flow patterns and the wetland water budget.

WETLAND ECOLOGY

Ecological patterns in wetlands reflect complex and dynamic interactions between physical and biological factors (Mitsch and Gosselink, 2000). The ecological comparison of natural, impaired, and augmented marsh and cypress wetlands in this study focuses primarily on the periphyton, wetland vegetation, and macroinvertebrate communities found in each. Differences in species composition, relative abundance, and biomass were used to compare and contrast community structure at the sites.

Methods of Ecological Data Collection and Interpretation

Ecological data were collected quarterly and semiannually in marsh and cypress wetlands using similar methods regardless of wetland type. The ecological sampling was primarily designed to facilitate comparisons among the groups of marsh wetlands (natural, impaired, and augmented), and among the groups of cypress wetlands. Data analysis involved a combination of descriptive and statistical methods. As noted earlier, all data and interpretive results for this section are reported in metric units. English units are only shown if they were the original unit of measure.

Periphyton
The periphyton community was assessed in each of the 10 wetlands using an artificial substrate sampler fitted with glass slides (25 x 76 mm). Periphyton growing on glass slides was collected as a surrogate for the periphyton typically found on wetland plant and sediment surfaces because this collection method provided consistent periphyton samples in all 10 wetlands (Stevenson and others, 1996). To determine community composition and periphyton biomass, samples were collected quarterly at the marsh wetlands during 2000-02, and at the cypress wetlands during 2002-04. A synoptic sampling of periphyton biomass and chlorophyll-*a* at all wetlands also occurred during September–October 2003.

The periphyton sampler (Wildco [TM]) was tethered to the staff gage at each wetland and floated at the water surface, so that the glass slides were immersed just below the water surface. Samplers remained deployed in the wetlands for 15 to 30 days. Each sampler was retrieved at the end of the sampling interval, placed in a plastic bag, and transported to the laboratory in a chilled cooler.

Two glass slides from each sampler were scraped with a single-edge razor blade and the algal material was mixed with a small aliquot of water and filtered onto glass fiber filters and frozen. Frozen samples were analyzed for biomass (ash-free dry mass) and chlorophyll-*a* concentration at the USGS Water Quality Laboratory in Ocala, Florida. Although glass slides were left in the field for 15 to 30 days, the biomass and chlorophyll-*a* data were normalized to a 21-day period for the purpose of comparison. Two additional glass slides were scraped, and the algal material was placed in a glass vial and preserved with 3 to 5 percent formalin. Preserved samples were shipped to Michigan State University in Ann Arbor, MI and analyzed to determine the composition of the algal community. Laboratory analysis methods are described in Stevenson and others (2002).

Wetland Vegetation
Vegetation sampling was designed to facilitate comparisons among the groups (natural, impaired, and augmented) of marsh wetlands, and among the groups of cypress wetlands. Differences in vegetation between marsh and cypress wetlands within groups were not of primary interest. The species composition and relative abundance of vegetation in all 10 wetlands were assessed in fixed plots in May and October 2002, May and October 2003, and May 2004. At each wetland site, three 1-m^2 vegetation plots were established and maintained for the duration of the study (app. 5). Vegetation plots were defined as transitional, intermediate, or deep, based on their elevation relative to the elevation at the wetland perimeter (Haag and others, 2005). Transitional plots were located 3 to 6 in. (7.6-15.2 cm)

below the seasonal high water elevation, which corresponds to the elevation of the wetland perimeter. Deep plots were located near a point of lowest elevation (maximum water depth) at each wetland. Intermediate plots were located at an elevation half-way between the elevation of the deep plots and the elevation of the transitional plots.

All emergent plants in the 1 -m^2 plots were identified to species, and their percent cover was estimated visually. No plants were removed, with the exception of an occasional specimen for species verification. Additional estimates of the relative abundance of herbaceous vegetation were made quarterly when macroinvertebrate and periphyton samples were collected in marsh wetlands during July 2000–July 2002 and in cypress wetlands during July 2002–July 2004. All plants were identified in 0.25 m2 plots in water depths of about 15 to 30 cm, at elevations similar to those of the intermediate plots.

Verification of species identification, when necessary, was provided by the University of South Florida Herbarium in Tampa, Florida. Plant names used herein follow Wunderlin (1998). Wetland plants were assigned a status based on the Florida Vegetative Index (Florida Department of Environmental Protection, 2004) or the Atlas of Florida Vascular Plants (Wunderlin and Hansen, 2004). Any plant not specifically listed in the index is considered an upland plant with the exception of vines and aquatic plants. Aquatic plants are those, including the roots, that (1) typically float on water or require water for their entire structural support; or (2) desiccate outside of water (Florida Department of State, 1994). The three wetland plant indicator categories (obligate wetland species, facultative wet wetland species and facultative wetland species) are defined according to Federal guidelines (Reed, 1988). Specifically, an obligate species is present in wetlands greater than 99 percent of the time, a facultative wet species is present in wetlands 67 to 99 percent of the time, and a facultative species is present in wetlands 34 to 66 percent of the time. Although both obligate and facultative wet species are widely recognized as useful indicators of wetlands, facultative species can be dominant plants in uplands as well as in wetlands and, therefore, are not considered to be reliable indicators of wetlands.

Vegetation assessment in a deep plot at a marsh wetland

The species composition of vegetation in marsh and cypress wetlands was compared using Jaccard's Similarity Index (Jongman and others, 1995). Jaccard's Index is a qualitative measure of similarity that expresses the percentage of species shared in common by two wetland communities. Data were grouped by plot elevation so that vegetation comparisons among the 10 wetlands were made between transitional plots, intermediate plots, or deep plots.

The biomass of vegetation in marsh wetlands was estimated quarterly during 2000-02. A 0.25-m^2 frame was placed on the wetland bottom at three widely separated locations in each marsh wetland on each sampling date. The frame was placed in water at depths less than about 0.3 m to facilitate sample collection. The relative proportions of the five dominant plant species in each frame were recorded based on visual estimates. Plants were clipped at their base at the sediment surface and all plant biomass in the frame was placed in a plastic bag and returned to the laboratory. Plants were dried in an oven on aluminum foil at 105 °C for 24 to 72 hours until a constant weight was obtained. Dried plants were weighed to the nearest gram. Plant biomass data are reported as dry weight in grams per square meter. The estimates of plant biomass were restricted to herbaceous vegetation growing in water depths of about 0.3 m; therefore, they are not representative of plant biomass in the entire wetland. Samples from the five marsh wetlands, however, can be compared because they all were collected at similar water depths and during the same time period.

Tree density was estimated in cypress wetlands during 2002. At each cypress wetland, five "reference" trees were chosen at five locations widely spaced throughout the wetland where water depth did not exceed 1 m. All cypress trees within a radius of 3.05 m from the reference trees were measured to determine tree diameter at breast height. The density of cypress trees at these locations was used to estimate the total number of cypress trees per acre in each of the five cypress wetlands and to compare the relative size of cypress trees in each wetland. The occurrence of fallen and leaning trees also was recorded.

Macroinvertebrates

Macroinvertebrates were sampled quarterly in the 10 wetlands in this study. A standard D-frame aquatic dip net about 30 cm wide with a mesh size of 0.5 mm was used to collect macroinvertebrate samples at three widely spaced locations in each marsh and cypress wetland on each sampling date. Samples were collected at water depths of 0.25 to 0.75 m at all wetlands to facilitate comparisons. Dip-net sweeps are an effective sampling method for wetland macroinvertebrates (Cheal and others, 1993; Rader and Richardson, 1994), although dip-net samples may underestimate the abundance of small-bodied taxa (Kratzer and Batzer, 2007). One distinct advantage of using the dip-net method for this study was that it could be used in all 10 wetlands regardless of wetland group or type. The net was used to sweep an area about 1 -m long, so that the total area swept by the net was about 0.33 m^2. All material in one dip-net sweep was placed in one or more 1 -L containers, preserved with 10-percent buffered formalin, and transported to the laboratory for analysis. A solution of rose bengal (100 mg/L) was added to stain the macroinvertebrates in the preserved samples at least 48 hours before samples were sorted to facilitate separation of biota from detritus and sediment.

The formalin preservative was then decanted, and each sample was rinsed with water to remove residual formalin. Each sample was then spread out in a shallow gridded pan and examined at 1 .75X magnification. All organisms were removed and stored in 70-percent ethanol until they could be identified. Non-insect macroinvertebrates were usually identified to order, and insects were identified to the lowest practical taxonomic level, usually to genus. (Diptera were identified to family.) References used for macroinvertebrate identification included Heard (1979), Merritt and Cummins (1984), Berner and Pescador (1988), Pennak (1989), Daigle (1991), Epler (1996), Thorp and Covich (1996), Rasmussen and Pescador (2002), Richardson (2003), and Thompson (2004). After identification, macroinvertebrates were dried in an oven at 100 °C for 24 to 48 hours, cooled, and weighed to obtain biomass estimates for each sample. Macroinvertebrate biomass data are reported as dry weight per square meter. Fish collected in dip-net samples were identified using Burgess (2004).

Several commonly used measures of community composition (metrics) were used for comparison of macro- invertebrates among the groups of marsh wetlands and among the groups of cypress wetlands, including mean taxa richness (the number of macroinvertebrate taxa per square meter), density (the number of macroinvertebrate organisms per square meter), biomass (the dry weight of macroinvertebrates per square meter), proportion of total Diptera and Chironomidae, and distribution of macroinvertebrate taxa among functional feeding groups (Merritt and others, 1996). Shannon diversity (Krebs, 1999), which incorporates both the number of species (richness) and the number of individuals in each species (evenness), also was calculated for each wetland. Each of these metrics describes different aspects of the macroinvertebrate community, and when used together, they can provide a basis for comparing and contrasting sites.

During early field reconnaissance, macroinvertebrates were collected in the 0.2- to 0.4-m-deep areas of each wetland with a 5-cm-diameter aluminum coring device, but a variety of factors made it difficult to obtain consistent 10-cm-long cores. Fibrous plant material hindered penetration of the core sampler at natural and impaired marsh sites, and the partially cut plant fragments hindered core retention. Tree roots prevented core penetration at natural and impaired cypress sites. Flocculent core samples could be collected at the augmented marsh and cypress sites, although there were few macroinvertebrates present (perhaps because of anoxic conditions in those thick sediments) and those organisms that were identified (Oligochaeta, Diptera larvae) were often in fragments. Because comparable semi-quantitative sediment core samples could not be collected at all sites, collection of sediment samples was discontinued.

Periphyton

Periphyton, also known as attached algae, grows in freshwater wetlands on all available substrates during periods of sustained inundation in response to nutrients and other water-quality constituents, and other physical and biochemical factors. Periphyton has a long history of use in the assessment of aquatic habitats. Specifically, the species composition of periphyton communities has been linked to a variety of water-quality constituents including pH, conductivity, nitrates, phosphorus, and others. Few studies have characterized algae in freshwater wetlands despite the widespread abundance of these wetlands (Goldsborough and Robinson, 1996), and wetland periphyton research in Florida has generally focused on the Everglades and surrounding areas (Lane and Brown, 2007).

Biomass and Chlorophyll-a

The median biomass of periphyton was lower in natural marshes (3.4-3.8 mg/m^2) than in augmented marshes (5.6-5.9 mg/m^2) in this study (table 14). The median periphyton biomass was lowest at W-29 Impaired Marsh (1.1 mg/m^2) compared to the other nine wetlands in the study. The median periphyton biomass also was lower at the natural cypress (1.3- 2.3 mg/m^2) and impaired cypress (1.9 mg/m^2) wetlands than at the augmented cypress (5.0-6.7 mg/m^2) wetlands.

A synoptic sampling of periphyton biomass and chlorophyll-a in all wetlands during September–October 2003 (table 15) also indicated that augmented marsh and cypress wetlands had higher periphyton biomass than natural wetlands. The median periphyton biomass was similar in natural and impaired cypress wetlands (2.20 and 2.64 mg/m^2, respectively), and augmented cypress wetlands had a substantially higher periphyton biomass (6.15 mg/m^2). Chlorophyll-a concentrations in periphyton were higher in the augmented marshes (2.70 µg/cm^2) than in the natural (1.47 µg/cm^2) or impaired marshes (0.27 µg/cm^2). Similarly, concentrations of chlorophyll-a were higher in the augmented cypress (5.68 µg/cm^2) than in the natural (0.55 µg/cm^2) or the impaired (1.76 µg/cm^2) cypress wetlands.

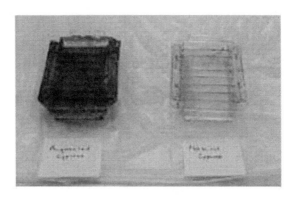

Periphyton biomass on glass-slide samplers was higher in augmented wetlands than in natural wetlands

Table 14. Median Biomass of Periphyton Samples Collected in Study Wetlands, 2002-04. [mg/m^2, milligrams per square meter]

Wetland	Number of samples	Periphyton biomass (mg/m^2)		
		Median	Minimum	Maximum
Green Swamp Natural Marsh	10	3.8	0.7	10.7
HRSP Natural Marsh	8	3.4	0.6	10.1
W-29 Impaired Marsh	5	1.1	0.5	2.3
Duck Pond Augmented Marsh	8	5.6	2.0	15.9
W-3 Augmented Marsh	8	5.9	0.5	15.2
Green Swamp Natural Cypress	9	1.3	0.6	5.0
S-68 Natural Cypress	6	2.3	0.3	5.3
W-19 Impaired Cypress	9	1.9	0.4	6.5
S-63 Augmented Cypress	6	6.7	1.6	23.3
W-5 Augmented Cypress	5	5.0	1.3	11.8

Table 15. Median Biomass and Chlorophyll-*a* of Periphyton Samples Collected in Study Wetlands During September–October 2003.
[mg/m^2, milligrams per square meter; µg/cm^2, micrograms per square centimeter]

Wetland	Number of samples	Biomass, (mg/m^2)	Chlorophyll-*a*, (µg/cm^2)
Natural marshes	6	4.40	1.47
Impaired marsh	4	2.29	0.27
Augmented marshes	4	6.60	2.70
Natural cypress	6	2.20	0.55
Impaired cypress	4	2.64	1.76
Augmented cypress	6	6.15	5.68

There are few studies of periphyton communities in Florida wetlands other than the Everglades (Lane and Brown, 2007). Goldsborough and Robinson (1996) tabulated results of biomass and chlorophyll-*a* data from a number of studies of freshwater wetlands, and the reported ranges for these algal community measures are broad. The range for chlorophyll-*a* reported in the present study (0.67-5.54 µg/cm^2), however, is within the broad ranges included in that summary paper (0.1-7.9 µg/cm^2). Moreover, the range for periphyton biomass reported in the present study (1.57-2.07 mg/cm^2) (data not shown) also is within the ranges reported in Goldsborough and Robinson (1996) (0.1-45 mg/cm^2).

Community Composition

The most abundant periphyton groups in most freshwater habitats are blue-green algae (Cyanophyta), green algae (Chlorophyta), diatoms (Bacillariophyta), and red algae (Rhodophyta), although other algal groups may be present (Stevenson and others, 1996). In general, wetlands supplied by rainwater, which has a low ionic content and low pH, would be expected to support a periphyton community dominated by green algae and acid-loving diatoms. Wetlands supplied with ground water, which has a higher pH and mineral content, would be expected to contain more blue-green algae and diatoms that prefer alkaline waters.

When algae in this study were compared on the basis of biovolume, green algae were the predominant group at natural marsh and cypress wetlands, as well as augmented marshes (figure 60). Desmids were more abundant at the unaugmented wetlands, with the exception of S-63 Augmented Cypress. Diatoms also were an important part of the total biovolume of algae at all wetlands except the unaugmented marshes. Filamentous and colonial bluegreen algae were present at low densities in most of the wetlands.

In studies of Everglades wetlands, desmids were more common at sites with low calcium carbonate and nutrient concentrations, whereas green algae and diatoms were more common at sites with moderate calcium carbonate and phosphorus concentrations (Browder and others, 1994). Similar patterns of algae abundance were not evident in the present study. One drawback of using algae as indicators of wetland condition is that they exhibit seasonal variation that may overshadow differences caused by other environmental factors (Stevenson and others, 1996).

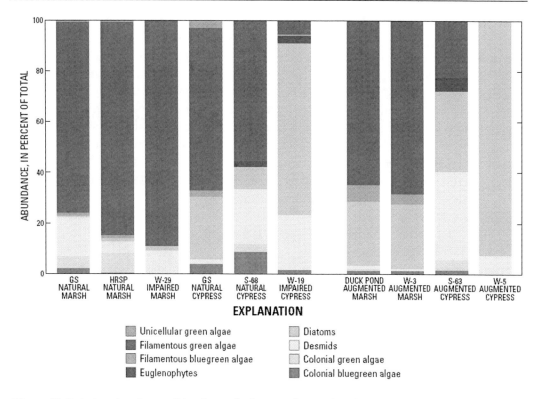

Figure 60. Relative abundance of dominant algal groups in marsh and cypress wetlands.

Diatoms are an important component of periphyton, and assessments of the diatom community can be used to compare wetlands because diatoms are relatively easy to identify and data are available that describe their ecological preferences (Lane and Brown, 2007). Diatom species richness was similar at the natural marshes (26.0) and S-68 Natural Cypress (27.0), but much lower at GS Natural Cypress (16.0) (table 16). The species richness was 21.0 at the two augmented cypress wetlands. The highest diatom species richness was found at W-29 Impaired Marsh (29.0), and the lowest value was found at W-19 Impaired Cypress (15.0).

A study of diatoms in 50 forested wetlands throughout Florida indicated that species richness averaged 19.0 at "reference" (undisturbed) sites and at sites influenced by agriculture (Reiss and Brown, 2005). Wetlands in urban settings in that study had higher diatom species richness (22.0). A parallel assessment of 70 marsh wetlands indicated a mean species richness of 18.4, with no difference in species richness observed between reference marshes and marshes that had experienced effects from agriculture or urban development (Lane and others, 2003).

Several species of diatoms were more abundant at natural and impaired sites in the present study than at augmented sites (table 16), including *Eunotia nagelii*, *Eunotia incisa*, *Frustulia rhomboides*, and *Pinnularia subcapitata*. Other taxa were more abundant at augmented sites than at the unaugmented sites, including species of *Gomphonema* and *Nitzchia*.

In the study of Florida forested wetlands by Reiss and Brown (2005), five diatom species were identified in 50 percent or more of the forested wetlands sampled. Four of those five species were found in the natural cypress wetlands in the present study, and all five species were found at W-19 Impaired Cypress. Only two of the species were found at the augmented cypress wetlands in the present study. Reiss and Brown (2005) also established lists of tolerant and intolerant diatom species for the set of Florida forested wetlands they sampled. Of those species listed as tolerant, only one species (*Navicula minima*) was identified at the cypress wetlands in the present study, where it was found in low numbers at most sites. Of the species listed by Reiss and Brown (2005) as intolerant or sensitive, *Eunotia naegelii* was found at the GS Natural Cypress, but not at the augmented or impaired cypress wetlands. *Frustulia rhomboides* and *Eunotia rhomboidea* and were common at the natural and impaired cypress wetlands, respectively, but not at the augmented cypress wetlands (table 16). The higher specific conductances prevailing at augmented cypress wetlands may explain the absence of these species at augmented sites compared to natural sites, which have much lower specific conductances. For example, in river habitats the optimum specific conductance for these three diatom species is low (65-90 µS/cm) (Potopova and Charles, 2003).

Table 16. Median Diatom Species Richness and Most Abundant Diatom Species in Study Wetlands

Wetland name	Median diatom species richness (range)	Most abundant diatom species				
GS Natural Marsh	26 (16–38)	*Cocconeis placentula euglypta*	*Eunotia incisa*	*Eunotia naegelii*	*Frustulia rhomboides*	*Pinnularia subcapitata*
HRSP Natural Marsh	26 (20–48)	*Acnanthes exigua*	*Eunotia incisa*	*Eunotia naegelii*	*Fragilaria brevistriata*	*Gomphonema gracile*
GS Natural Cypress	16 (10–39)	*Acnanthes exigua*	*Eunotia incisa*	*Eunotia naegelii*	*Pinularia brau-nii amphicephala*	*Pinnularia subcapitata*
S-68 Natural Cypress	27 (21–47)	*Eunotia naegelii*	*Eunotia paludosa*	*Eunotia septentrionalis*	*Frustulia rhomboides*	*Pinnularia subcapitata*
W-19 Impaired Cypress	15 (10–26)	*Eunotia incisa*	*Eunotia rhomboidea*	*Frustulia rhomboides crassinerva*	*Gomphonema affine*	*Navicula minima*
W-29 Impaired Marsh	29 (8–34)	*Acnanthes exigua*	*Eunotia naegelii*	*Frustulia brevis*	*Frustulia rhomboides*	*Pinnularia subcapitata*
Duck Pond Augmented Marsh	29 (14–51)	*Cymbella laevis*	*Eunotia naegelii*	*Fragilaria brevistriata*	*Frustulia rhomboides*	*Nitzschia paleacea*
W-3 Augmented Marsh	22 (12–31)	*Cymbella laevis*	*Gomphonema parvulum*	*Fragilaria brevistriata*	*Nitzschia archibaldii*	*Pinnularia subcapitata*
S-63 Augmented Cypress	21 (17–28)	*Gomp-honema angustum*	*Gomphonema gracile*	*Navicula minima*	*Nitzschia amphibia*	*Sellaphora pupula*
W-5 Augmented Cypress	21 (8–34)	*Acnanthes biasolet-tiana*	*Cocconeis placentula euglypta*	*Cocconeis placentula lineata*	*Gomphonema parvulum*	*Gomphonema pseudoten-ellum*

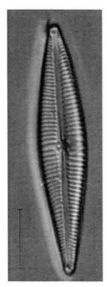

Photograph provided by R.J. Stevenson, Michigan State University

The diatom *Gomphonema gracile* was found widely in augmented marshes

Studies at 70 Florida marsh wetlands also indicated that species in the genera *Anomoeoneis, Eunotia,* and *Frustulia* were generally found to be sensitive to human disturbances (Lane and others, 2003). *Eunotia naegelli, Eunotia rhomboidea,* and *Frustulia rhomboides* were indicative of reference sites (Lane and others, 2003). Although these three species were commonly found at the natural and impaired marshes in the present study, they were not widely found at the augmented marshes. Species of *Gomphonema, Navicula,* and *Nitzchia* were found to be indicative of disturbed conditions in marsh wetlands by Lane and others (2003). In the present study *Gomphonema gracile, Navicula minima, Nitzchia amphibia, and Nitzchia paleacea* were found widely in the augmented marshes, but were not common in the natural marshes. For example, the species *Navicula minima* has an optimum specific conductance of 319 µS/cm in river habitats, and a range of 140-729 µS/cm (Potopova and Charles, 2003), indicating that it would not be expected in high numbers in natural wetlands with their characteristically low specific conductances.

Diatom species have varying sensitivity to changes in water-quality properties, including pH and nutrients. The Van Dam Ecological Indicator values for diatom species are among the most complete references for assessing various environmental conditions (Van Dam and others, 1994). Several of these indices were used to characterize the sites in the present study, including the following:

- *pH Index*—Diatoms are sensitive to pH and the index value, which ranges from 1 to 5, indicates acidic to alkaline conditions, respectively.
- *Trophic State Index*—Diatoms are sensitive to nutrient concentrations and the index values, which range from 1 to 6, indicate an increasing proportion of diatoms tolerant to elevated nutrient concentrations.
- *Index of Nitrogen Uptake Metabolism*—Diatoms vary in nitrogen uptake ability and the indicator values, which range from 1 to 4, increase with organic enrichment.

Table 17. Van Dam Ecological Indicator Values (Van Dam and Others, 1994) for Diatoms in Study Wetlands

Wetland name	Van Dam Trophic Index mean value	Van Dam Nitrogen Index mean value	Van Dam pH Index mean value
GS Natural Marsh	2.21	1.41	2.41
HRSP Natural Marsh	2.61	1.38	2.59
W-29 Impaired Marsh	2.03	1.73	2.21
GS Natural Cypress	1.90	1.27	2.28
S-68 Natural Cypress	1.38	1.10	2.02
W-19 Impaired Cypress	1.98	1.34	2.36
Duck Pond Augmented Marsh	4.00	1.67	3.25
W-3 Augmented Marsh	4.55	1.97	3.41
S-63 Augmented Cypress	4.42	2.23	3.62
W-5 Augmented Cypress	4.77	2.00	3.92

Table 18. Jaccard's Similarity Index matrices (Using all Species Greater than 1 Percent of Abundance) for Vegetation in Fixed Plots in Marsh Wetlands, 2000-04.

		GS Natural Marsh	HRSP Natural Marsh	W-29 Impaired Marsh	Duck Pond Augmented Marsh	W-3 Augmented Marsh
Deep plots	GS Natural Marsh	4 species	40%	14%	0%	0%
	HRSP Natural Marsh		3 species	17%	0%	20%
	W-29 Impaired Marsh			4 species	0%	20%
	Duck Pond Augmented Marsh W-3				6 species	13%
	Augmented Marsh					3 species
Intermediate plots	GS Natural Marsh	8 species	6%	11%	5%	8%
	HRSP Natural Marsh		11 species	10%	9%	6%
	W-29 Impaired Marsh			12 species	14%	6%
	Duck Pond Augmented Marsh				13 species	27%
	W-3 Augmented Marsh					6 species
Transitional plots	GS Natural Marsh	9 species	19%	20%	11%	11%
	HRSP Natural Marsh		10 species	23%	16%	16%
	W-29 Impaired Marsh			6 species	20%	13%
	Duck Pond Augmented Marsh				12 species	9%
	W-3 Augmented Marsh					12 species

Van Dam Ecological Indicator values were calculated for diatom samples collected at the 10 wetlands in the present study (table 17). The pH index values indicate the prevalence of diatoms preferring more acidic conditions at the natural wetlands, whereas diatoms at the augmented wetlands were typical of a more alkaline pH. The trophic index values were consistently lower at the natural (1.38-2.61) and impaired (1.98-2.03) wetlands than at the augmented wetlands (4.00-4.77). Similarly, nitrogen index values were lower at the natural (1.10-1.41) and impaired (1.34-1.73) wetlands than at the augmented wetlands (1.67-2.23). These patterns of indicator values indicate that the diatom communities at augmented sites include species that may be able to take advantage of the nutrients released by the partially decomposed organic material that accumulates in these wetlands.

Wetland Vegetation

Differences in the relative abundance of aquatic plants and woody vegetation in wetlands are attributable to differences in a number of abiotic factors, including the areal extent of flooding, flood duration, water depth, and nutrient availability.

Comparison of Vegetation Communities

When vegetation in marsh wetlands was compared in deep plots, the greatest Jaccard's Similarity Index value (40 percent) was found between the two natural marshes where *Panicum hemitomon* and *Pontederia cordata* were found, followed by 20-percent similarity at W-29 Impaired Marsh and W-3 Augmented Marsh, where *Panicum hemitomon* and *Nymphaea odorata* were found (table 18). Deep plots at GS Natural Marsh and HRSP Natural Marsh were flooded more than 65 and 71 percent of the year, respectively, during the recent period in the study (table 19).

Vegetation in Duck Pond Augmented Marsh was not similar to that of any other marsh site (table 18), with the exception of W-3 Augmented Marsh, which shared a single plant species (*Sagittaria latifolia*). The deep plots at Duck Pond Augmented Marsh were flooded 100 percent of the time during the recent period, and to a much greater depth than any of the other sites (table 19). Deep plots at W-3 Augmented Marsh were flooded more than 61 percent of the time. Overall, the number of aquatic plant species in deep plots was low at the five marsh sites, and therefore, the number of shared species also was low.

Although intermediate plots at the marsh sites contained more vegetation species than deep plots, Jaccard's Similarity Index was generally low between sites. One exception was between the augmented marshes (27 percent), where the four shared species were *Leersia hexandra*, *Panicum hemitomon*, *Sagittaria latifolia* (all obligate plants), and the vine *Berschemia scandens*. Intermediate plots at Duck Pond Augmented Marsh were flooded 91 percent of the time, and at W-3 Augmented Marsh 61 percent of the time (table 19).

Transition plots at the marsh sites also had relatively more vegetation species than deep plots, although the amount of time that these plots were flooded during the recent period varied from 0 percent at W-3 Augmented Marsh to a maximum of 31 to 53 percent of the time at the two natural marsh wetlands (table 19). The greatest observed similarities between transitional plots were among the natural and impaired sites, where shared species included several facultative species (*Amphicarpum muhlenbergianum*, *Andropogon virginicus*, *Lachnanthes caroliana*), and the obligate species *Panicum hemitomon*.

When vegetation in cypress wetlands was compared, the greatest Jaccard's Similarity Index among deep plots (14 percent) was between S-68 Natural Cypress and S-63 Augmented Cypress (table 20). The shared species were *Panicum hemitomon* and *Rhynchospora corniculata* (both obligate). Deep plots at these two sites were flooded more than 96 and 86 percent of the time, respectively. Jaccard's Similarities were also low among intermediate plots, although S-63 Augmented Cypress shared two species each with W-19 Impaired Cypress (*Acer rubrum* and *Myrica cerifera*) and W-5 Augmented Cypress (*Rhynchospora mileacea* and *Lycopus rubellus*) (table 20). Intermediate plots at W-5 Augmented Cypress were flooded more then 62 percent of the time. Transition plots at the cypress wetlands had minimal Similarity Indices (table 20). S-68 Natural Cypress and S-63 Augmented Cypress shared three species: *Amphicarpum muhlenbergianum* (facultative wet), *Andropogon virginicus* (facultative), and *Aristida strict* var. *beyrichiana* (facultative). Transitional plots at these sites were flooded 52 and 30 percent of the time, respectively.

W-29 Impaired Marsh is of particular interest because it illustrates the possible effects of changes in ground-water pumping and rainfall on wetland vegetation. The flooding characteristics and percentages of time that plots were inundated were substantially different at W-29 Impaired Marsh during 2000-02, when rainfall was about average, than during 2002-04 when rainfall was above average and ground-water pumping had decreased (table 21). During the average rainfall period, deep plots at W-29 were more similar to the deep plots at the natural marshes than those at the augmented marshes. These differences did not extend to the intermediate or transition plots.

Table 19. The Percentage of Time That Fixed Vegetation Plots Were Flooded During the Recent Period (2000–02 or 2002–04), Based on Stage Data and Bathymetry.
[>, greater than]

Wetland name (and data collection period)	Percentage of time flooded		
	Deep plots	Intermediate plots	Transitional plots
GS Natural Marsh (2000–02)	>65	65	31
HRSP Natural Marsh (2000–04)	>71	71	53
W-29 Impaired Marsh (2000–02[1])	>18	12	0
W-29 Impaired Marsh (2002–04[2])	>99	99	67
Duck Pond Augmented Marsh (2000–04)	100	91	5
W-3 Augmented Marsh (2000–02)	>61	61	0
GS Natural Cypress (2002–04)	>77	77	62
S-68 Natural Cypress (2002–04)	>96	80	52
W-19 Impaired Cypress (2002–04)	>93	93	61
S-63 Augmented Cypress (2002–04)	>86	>86	30
W-5 Augmented Cypress (2002–04)	>62	>62	55

[1] Period of average rainfall and ground-water pumping.
[2] Period of above-average rainfall and reduced ground-water pumping.

Table 20. Jaccard's Similarity Index Matrices (Using all Species Greater than 1 Percent of Abundance) for Vegetation in Fixed Plots in Cypress Wetlands, 2000-04.

		GS Natural Cypress	S-68 Natural Cypress	W-19 Impaired Cypress	S-63 Augmented Cypress	W-5 Augmented Cypress
Deep plots	GS Natural Cypress	1 species	0%	0%	0%	0%
	S-68 Natural Cypress		3 species	0%	14%	0%
	W-19 Impaired Cypress			6 species	0%	0%
	S-63 Augmented Cypress				11 species	0%
	W-5 Augmented Cypress					1 species
Intermediate plots	GS Natural Cypress	4 species	0%	0%	7%	0%
	S-68 Natural Cypress		9 species	0%	5%	0%
	W-19 Impaired Cypress			8 species	18%	0%
	S-63 Augmented Cypress				11 species	13%
	W-5 Augmented Cypress					7 species
Transitional plots	GS Natural Cypress	9 species	6%	7%	0%	0%
	S-68 Natural Cypress		10 species	7%	14%	0%
	W-19 Impaired Cypress			6 species	0%	7%
	S-63 Augmented Cypress				14 species	5%
	W-5 Augmented Cypress					9 species

The influence of this difference in rainfall and ground-water pumping over time is also evident for Jaccard's Similarity Indices among plots at individual wetlands during the two periods (table 21). Within each marsh, the vegetation in the deep and intermediate plots generally was more similar over time (comparing the average period and the wetter period) at the augmented wetlands than at the natural wetlands because water levels were not controlled as much by rainfall and pumping, but were kept relatively constant throughout the entire 4-year period. This pattern was not consistent at the natural and augmented cypress wetlands. The lowest similarities over time were at W-29 Impaired Marsh (16-33 percent) and at W-19 Impaired Cypress (0-33 percent), because these two wetlands were most vulnerable to ground-water pumping and rainfall variation.

Use of the Jaccard's Similarity Index to establish similarity between vegetation communities in the wetlands in this study was limited by the fact that the most abundant species were rarely the same between individual wetlands. Initially, the Jaccard's Similarity

Indices were calculated using only the abundant (common) species because many previous qualitative wetland assessments used relative abundance of common plant species to characterize the wetlands (Jongman and others, 1995). Among the pairs of marsh wetlands compared using only abundant species, however, most of the pairs of marsh wetlands in the current study shared only one or two plant species. The index was even less useful for comparing cypress wetlands, where there are few herbaceous plant species in the deep and intermediate plots. The majority of pairs of cypress wetlands compared using the index shared only one species (pond cypress), and 7 of the 10 possible cypress wetland comparisons would have had no species in common if pond cypress trees had not been included in the calculations.

Species Richness

Species richness is a commonly used measure of community composition in ecological studies, and is simply a count of the number of different species in a sample or group of samples. In the fixed vegetation plots sampled semiannually in this study, the mean species richness of plants at the natural marshes (17) and the natural cypress wetlands (16) was slightly lower than the mean species richness at the augmented marsh wetlands (19) and the augmented cypress wetlands (19). Mean species richness also was lower at W-29 Impaired Marsh (14) and at W-19 Impaired Cypress (16) than at the augmented wetlands.

When the species richness data from fixed plots sampled semiannually were combined with the data from random plots sampled quarterly, mean species richness also was generally lower in natural marshes (17-21) and natural cypress wetlands (14-20) than in augmented marshes (23-29) and augmented cypress wetlands (18-24) (tables 22 and 23). Species richness at W-29 Impaired Marsh (15) was lower than at the natural marshes, but at W-19 Impaired Cypress species richness (17) was similar to that of the natural cypress.

Table 21. Jaccard's Similarity Index Comparing Vegetation in Fixed Plots Sampled During 2000-02 (the Period of Average Rainfall) with Vegetation in Fixed Plots Sampled During 2002-04 (the period of above-average rainfall and reduced ground-water pumping)

Wetland name	Jaccard's Similarity Index (percent)		
	Deep plots	Intermediate plots	Transitional plots
GS Natural Marsh	25	38	56
HRSP Natural Marsh	67	30	40
W-29 Impaired Marsh	25	33	16
Duck Pond Augmented Marsh	83	50	33
W-3 Augmented Marsh	100	50	50
GS Natural Cypress	100	50	55
S-68 Natural Cypress	67	44	90
W-19 Impaired Cypress	17	0	33
S-63 Augmented Cypress	45	64	33
W-5 Augmented Cypress	100	29	67

Sampling randomly located plots at the marshes improved the estimates of species richness by 31-40 percent at the natural marshes and by 32-53 percent at the augmented marshes. The addition of random plots improved those estimates by only 18-27 percent at the natural cypress wetlands and by 13-14 percent at the augmented cypress wetlands. Overall, the greatest number of species at wetlands in this study was found at two of the augmented wetlands. At Duck Pond Augmented Marsh, which had 29 species, more than half of the total wetland area was flooded 81 percent of the time (table 12), enabling many obligate species to remain established. In contrast, at S-63 Augmented Cypress, which had 24 species, more than half of the total wetland area was flooded only 33 percent of the time. Moreover, S-63 Augmented Cypress had a flooded area that fluctuated rapidly and frequently during the study, and was often completely dry. The frequency and extent of fluctuations in the hydrograph and the extent of flooded area at S-63 Augmented Cypress likely contributed to the unusually high density and species richness of emergent species at this site.

Species richness in wetlands is influenced by many factors. Studies of wetlands that are shallow depressions indicate that species composition can vary considerably over time, and also vary spatially within the same wetland (Swanson and others, 2003). The importance of hydrologic conditions to species richness has been observed in studies of natural wetlands. Studies of emergent wetlands in the northwestern United States (Magee and Kentula, 2005) found that the richest assemblages of plants were present in wetlands with relatively low water-level variability. Wetland size also is an important influence on species richness. A study of 58 large marsh and swamp wetlands in southeastern Ontario, Canada, indicated that plant species richness was positively correlated with wetland area (Houlahan and others, 2006).

About 20 percent of all the species identified in that study were found in only one wetland. This observation agrees with the relatively low similarity indices obtained for wetland plant species comparisons in the present study. Furthermore, 49 of the 58 wetlands in the Ontario study contained at least one species unique to that wetland. Those results suggest that no single wetland, regardless of size, can conserve the landscape diversity of aquatic plants, and that small wetlands may be critically important for the conservation of rare species.

Relative Abundance of Wetland Plants by Indicator Category

The relative abundance of wetland plant species in various indicator categories (obligate, facultative wet, facultative, facultative upland, upland, and undetermined) (Florida Department of Environmental Protection, 2004) differed among some of the wetland groups in this study (figure 61). The natural and impaired marshes had a somewhat higher percentage (52-53 percent) of obligate species than W-3 Augmented Marsh (38 percent), but the percentage was similar to Duck Pond Augmented Marsh. Natural marshes had a higher percentage of facultative wet species than Duck Pond Augmented Marsh but a similar percentage to W-3 Augmented Marsh. The impaired marsh, however, had a much lower percentage of facultative wet species (7 percent). Natural and augmented marshes had similar percentages of facultative species (14 percent and 15 percent, respectively), whereas W-29 Impaired Marsh had twice as many facultative species (33 percent).

The natural cypress and the augmented cypress wetlands did not differ in their percentage of obligate plant species (39 percent and 40 percent, respectively), whereas W-19 Impaired Cypress had only 29 percent obligate species. Natural and augmented cypress also had the same percentage of facultative wet species (27 percent), but W-19 Impaired Cypress had more facultative wet species (41 percent). Natural cypress and augmented cypress wetlands had similar percentages of facultative species (25 and 22 percent, respectively), and the W-19 Impaired Cypress had 18 percent facultative species.

The proportion of facultative upland and undetermined plant species varied somewhat among sites, and no patterns were evident. Although facultative upland plants are rarely found in wetlands, they may be present at the wetland edge or in areas with a higher elevation within a wetland, such as on hummocks. Sample plots in the natural marshes had no facultative upland or undetermined species, whereas they constituted 0 to 9 percent of the plants in augmented marshes and 7 percent of the plants in W-29 Impaired Marsh. The percentage of facultative upland and undetermined species averaged 6 percent at the natural cypress wetlands, ranged from 4 to 11 percent at the augmented cypress wetlands, and was 6 percent at W-19 Impaired Cypress.

It is widely accepted that the relative abundance of plants in different indicator categories is not a precise descriptor of wetland hydrologic conditions. For example, although many obligate wetland species are found in permanently or semi- permanently flooded wetlands, a number of obligate species also are present in wetlands that are temporarily or seasonally flooded. In a given wetland, a high proportion of facultative plant species indicates relatively dry conditions during the most recent growing season (Adamus and others, 1991). Further quantitative studies are needed before plant indicator status can be used as stand-alone evidence of short- or long-term hydrologic conditions. One such study is underway in the northern Tampa Bay area to determine the frequency at which individual wetland plant species are found at measured depths in cypress wetlands (GPI Southeast, Inc., 2006). Tampa Bay Water and SWFWMD also are applying a regional annual Wetland Assessment Procedure to describe the occurrence of wetland plants by indicator status, and the associated changes in wetland hydrology over time (Southwest Florida Water Management District and Tampa Bay Water, 2005). These detailed data will be useful in future assessments of wetland plant distribution, zonation patterns, and plant tolerance to changing wetland hydrology.

High density of emergent vegetation at S-63 Augmented Cypress wetland

Table 22. Plant Species in Fixed and Randomly Located Plots in Marsh Wetlands.

[bold type indicates abundant species (more than 10 percent of the plant community). species type: fac, facultative; facw, facultative wet; facu, facultative upland; obl, obligate; --, not classified]

GS Natural Marsh (17 species)		HRSP Natural Marsh (21 species)		W-29 Impaired Marsh (15 species)		Duck Pond Augmented Marsh (29 species)		W-3 Augmented Marsh (23 species)	
Species name	Type	Species name	Type	Species name	Type	Species name	Type	Species name	Type
Amphicarpum muhlenbergianum	FACW	Amphicarpum muhlenbergianum	FACW	Amphicarpum muhlenbergianum	FACW	Ampelopsis arborea	FAC	Amphicarpum muhlenbergianum	FACW
Andropogon virginicus	FAC	Andropogon virginicus	FAC	Andropogon virginicus	FAC	Amphicarpum muhlenbergianum	FACW	Andropogon glomeratus var. pumilus	--
Carex joorii	FACW	Erigeron quercifolius	FACW	Conyza canadensis	FACU	Andropogon glomeratus var. pumilus	--	Berchemia scandens	FACW
Carex verrucosa	FACW	Juncus marginatus	FACW	Eupatorium capillifolium	FAC	Andropogon virginicus	FAC	Callicarpa americana	FACU
Eriocaulon compressum	OBL	Lachnanthes caroliana	FAC	Euthamia caroliniana	FAC	Aristida palustris	OBL	Carex joorii	FACW
Lachnanthes caroliana	FAC	Leersia hexandra	OBL	Hypericum fasciculatum	OBL	Centella asiatica	FACW	Hydrocotyle umbellata	FACW
Panicum hemitomon	OBL	Ludwigia linearis	OBL	Lachnanthes caroliana	FAC	Chara sp.	--	Leersia hexandra	OBL
Polygala lutea	FACW	Nymphaea odorata	FACW	Nymphaea odorata	OBL	Cyperus haspan	OBL	Ludwigia repens	OBL
Polygala rugelii	FACW	Oxypolis filiformis	FACW	Panicum hemitomon	OBL	Eleocharis equisetoides	OBL	Mikania scandens	FACW
Pontederia cordata	OBL	Panicum hemitomon	OBL	Paspalum setaceum	FAC	Eleocharis vivipara	OBL	Myrica cerifera	FAC
Proserpinaca pectinata	OBL	Panicum verrucosum	OBL	Rhynchospora microcarpa	OBL	Erigeron quercifolius	FAC	Nymphaea odorata	OBL
Rhynchospora cephalantha	OBL	Panicum virgatum	OBL	Saccharum baldwinii	OBL	Fuirena squarrosa	OBL	Panicum hemitomon	OBL
Rhynchospora fascicularis	FACW	Pluchea rosea	FACW	Sagittaria graminea	OBL	Hydrocotyle umbellata	FACW	Pontederia cordata	OBL
Saccharum giganteum	OBL	Polygala lutea	FACW	Utricularia purpurea	OBL	Juncus marginatus	FACW	Pteridium aquilinum	--
Sagittaria graminea	OBL	Polygonum hydropiperoides	OBL	Nyris fimbriata	OBL	Juncus megacephalus	OBL	Ptilimnium capillaceum	FACW
Utricularia purpurea	OBL	Pontederia cordata	OBL			Leersia hexandra	OBL	Quercus laurifolia	FACW
Nyris fimbriata	OBL	Proserpinaca pectinata	OBL			Ludwigia microcarpa	OBL	Rubus cuneifolius	FAC
		Rhynchospora inundata	OBL			Mikania scandens	FACW	Sagittaria latifolia	OBL
		Sagittaria graminea	OBL			Naphar advena	OBL	Salix caroliniana	OBL
		Scleria baldwinii	FACW			Nymphoides aquatica	OBL	Serenoa repens	FACU
		Utricularia foliosa	OBL			Panicum hemitomon	OBL	Smilax bona-nox	FAC
						Panicum rigidulum	FACW	Typha latifolia	OBL
						Phyla nodiflora	FAC	Nyris fimbriata	OBL
						Pontederia cordata	OBL		
						Proserpinaca palustris	OBL		
						Rhynchospora colorata	FACW		
						Rhynchospora microcarpa	OBL		
						Sagittaria latifolia	OBL		
						Setaria parviflora	FAC		

Table 23. Plant Species in Fixed and Randomly Located Plots in Cypress Wetlands.

[bold type indicates abundant species (more than 10 percent of the plant community). species type: fac, facultative; facw, facultative wet; facu, facultative upland; obl, obligate; --, not classified]

GS Natural Cypress (14 species)		S-68 Natural Cypress (20 species)		W-19 Impaired Cypress (17 species)		S-83 Augmented Cypress (24 species)		W-5 Augmented Cypress (18 species)	
Species name	Type	Species name	Type	Species name	Type	Species name	Type	Species name	Type
Cephalanthus occidentalis	OBL	Amphicarpum muhlenbergianum	OBL	Acer rubrum	FACW	Acer rubrum	FACW	Calicarpa americana	FACU
Ilex cassine	OBL	Andropogon virginicus	OBL	Carex longii	FACW	Amphicarpum muhlenbergianum	FACW	Dichanthelium commutatum	FAC
Lachnanthes caroliana	FAC	Andropogon virginicus var. glaucus	FAC	Carex verrucosa	FACW	Andropogon virginicus	FAC	Erechtites hieracifolia	FAC
Ludwigia lanceolata	OBL	Aristida condensata	--	Dichanthelium ensifolium var. unciphyllum	FAC	Aristida stricta var. beyrichiana	OBL	Lycopus rubellus	OBL
Lyonia lucida	FACW	Aristida palustri	OBL	Dichanthelium sp.	--	Aster elliottii	OBL	Melothria pendula	FACW
Osmunda cinnamomea	FACW	Aristida stricta var. beyrichiana	FAC	Habenaria floribunda	FACW	Blechnum serrulatum	FACW	Ophismenus hirtellus	FAC
Sagittaria graminea	OBL	Coelorachis rugosa	FACW	Lemna obscura	OBL	Coelorachis rugosa	FACW	Panicum anceps	FAC
Serenoa repens	FACU	Dichanthelium ensifolium var. unciphyllum	FAC	Melothria pendula	FACW	Cyperus distinctus	OBL	Panicum rigidulum	FACW
Smilax laurifolia	FACW	Dichanthelium erectifolium	OBL	Mikania scandens	FACW	Ludwigia repens	OBL	Polygonum hydropiperoides	OBL
Taxodium ascendens	OBL	Eupatorium capillifolium	OBL	Myrica cerifera	FAC	Lycopus rubellus	OBL	Quercus laurifolia	FACW
Toxicodendron radicans	OBL	Hypericum fasciculatum	FAC	Paspalum repens	OBL	Mikania scandens	FACW	Rhynchospora corniculata	OBL
Vitis rotundifolia	FAC	Hypericum myrtifolium	FAC	Ptilimnium capillaceum	FACW	Myrica cerifera	FAC	Rhynchospora miliacea	OBL
Woodwardia virginica	FACW	Ilex glabra	FACW	Serenoa repens	FACU	Panicum hemitomon	OBL	Riccia fluitans	--
Xyris fimbriata	OBL	Lachnanthes caroliana	FAC	Taxodium ascendens	OBL	Panicum rigidulum	FACW	Sagitaria graminea	OBL
		Panicum hemitomon(A)	OBL	Toxicodendron radicans	FAC	Persea palustris	OBL	Serenoa repens	FACU
		Pluchea rosea	FACW	Utricularia foliosa	OBL	Pluchea odorata	FACW	Smilax bona-nox	FAC
		Rhynchospora corniculata	OBL	Utricularia inflata	OBL	Rhynchospora corniculata	OBL	Taxodium ascendens	OBL
		Serenoa repens	FACU			Rhynchospora microcarpa	OBL	Thelypteris palustris	FACW
		Taxodium ascendens	OBL			Rhynchospora miliacea	OBL		
		Utricularia purpurea	OBL			Rubus cuneifolius	FAC		
						Saccharum baldwinii	OBL		
						Serenoa repens	FACU		
						Taxodium ascendens	OBL		
						Woodwardia virginica	FACW		

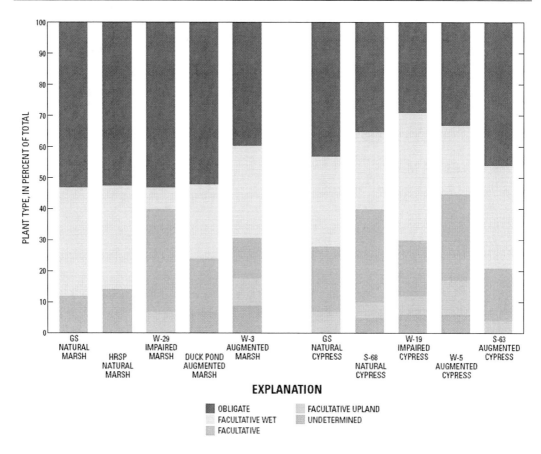

Figure 61. Relative abundance of obligate, facultative wet, facultative, and facultative upland plants in marsh and cypress wetlands.

Plant Biomass in Marshes

Estimates of plant biomass in marshes (expressed as dry weight per square meter) were restricted to herbaceous vegetation growing in water depths of about 0.3 m and, therefore, are not representative of plant biomass throughout each wetland. Samples from the five marsh wetlands can be compared, however, because they were collected at similar water depths and during the same time periods. Duck Pond Augmented Marsh and W-3 Augmented Marsh had higher average vegetation biomass (717 g/m^2 and 581 g/m^2, respectively) than GS Natural Marsh and HRSP Natural Marsh (308 and 452 g/m^2, respectively) (table 24). Vegetation biomass at W-29 Impaired Marsh (384 g/m^2) was within the range of values for the natural marshes. The higher biomass of herbaceous vegetation in augmented marsh wetlands may be related to the higher concentrations of phosphorus made available as accumulated dead plant material slowly decays. For example, concentrations of total phosphorus were substantially higher in W-3 Augmented Marsh (median 0.03 mg/L) than in the natural and impaired marshes (median 0.01 mg/L). In Duck Pond Augmented Marsh, however, the median concentration of total phosphorus was only 0.01 mg/L; at this site, the high leakance rate may prevent phosphorus accumulation. Natural wetlands in this study appeared to be phosphorus limited, based on the high nitrogen-to-phosphorus ratios found in their surface waters (figure 44).

Table 24. Biomass of Vegetation in Marsh Wetlands
[Min., minimum value; max., maximum value]

Wetland name	Number of samples	Plant biomass, in grams of dry weight per square meter		
		Mean	Min.	Max.
Green Swamp Natural Marsh	19	308	248	372
HRSP Natural Marsh	19	452	244	548
W-29 Impaired Marsh	9	384	332	427
Duck Pond Augmented Marsh	19	717	619	856
W-3 Augmented Marsh	21	581	397	800

Tree Density and Size in Cypress Wetlands

The mean density of cypress trees in the two natural cypress wetlands (2,985 trees/ha) was more than 25 percent greater than in the two augmented wetlands (2,322 trees/ha) and W-19 Impaired Cypress (2,226 trees/ha). The mean percentages of fallen trees, dead trees, and stumps were substantially smaller in the two natural wetlands (10.1 percent) than in the two augmented wetlands (28.0 percent) or W-19 Impaired Cypress (34.6 percent). Persistent dry conditions in W-19 Impaired Cypress and in the augmented wetlands prior to augmentation are the presumed reason for the relatively high number of dead trees at these sites.

The 10.5-cm mean diameter of cypress trees in the natural wetlands was smaller than the 12.5-cm diameter in the augmented wetlands, and 17.6-cm diameter in the impaired wetland. The larger mean diameter and lower mean density of trees in augmented and impaired wetlands may be the cumulative result of years of failed seed germination and poor seedling survival, resulting in an absence of young trees. Cypress can only germinate on dry land (Demaree, 1932). Moreover, the regeneration of *Taxodium* spp. requires a sequence of hydrologic conditions unlikely to exist under altered hydrologic regimes prevalent in augmented wetlands or impaired wetlands, specifically, prolonged flooding, followed by drawdown, quickly followed by moderate water levels (Dickson and Broyer, 1972; Deghi, 1984). A greater cypress tree growth rate at S-63 Augmented Cypress, compared to unaugmented wetlands, was observed when Tampa Bay Water staff was monitoring the wetland in the mid-1990s (Chris Shea, Tampa Bay Water, written commun., 2007). The availability of nutrients released by partially decayed wetland vegetation may contribute to enhanced tree growth.

Effects of Environmental Stressors on Wetland Plant Communities

Numerous environmental stressors related to human activities, including physical disturbance, nutrient enrichment, and disturbance to the hydrologic regime resulting in desiccation, excessive inundation, and increased or decreased hydroperiod, have been associated with an increase or decrease in abundance of some plants species in wetlands (Wilcox, 1995; Shay and others, 1999; Kowalski and Wilcox, 2003). Doherty and others (2000a) surveyed wetland studies in Florida and developed lists of "tolerant" and "intolerant" plant taxa that decreased or increased, respectively, in response to numerous stressors. The relative abundance of these plant species, therefore, could be used to indicate the amount of overall disturbance from environmental stressors that has occurred in Florida wetlands. In the present study, there was a relatively higher percentage of intolerant species and a lower percentage of tolerant species at natural marsh and cypress wetlands compared to augmented and impaired wetlands (figure 62). At augmented marsh and cypress wetlands there were relatively more tolerant species than intolerant species (table 25). However, the overall differences were small and could not be used to reliably distinguish natural from augmented sites.

Although the amount of physical disturbance in the vicinity of wetlands in this study varied, areas surrounding natural wetlands generally were the least disturbed. The natural marsh and cypress wetlands are surrounded by flatwoods or unmanaged pine flatwoods. Some wetlands on well fields are near paved roads, which can change the pattern of surface-water flow and decrease runoff to the wetlands. At W-5 Augmented Cypress, an unpaved road breached the wetland perimeter and increased runoff from the wetland. At Duck Pond Augmented Marsh, the area directly adjacent to the wetland edge is regularly mowed, and the area adjacent to that is an agriculturally managed pine plantation. The widespread practice of clearing the areas surrounding wetlands prior to agricultural and urban land use facilitates the invasion of wetlands by weedy (tolerant) plant species (Rochow, 1998; Angeler and Garcia, 2005). Habitat fragmentation and physical disturbance also tend to favor plant species that can disperse their seeds widely, such as *Typha* sp., *Salix caroliniana*, and *Eupatorium capillifolium*. These particular species were found at the augmented and impaired marshes in the present study. Land clearing within 250 m of the edge of wetlands in southeastern Ontario, Canada, was shown to interfere with critical seed sources (Houlahan and others, 2006). That study suggested that wetlands cannot be managed in isolation from their surrounding uplands or other adjacent wetlands without impairing germination and growth of indigenous plant species.

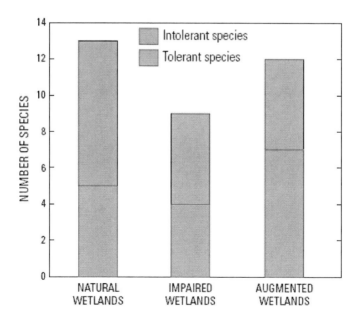

Figure 62. Number of tolerant and intolerant plant species at natural, impaired, and augmented wetlands.

One of the changes associated with reduced hydroperiod and lower water levels is a reduction in the size of the wetland flooded area (Mortellaro and others, 1995). Differences in wetland topography, exemplified by Duck Pond Augmented Marsh and S-63 Augmented Cypress, can lead to substantially different effects on the size of wetland flooded area when wetland water levels are reduced. Even slight water-level reductions (as measured at the staff gage) at S-63 Augmented Cypress may eliminate large areas of flooding and the associated aquatic plant habitat, whereas water-level reductions of a similar magnitude at Duck Pond Augmented Marsh resulted in little change in the flooded area and aquatic plant habitat along the wetland edge. The reduction in wetland flooded area can increase distances between wetlands, fragmenting the aquatic habitats available to wetland plants.

Wetland plants may not be useful as sole indicators of changes in the hydrologic regime (Tiner, 1991), but may be relied upon with more success when used in conjunction with measurement of physical characteristics including flood frequency and flood duration (Haag and others, 2005). The Wetland Assessment Procedure used by SWFWMD and Tampa Bay Water (2005) relates changes in wetland plant distribution to changes in wetland hydrologic regime on a yearly basis, and ultimately over longer time periods. Magee and Kentula (2005) studied emergent wetlands in the northwestern United States and found that large increases in annual water depth will likely exclude many emergent marsh species and favor aquatic assemblages more typically found in permanently flooded ponds. However, Kirkman and others (1999) discuss the difficulty of extracting useful metrics from depression wetlands for which normal hydrologic variability is great, because some plant species can withstand intense hydrologic stress and many species are adapted to a wide variety of hydrologic conditions.

In addition to sensitivity to physical disturbance, some wetland plants have varying tolerance to changes in water quality. In studies of lakes in Florida, for example, a number of wetland plants were found in lakes with low phosphorus concentrations, but not in lakes with higher concentrations (Doherty and others, 2000a). Several of the plant taxa found in that study (*Eriocaulon* spp., *Hypericum* spp., *Lacnanthes caroliniana*, *Utricularia purpurea*, and *Xyris* spp.) were found only in unaugmented wetlands in the current study. The natural and impaired wetlands derive their phosphorus from rainfall, and therefore, have relatively low phosphorus concentrations. Several wetland plant species also have been associated with low nitrogen concentrations in lakes, including *Eriocaulon* spp., *Hypericum* spp., *Leersia hexandra*, and *Xyris* spp. These species were found at several of the natural and impaired wetlands in the present study, although total nitrogen was relatively higher at those sites than at the augmented sites. Craft and others (1995) reported increased growth of *Chara* spp. in wetlands with moderate phosphorus enrichment, and evidence of replacement of *Utricularia* spp. by *Chara* at those sites. Duck Pond Augmented Marsh, which had a relatively low total phosphorus concentration, was the only site in the study containing *Chara* spp.; conversely, *Utricularia* was not found at this site. *Chara* spp. thrive in the presence of high calcium concentrations such as those found at Duck Pond Augmented Marsh. Houlahan and others (2006) found a strong negative correlation between nutrient concentrations and plant species richness, whereby eutrophication of wetlands led to reduced species richness. However, the range of nutrient concentrations in the wetlands in the present study cannot be characterized as eutrophic. Cattails (*Typha* spp.) have been observed to have a competitive advantage at sites with elevated nutrient concentrations and high rates of silt accumulation (Wilcox and others, 1984). W-3 Augmented Marsh is one of the two sites in this study where cattails were established, and this site had the highest phosphorus concentration as well as the thickest accumulation of soft sediments. Newman and others (1998) found that the combination of elevated nutrients and increased water depth favors the growth of cattail in the Everglades.

The higher pH of augmentation water may alter vegetation community in augmented wetlands compared to natural wetlands. For example, *Eriocaulon spp.*, *Lacnanthes caroliniana*, *Utricularia purpurea*, and *Xyris* spp. were found in the present study at natural marsh and cypress wetlands, where the pH is low (4.2-4.8), but not at augmented sites where the pH typically is above 7.0. Conversely, *Mikania scandens*, *Sagittaria latifolia*, and *Typha* spp. were found at the augmented marshes. These are species that tend to be found in Florida lakes at relatively high values of pH (Doherty and others, 2000a).

Table 25. Wetland Plants That Tend to Decrease or Increase in Abundance with Disturbance [Data are from Doherty and others, 2000; A, abundant; P, present]

Species name	GS Natural Marsh	HRSP Natural Marsh	GS Natural Cypress	S-68 Natural Cypress	W-29 Impaired Marsh	W-19 Impaired Cypress	Duck Pond Augmented Marsh	W-3 Augmented Marsh	S-63 Augmented Cypress	W-5 Augmented Cypress
Plant taxa that typically decrease in abundance with disturbance										
Bacopa caroliniana										
Eleocharis (not E. baldwinii)							A			
Eriocaulon	A									
Hypericum fasciculatum				A	A					
Juncus repens										
Nymphaea					A			A		
Nymphoides aquatica							A			
Polygala										
Pontederia cordata	A	A								
Rhynchospora corniculata, R. inundata		A		A					A	A
Sagittaria	A	A	P		A		A	A		A
Sphagnum	A									
Utricularia inflata, U. purpurea	A	A			A	A				
Xyris fimbriata	A		P	A	A					
Plant taxa that typically increase in abundance with disturbance										
Amphicarpum	A	A		P	A		A	P	P	
Andropogon	P	A		A	A		A	P	A	
Axonopus										
Blechnum									A	
Erianthus										
Eupatorium				P	A					
Euthamia minor					A					
Lycopus									A	P
Paederia										
Paspalum notatum										
Pinus spp.										
Rubus spp.									P	
Smilax spp., S. glauca			P					P		P
Woodwardia			A						P	

It is difficult to distinguish between the natural variability of plant communities in the 10 wetlands in the present study and plant responses to hydrologic changes associated with augmentation, even though wetland plants are sensitive to hydrologic change (Wilcox, 1995) and have been used to assess conditions in wetlands in the northern Tampa Bay area (Rochow, 1994). In part, this may be due to the small number of wetlands in each group and of each type in this study, and the relatively short duration of the assessment period. The number of shared vegetation species in fixed plots at comparable locations in the hydrologic gradient was relatively low among the same type of wetlands (marsh or cypress) in the same group (natural or augmented), and therefore, similarity indices were not useful in determining differences among wetland groups.

Macroinvertebrates

The composition of macroinvertebrate communities reflects the biological conditions in wetlands at the most fundamental The composition of macroinvertebrate communities reflects the biological level (Doherty and others, 2000a). Macroinvertebrates are a trophic link between primary producers, plant-derived detritus, and higher trophic levels such as fish, amphibians, and waterfowl. Because of these food-web linkages, the taxa richness and abundance of macroinvertebrates, and the relative abundance of selected taxonomic groups, have been used to indicate overall aquatic ecosystem condition. Macroinvertebrates in depression wetlands are found along a continuum of abiotic conditions. The tolerances of macroinvertebrates to changing water depth and water quality vary between and among taxonomic groups.

Marsh Macroinvertebrate Communities

The macroinvertebrate taxonomic groups (Order: Family) found with the greatest frequency in the two natural marsh wetlands were mayflies (Ephemeroptera: Baetidae), dragonflies and damselflies (Odonata: Coenagrionidae, Aeschnidae, Libellulidae), true bugs (Hemiptera: Belastomatidae, Notonectidae), beetles (Coleoptera: Dytiscidae, Haliplidae), and true flies (Diptera: Chironomidae) (tables 26, 27). Numerically, the most abundant families were Cambaridae, Chaoboridae, Chironomidae, Dytiscidae, and Libellulidae. Crayfish (Procambarus) were found in about 24 percent of samples in GS Natural Marsh and in 90 percent of the samples at HRSP Natural Marsh (table 27). Mean taxa richness was 15.4 taxa/m^2 at GS Natural Marsh and 19.9 taxa/m^2 at HRSP Natural Marsh (figure 63C). The higher taxa richness at HRSP Natural Marsh primarily was attributable to more species of Odonata at this site. Twenty families of macroinvertebrates were collected at GS Natural Marsh and 18 families were collected at HRSP Natural Marsh (table 26). Shannon diversity was similar at the two natural marshes (1.40-1.51) (figure 64). Macroinvertebrate biomass also was similar at the two natural marshes, but mean macroinvertebrate density (primarily of Diptera in the family Chaoboridae) was substantially higher at HRSP Natural Marsh (173.4 individuals/m^2) than at GS Natural Marsh (73.1 individuals/m^2) (figure 63A-B).

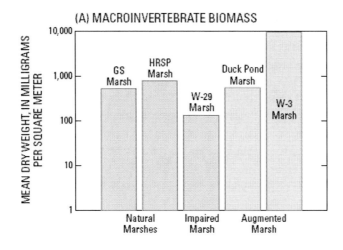

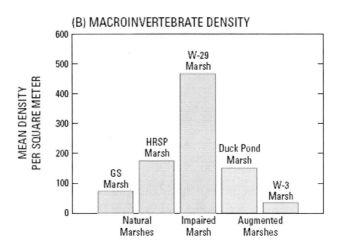

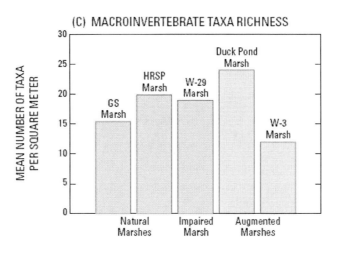

Figure 63. Biomass, density, and taxa richness of macroinvertebrates in marsh wetlands

Hemiptera and Coleoptera were less abundant at W-29 Impaired Marsh than in the natural marshes (table 27). The freshwater shrimp Palaemonetes paludosus was present in 100 percent of samples from this site (table 27) at a relatively high mean density (35.3 individuals/m^2). Taxa richness (19.0 taxa/m^2) at W-29 Impaired Marsh was similar to HRSP Natural Marsh (figure 63C), although only 10 families of macro- invertebrates were collected at this site (table 26). Shannon diversity was much lower (1.00) than at the natural marshes (figure 64), primarily because the macroinvertebrate density was much higher (greater than 450 individuals/m^2) (figure 63B). Diptera (Chironomidae and Chaoboridae) contributed most to the higher densities of macroinvertebrates (table 27), but because these organisms are small, the macroinvertebrate biomass at W-29 Impaired Marsh (134.1 mg/m^2) was substantially lower than at either of the natural marshes (figure 64A).

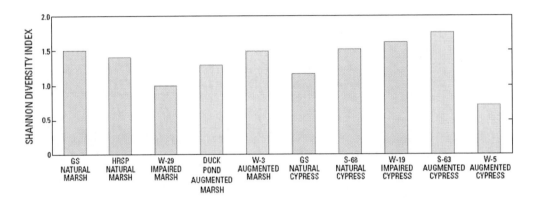

Figure 64. Shannon diversity of macroinvertebrates in marsh and cypress wetlands.

Table 26. Summary of Macroinvertebrate Community Assessment. [mg, Milligrams; m^2, Square Meter; Coleoptera Families in Lime Green; Crustacea Families in Black; Decapoda Families in Red; Diptera Families in Dark Green; Ephemeroptera Families in Pink; Gastropoda Families in Blue; Odonata Families in Orange]

Wetland name (and number of samples)	Total number of families	Most abundant families	Mean biomass (mg/m^2)	Mean taxa richness	Mean density (individuals/m^2)	Mean Shannon diversity
GS Natural Marsh (21)	20	Cambaridae, Chironomidae, Dytiscidae, Libellulidae	529.1	15.4	73.1	1.51
HRSP Natural Marsh (21)	18	Cambaridae, Chaoboridae, Chironomidae, Libellulidae	787.7	19.9	173	1.40
W-29 Impaired Marsh (9)	10	Baetidae, Chaoboridae, Chironomidae, Palaemonidae	134.1	19.0	450	0.99
Duck Pond Augmented Marsh (21)	23	Baetidae, Caenidae, Chironomidae, Planorbidae	543	24.0	148	1.29

Table 26. (Continued)

Wetland name (and number of samples)	Total number of families	Most abundant families	Mean biomass (mg/m^2)	Mean taxa richness	Mean density (individuals/m^2)	Mean Shannondiversity
W-3 Augmented Marsh (21)	16	Ampullariidae, Chironomidae, Physidae, Planorbidae	9,593	11.9	35.0	1.49
GS Natural Cypress (21)	13	Baetidae, Cambaridae, Chaoboridae, Chironomidae	606	13.0	82.7	1.16
S-68 Natural Cypress (21)	14	Caenidae, Cambaridae, Chironomidae, Coenagrionidae	65.6	14.5	55.6	1.52
W-19 Impaired Cypress (18)	17	Baetidae, hironomidaeCoenagrionidae, Hyalellidae	253.5	20.5	135.7	1.61
S-63 Augmented Cypress (21)	22	Baetidae,ChironomidaeCoenagrionidae, Physidae	302	20.5	129.3	1.76
W-5 Augmented Cypress (18)	20	Baetidae,Chironomidae, Coenagrionidae, Hyalellidae	244.7	21.2	553.3	0.71

At W-3 Augmented Marsh, 16 families of macroinvertebrates were collected (table 26), but only glass shrimp (*Paleomonetes paludosus)*, true flies (Diptera: Chaoboridae, Chironomidae), and snails (Gastropoda: Ampullariidae, Physidae, Planorbidae) were abundant (table 27). Dragonflies and damselflies (Odonata) were notably absent at W-3 Augmented Marsh compared to the natural and impaired marshes, with only one species collected (table 27). Mean taxa richness was lowest at W-3 Augmented Marsh (11.9 taxa/m^2), and W-3 Augmented Marsh also had a much lower mean density of macroinvertebrates (35.0 individuals/m^2) than any of the other marshes (figure 63B-C). However, because snails were abundant, the biomass at W-3 Augmented Marsh was much higher (9,600 mg/m^2) than at any other wetland (figure 63A). Shannon diversity at W-3 Augmented Marsh (1.49) was similar to the natural marshes (figure 64), in part because of the large number of snail species.

The macroinvertebrate community at Duck Pond Augmented Marsh was more similar to the natural marshes than to W-3 Augmented Marsh. Mayflies (Ephemeroptera: Baetidae, Caenidae), true flies (Diptera: Chironomidae), and snails (Gastropoda: Planorbidae) were abundant at Duck Pond Augmented Marsh (table 26), and mean taxa richness was higher (24.0 taxa/m^2) than any of the other marshes (figure 63C). Twenty- three families of macroinvertebrates were collected at Duck Pond Augmented Marsh (table 26), and Shannon diversity was 1.29 (figure 64). The mean biomass of macroinvertebrates at Duck Pond Augmented Marsh (543 mg/m^2) was similar to GS Natural Marsh, and mean macroinvertebrate density (148.3 individuals/ m^2) was similar to HRSP Natural Marsh (figure 63A-B).

Cypress Macroinvertebrate Communities

In the two natural cypress wetlands, crayfish (Decapoda: Cambaridae) were found in about 50 percent of the samples (table 28). Other taxa with a high frequency of occurrence included mayflies (Ephemeroptera: Baetidae, Caenidae), damselflies (Odonata: Coenagrionidae), beetles (Coleoptera: Dytiscidae), and true flies (Diptera: Chaoboridae, Chironomidae) (table 28). There were 13 families of macroinvertebrates collected at GS Natural Cypress and 14 families at S-68 Natural Cypress (table 26), and taxa richness also was similar (13.0 and 14.5 taxa/m^2, respectively) (figure 65C). Shannon diversity was 1.16 at GS Natural Cypress and 1.52 at S-68 Natural Cypress (figure 64). Macroinvertebrate biomass was much higher at GS Natural Cypress (606 mg/m^2) than at S-68 Natural Cypress (65.6 mg/m^2) (figure 65A), because of the presence of several large crayfish (Decapoda) and drag-onflies (Odonata: Aeschnidae) (table 28). However, macroinvertebrate density was relatively low in both natural cypress wetlands (82.7 and 55.6 individuals/m^2) (table 26; figure 65B).

At W-19 Impaired Cypress, taxa with a high frequency of occurrence included amphipods (Amphipoda: Hyalellidae), mayflies (Ephemeroptera: Baetidae), damselflies (Odonata: Coenagrionidae), and true flies (Diptera: Chironomidae) (table 28). A total of 17 families of macroinvertebrates were collected (table 26). Taxa richness (20.5 taxa/m^2), mean density (135.7 individuals/m^2), and mean biomass (253.5 mg/m^2) of macroinvertebrates at W-19 Impaired Cypress were all substantially higher than at either of the natural cypress wetlands (figure 65), whereas Shannon diversity (1.61) was similar to that of S-68 Natural Cypress (figure 64).

In both of the augmented cypress wetlands, taxa with a high frequency of occurrence included crayfish (Decapoda: Cambaridae), mayflies (Ephemeroptera: Baetidae), damselflies (Odonata: Coenagrionidae), and true flies (Diptera: Chironomidae) (table 28). At S-63 Augmented Cypress, snails (Gastropoda: Physidae) were also abundant, whereas at W-5 Augmented Cypress, amphipods (Amphipoda: Hyalellidae) were found in more than 75 percent of the samples and were extremely abundant (mean density 428 individuals/m^2) (table 28). Mean taxa richness and the number of macroinvertebrate families collected were substantially higher at both augmented cypress wetlands compared to the natural cypress wetlands (figure 65C and table 26). The relatively even distribution of individuals in taxonomic groups at S-63 Augmented Cypress resulted in the highest Shannon diversity value (1.76) in the study (figure 64). In contrast, because of the abundance of amphipods, Shannon diversity was much lower at W-5 Augmented Cypress than at the other wetlands (figure 64). Mean macroinvertebrate biomass was similar between S-63 Augmented Cypress (302 mg/m^2) and W-5 Augmented Cypress (244.7 mg/m^2) (figure 65A), but because amphipods had a high frequency of occurrence and were abundant at W-5 Augmented Cypress, the mean density of macroinvertebrates at that site was substantially higher than at S-63 Augmented Cypress.

Functional Feeding Groups

As noted earlier, macroinvertebrates are a trophic link between primary producers and plant-derived detritus, and the higher trophic levels in the food web such as fish, amphibians, and waterfowl. The distribution of macroinvertebrates in functional feeding groups in wetlands reflects these linkages between food resources and how organisms take advantage of them (Merritt and Cummins, 1984; Merritt and others, 1996; Merritt and others, 1999). The macroinvertebrates collected from the 10 wetlands in the present study can be grouped into several major functional feeding groups, including generalists, predators, herbivores, collector-gatherers, filtering collectors, scrapers, and shredders (tables 27 and 28). The proportion of taxa in each of these feeding groups varied among natural, impaired, and augmented wetlands (figure 66).

Table 27. Mean density, frequency of occurrence, and functional feeding group classification of macroinvertebrates in marsh wetlands [m², square meter; SD, standard deviation; C, collector-gatherer; F, filtering collector; G, generalist; H, herbivore; P, predator; S, scraper; SH, shredder; sp., species; *, multiple feeding groups]

Macroinvertebrate taxonomy and feeding group classification		GS Natural Marsh (21 samples)		HRSP Natural Marsh (21 samples)		W-29 Impaired Marsh (9 samples)		Duck Pond Augmented Marsh (21 samples)		W-3 Augmented Marsh (15 samples)	
		Mean density per m² ± SD	Occurrence frequency (percent)	Mean density per m² ± SD	Occurrence frequency (percent)	Mean density per m² ± SD	Occurrence frequency (percent)	Mean density per m² ± SD	Occurrence frequency (percent)	Mean density per m² ± SD	Occurrence frequency (percent)
Hirudinea	P										
Crustacea											
Amphipoda											
Hyalellidae											
Hyalella azteca	S	0.4 ± 1.4	9.5								
Decapoda											
Cambaridae											
Procambarus alleni	G	2.6 ± 6.1	23.8	11.9 ± 12.6	90.5			0.7 ± 1.3	23.8		
Palaemonidae											
Palaemonetes paludosus	SH					35.3 ± 38.4	100				
Insecta											
Ephemeroptera											
Baetidae											
Callibaetis floridanus	C	0.1 ± 0.7	4.8	3.6 ± 4.2	52.4	7.3 ± 12.6	33.3	20.4 ± 32.3	42.9	0.4 ± 1.4	9.5
Caenidae											
Caenis diminuta	C							14.3 ± 31.9	33.3		
Odonata											
Lestidae											
Lestes disjunctus	P			5.9 ± 15.0	14.3						
Coenagrionidae											
Enallagma civale	P			1.3 ± 3.6	14.3	2.7 ± 4.6	33.3				
Enallagma dubium	P										
Enallagma pallidum	P			0.4 ± 2.0	4.8	0.7 ± 1.3	22.2	2.3 ± 4.5	28.6		
Enallagma sp.	P	0.1 ± 0.7	4.8	0.3 ± 1.3	4.8						
Ischnura posita	P			3.3 ± 5.4	33.3						9.5

Table 27. (Continued)

Macroinvertebrate taxonomy and feeding group classification		GS Natural Marsh (21 samples)		HRSP Natural Marsh (21 samples)		W-29 Impaired Marsh (9 samples)		Duck Pond Augmented Marsh (21 samples)		W-3 Augmented Marsh (15 samples)	
		Mean density per m² ± SD	Occurrence frequency (percent)	Mean density per m² ± SD	Occurrence frequency (percent)	Mean density per m² ± SD	Occurrence frequency (percent)	Mean density per m² ± SD	Occurrence frequency (percent)	Mean density per m² ± SD	Occurrence frequency (percent)
Ishnura sp.	P										
Aeschnidae	P										
Anax junius		1.7 ± 2.9	33.3	0.3 ± 0.9	9.5	3.0 ± 3.0	66.7				
Anax longipes		0.1 ± 0.7	4.8	0.4 ± 1.4	9.5						
Coryphaeschna adnexa			23.8	0.3 ± 0.9	9.5						
Gomphaeschna antilope	P										
Libellulidae	P										
Libellula auripennis		3.3 ± 5.0	42.9	1.0 ± 2.9	14.3	0.7 ± 1.3	22.2	0.6 ± 1.5	14.3	0.4 ± 1.4	9.5
Libellula semifasciata				7.1 ± 8.8	52.4	1.3 ± 3.0	22.2				
Erythemis simplicollis				3.0 ± 13.1	9.5						
Pachydiplax longipennis				2.0 ± 4.3	19.0						
Tramea Carolina		2.9 ± 6.7	19.0	0.1 ± 0.7	4.8						
Hemiptera											
Belastomatidae	P										
Belastoma sp.		1.7 ± 3.4	28.6	2.7 ± 4.2	38.1			0.4 ± 1.1	14.3	0.3 ± 1.3	4.8
Lethocerus sp.		0.1 ± 0.7	4.8								
Corixidae	P										
Trichocorixa sp.				0.6 ± 1.8	9.5						
Gerridae	P										
Gerris sp.											
Naucoridae	P										
Pelocoris sp.			4.8			0.7 ± 2.0	11.1	2.0 ± 3.9	23.8		
Nepidae	P										
Ranatra sp.		0.4 ± 1.1	14.3	0.3 ± 0.9	9.5						
Notonectidae	P										
Buenoa sp.		0.3 ± 0.9	9.5	3.1 ± 7.9	33.3					0.4 ± 2.0	4.8
Notonecta sp.				2.6 ± 3.7	42.9						

Table 27. (Continued)

Macroinvertebrate taxonomy and feeding group classification		GS Natural Marsh (21 samples)		HRSP Natural Marsh (21 samples)		W-29 Impaired Marsh (9 samples)		Duck Pond Augmented Marsh (21 samples)		W-3 Augmented Marsh (15 samples)	
		Mean density per m² ± SD	Occurrence frequency (percent)	Mean density per m² ± SD	Occurrence frequency (percent)	Mean density per m² ± SD	Occurrence frequency (percent)	Mean density per m² ± SD	Occurrence frequency (percent)	Mean density per m² ± SD	Occurrence frequency (percent)
Veliidae											
Microvelia sp.	P										
Megaloptera											
Corydalidae											
Chauliodes sp.	P										
Sialidae											
Sialis sp.	P										
Coleoptera											
Chrysomelidae											
Disonycha sp.	H	0.3 ± 1.3	4.8					0.7 ± 3.3	4.8		
Curculionidae											
Onychylis sp.	H	0.1 ± 0.7	4.8	0.3 ± 0.9	9.5			1.7 ± 3.7	23.8		
Dytiscidae											
Celina sp.	P	0.1 ± 0.7	4.8								
Copelatus sp.	P	4.3 ± 10.2	23.8								
Coptotomus interrogatus	P	4.9 ± 6.9	47.6	1.1 ± 2.0	28.6			0.3 ± 1.3	4.8		
Cybister fimbriolatus	P	2.0 ± 3.0	38.1	0.3 ± 1.3	4.8	5.7 ± 8.9	55.6	1.9 ± 2.6	42.9	0.1 ± 0.7	4.8
Hydaticus bimarginatus	P	0.9 ± 2.4	14.3	0.3 ± 0.9	9.5			2.3 ± 6.4	19.0		
Hydroporus sp.	P	0.1 ± 0.7	4.8								
Laccophilus proximus	P										
Thermonectus basillaris	P										
Elmidae											
Stenelmis sp.	C			0.1 ± 0.7	4.8						
Haliplidae											
Peltodytes sp.	H	0.7 ± 1.3	23.8	1.0 ± 2.7	19.0			0.4 ± 1.4	9.5		
Hydrophilidae											
Berosus sp.	P	0.3 ± 1.3	4.8								

Table 27. (Continued)

Macroinvertebrate taxonomy and feeding group classification		GS Natural Marsh (21 samples) Mean density per m² ± SD	Occurrence frequency (percent)	HRSP Natural Marsh (21 samples) Mean density per m² ± SD	Occurrence frequency (percent)	W-29 Impaired Marsh (9 samples) Mean density per m² ± SD	Occurrence frequency (percent)	Duck Pond Augmented Marsh (21 samples) Mean density per m² ± SD	Occurrence frequency (percent)	W-3 Augmented Marsh (15 samples) Mean density per m² ± SD	Occurrence frequency (percent)
Enochrus sp.	P							1.0 ± 2.0	23.8		
Hydrobiomorpha casarua	P	1.7 ± 5.0	14.3					0.3 ± 1.3	4.8		
Hydrochara sp.	P										
Tropisternus lateralis	P			0.6 ± 1.5	14.3						
Hydrophilus triangularis	P										
Noteridae											
Mesonoterus addendus	P			0.7 ± 2.3	9.5						
Pronoterus semipunctatus	P	0.1 ± 0.7	4.8	0.3 ± 0.9	9.5						
Suphisellus gibbulus	P							1.3 ± 2.4	28.6		
Ptilodactylidae											
Anchytarsus bicolor	H							0.9 ± 1.9	19.0		
Scirtidae/Helodidae											
Prinocyphon sp.	C	0.1 ± 0.7	4.8					0.4 ± 1.1	14.3		
Trichoptera											
Hydropsychidae											
Potamyia sp.	F							2.3 ± 6.1	23.8		
Hydroptilidae											
Oxyethira sp.	H	0.1 ± 0.7	4.8								
Lepidoptera											
Pyralidae	H									0.1 ± 0.7	4.8
Diptera											
Ceratopogonidae	P	1.6 ± 7.2	4.8			2.7 ± 4.1	44.4	0.9 ± 2.0	9.5		
Chaoboridae	P	0.1 ± 0.7	4.8	106.0 ± 248.6	42.9	65.0 ± 59.8	100.0			1.6 ± 5.5	9.5
Chironomidae	*	40.7 ± 70.8	71.4	12.6 ± 25.7	33.3	341.7 ± 314.6	100.0	59.0 ± 74.8	100.0	4.1 ± 17.0	14.3
Culicidae	F										
Dixidae	C										
Sciomyzidae	P										

Table 27. (Continued)

Macroinvertebrate taxonomy and feeding group classification		GS Natural Marsh (21 samples)		HRSP Natural Marsh (21 samples)		W-29 Impaired Marsh (9 samples)		Duck Pond Augmented Marsh (21 samples)		W-3 Augmented Marsh (15 samples)	
		Mean density per m² ± SD	Occurrence frequency (percent)	Mean density per m² ± SD	Occurrence frequency (percent)	Mean density per m² ± SD	Occurrence frequency (percent)	Mean density per m² ± SD	Occurrence frequency (percent)	Mean density per m² ± SD	Occurrence frequency (percent)
Stratiomyidae	C							1.1 ± 4.6	9.5		
Tabanidae	P							0.1 ± 0.7	4.8		
Tanyderidae	C										
Tipulidae	C									0.3 ± 1.3	4.8
Mollusca											
Gastropoda											
Ampullariidae											
Pomacea paludosa	S									4.6 ± 6.5	66.7
Ancylidae											
Laevapex fuscus	S									1.4 ± 4.1	19.0
Lymnaeidae											
Fossaria cubensis	S							2.3 ± 4.5	23.8	2.4 ± 3.6	42.9
Physidae											
Haitia cubensis	S							11.9 ± 19.2	57.1	5.0 ± 8.6	38.1
Planorbidae											
Gyraulus parvus	S							13.7 ± 29.7	28.6	0.3 ± 0.9	9.5
Micromenetus dilatus	S							1.1 ± 2.4	23.8		
Planorbella duryi	S							2.3 ± 4.0	33.3	1.9 ± 4.6	19.0
Planorbella scalaris	S									3.1 ± 5.0	42.9
Planorbella trivolvis	S									7.3 ± 7.3	71.4
Viviparidae											
Viviparus georgianus	S							0.1 ± 0.9	9.5	0.7 ± 2.3	9.5
Bivalvia											
Sphaeriidae											
Musculium lacustre	F									0.1 ± 0.7	4.8

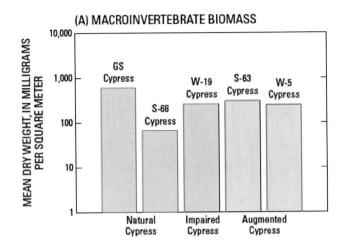

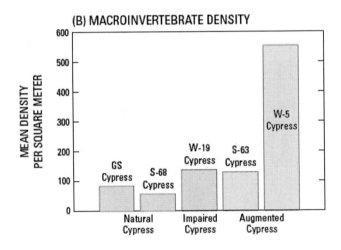

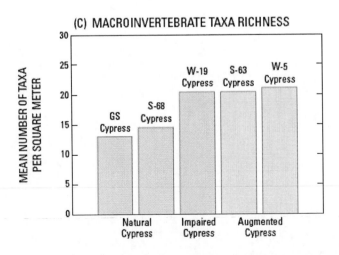

Figure 65. Biomass, density, and taxa richness of macroinvertebrates in cypress wetlands

Predator taxa were abundant in all study wetlands, both in number of taxa and number of individuals (tables 27 and 28). Batzer and Wissinger (1996) also reported that predatory insects were abundant in seasonally flooded marshes. Collector-gatherers also are an important feeding group in marsh and cypress wetlands, as indicated by the relatively high densities (3-20 individuals/m^2) of mayfly nymphs (*Callibaetis floridanus* and *Caenis diminuta*), which were found at all sites in the study. Herbivore taxa were more numerous at GS Natural Cypress and Duck Pond Augmented Marsh than at the other sites, but in general were low in frequency of occurrence (5-25 percent of samples) and density (generally less than 2 individuals/m^2) at all sites (tables 27 and 28). Haack and others (1989) reported that many wetland plants contain secondary compounds that inhibit herbivory by insects. Moreover, the low pH of natural wetlands can slow down the microbial mineralization that conditions leave and makes them more palatable to herbivores. Collectively, these factors may limit the number of herbivores found in isolated wetlands.

Shredders were largely absent in both marsh and cypress wetlands in the present study, although there were a few Tipulidae (Diptera) collected in the impaired and augmented cypress wetlands and at W-3 Augmented Marsh. Although some members of this Diptera family are shredders, the specimens were not identified below the family level, and thus, were conservatively grouped as collector-gatherers. Batzer and others (2005) reported that shredders are largely absent in many southern forested wetlands, including forested wetlands in northern Florida (Haack and others, 1989). Although typically classified as a generalist, the glass shrimp *Paleomonetes paludosus*, was categorized as a facultative shredder in studies in the Kissimmee River basin (Merritt and others, 1999) and in the present study. *Paleomonetes paludosus* was only found in high numbers at W-29 Impaired Marsh in the present study. During the early part of the study, dead leaves from maiden- cane were plentiful at the site, providing an abundant potential food for this species. Beck and Cowell (1976) studied stomach contents of *Paleomonetes paludosus* and found abundant vascular plant material, along with large amounts of algae, indicating that this species may function as a shredder at other sites as well.

Photograph provided by D. Denson, Florida Department of Environmental Protection

Damselflies. such as *Enallagma* sp., are abundant macroinvertebrate predators in wetlands

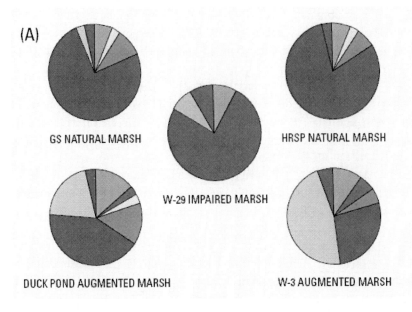

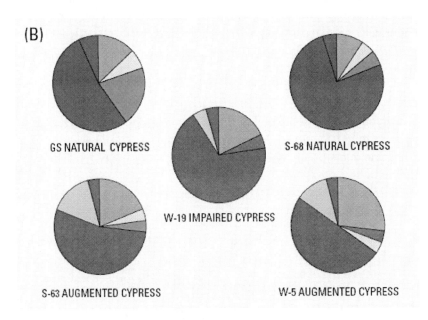

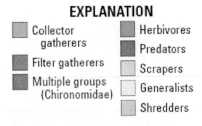

Figure 66. Proportion of macroinvertebrate functional feeding groups (determined by number of taxa) in (A) marsh wetlands and (B) cypress wetlands

Table 28. Mean Density, Frequency of Occurrence, and Functional Feeding Group Classification of Macroinvertebrates in Cypress Wetlands. [m², square meter; SD, standard deviation; C, collector-gatherer; F, filtering collector; G, generalist; H, herbivore; P, predator; S, scraper; SH, shredder; sp., species; *, multiple feeding groups]

Macroinvertebrate taxonomy and feeding group classification		GS Natural Cypress (21 samples)		S-68 Natural Cypress (18 samples)		W-19 Impaired Cypress (18 samples)		S-63 Augmented Cypress (18 samples)		W-5 Augmented Cypress (18 samples)	
		Mean density per m² ± SD	Occurrence frequency (percent)	Mean density per m² ± SD	Occurrence frequency (percent)	Mean density per m² ± SD	Occurrence frequency (percent)	Mean density per m² ± SD	Occurrence frequency (percent)	Mean density per m² ± SD	Occurrence frequency (percent)
Hirudinea	P							0.2 ± 0.7	5.6	0.2 ± 0.7	5.6
Crustacea											
Amphipoda											
Hyalellidae											
Hyalella azteca	G	3.4 ± 3.9	52.4			48.3 ± 57.1	72.2			438.0 ± 528.0	77.8
Decapoda											
Cambaridae											
Procambarus alleni	G			2.5 ± 3.5	50.0			2.8 ± 3.8	44.4	1.5 ± 2.6	33.3
Palaemonidae											
Palaemonetes paludosus	SH										
Insecta											
Ephemeroptera											
Baetidae											
Callibaetis floridanus	C	6.3 ± 6.9	61.9	2.2 ± 4.9	27.8	9.2 ± 8.1	100.0	15.0 ± 28.1	66.7	8.3 ± 11.4	61.1
Caenidae											
Caenis diminuta	C			3.3 ± 5.8	38.9			0.2 ± 0.7	5.6	1.7 ± 3.1	27.8
Odonata											
Lestidae											
Lestes disjunctus	P					4.3 ± 6.1	50.0				
Coenagrionidae											
Enallagma civale	P			1.3 ± 4.4	11.1	0.3 ± 1.4	5.6			8.3 ± 31.7	16.7
Enallagma dubium	P							5.2 ± 7.2	50.0	1.3 ± 4.4	11.1
Enallagma pollidum	P			4.3 ± 8.8	44.4			3.0 ± 5.1	38.9	12.3 ± 34.0	38.9
Enallagma sp.	P			0.8 ± 2.0	16.7			0.3 ± 1.0	11.1		

Table 28. (Continued)

Macroinvertebrate taxonomy and feeding group classification		GS Natural Cypress (21 samples)		S-68 Natural Cypress (18 samples)		W-19 Impaired Cypress (18 samples)		S-63 Augmented Cypress (18 samples)		W-5 Augmented Cypress (18 samples)	
		Mean density per m² ± SD	Occurrence frequency (percent)	Mean density per m² ± SD	Occurrence frequency (percent)	Mean density per m² ± SD	Occurrence frequency (percent)	Mean density per m² ± SD	Occurrence frequency (percent)	Mean density per m² ± SD	Occurrence frequency (percent)
Ishnura posita	P			2.3 ± 4.6	27.8	4.2 ± 6.1	44.4	2.8 ± 5.6	27.8	11.3 ± 35.0	38.9
Ishnura sp.	P										
Aeschnidae											
Anax junius	P	1.3 ± 2.8	23.8			0.8 ± 1.7	22.2				
Anax longipes	P										
Coryphaeschna adnexa	P			0.5 ± 1.2	16.7						
Gomphaeschna antilope	P										
Libellulidae											
Libellula auripennis	P			1.0 ± 2.3	16.7	1.5 ± 3.1	22.2				
Libellula semifasciata	P	2.9 ± 7.1	42.9			0.3 ± 1.0	11.1	4.5 ± 7.2	38.9		
Erythemis simplicollis	P			3.0 ± 12.0	11.1						
Pachydiplax longipennis	P			1.8 ± 4.0	27.8	2.2 ± 3.5	38.9	4.8 ± 10.9	27.8	1.2 ± 2.9	22.2
Tramea carolina	P										
Hemiptera											
Belastomatidae											
Belastoma sp.	P							0.5 ± 1.2	16.7		
Lethocerus sp.	P										
Corixidae											
Trichocorixa sp.	P	0.9 ± 2.4	14.3								
Gerridae											
Gerris sp.	P										
Naucoridae											
Pelocoris sp.	P										
Nepidae											
Ranatra sp.	P	0.3 ± 0.9	9.5	0.2 ± 0.7	5.6	0.3 ± 1.0	11.1	0.3 ± 1.0	11.1	0.3 ± 1.0	11.1
Notonectidae											
Buenoa sp.	P										

Table 28. (Continued)

Macroinvertebrate taxonomy and feeding group classification		GS Natural Cypress (21 samples)		S-68 Natural Cypress (18 samples)		W-19 Impaired Cypress (18 samples)		S-63 Augmented Cypress (18 samples)		W-5 Augmented Cypress (18 samples)	
		Mean density per m² ± SD	Occurrence frequency (percent)	Mean density per m² ± SD	Occurrence frequency (percent)	Mean density per m² ± SD	Occurrence frequency (percent)	Mean density per m² ± SD	Occurrence frequency (percent)	Mean density per m² ± SD	Occurrence frequency (percent)
Noterus sp.	P										
Veliidae											
Microvelia sp.	P									1.3 ± 2.4	27.8
Megaloptera											
Corydalidae											
Chauliodes sp.	P			0.7 ± 1.6	16.7			0.3 ± 1.0	11.1		
Sialidae											
Sialis sp.								1.5 ± 5.7	11.1	0.5 ± 1.5	11.1
Coleoptera											
Chrysomelidae	H										
Disonycha sp.	H	0.4 ± 1.4	9.5								
Curculionidae	H										
Oosydyus sp.	H	0.4 ± 1.4	9.5	0.3 ± 0.9	9.5						
Dytiscidae	P										
Celina sp.	P										
Copelatus sp.	P										
Coptotomus interrogatus	P										
Cybister fimbriolatus	P			1.1 ± 2.0	28.6	0.7 ± 1.3	22.2				
Hydaticus bimarginatus	P									0.2 ± 0.7	5.6
Hydroporus sp.	P										
Laccophilus proximus	P										
Thermonectes basillaris	P	0.6 ± 1.5	14.3								
Elmidae	C										
Stenelmis sp.	C	1.3 ± 5.9	4.8								
Haliplidae	H										
Peltodytes sp.	H										
Hydrophilidae											

Table 28. (Continued)

Macroinvertebrate taxonomy and feeding group classification		GS Natural Cypress (21 samples) Mean density per m² ± SD	Occurrence frequency (percent)	S-68 Natural Cypress (18 samples) Mean density per m² ± SD	Occurrence frequency (percent)	W-19 Impaired Cypress (18 samples) Mean density per m² ± SD	Occurrence frequency (percent)	S-63 Augmented Cypress (18 samples) Mean density per m² ± SD	Occurrence frequency (percent)	W-5 Augmented Cypress (18 samples) Mean density per m² ± SD	Occurrence frequency (percent)
Berosus sp.	C										
Enochrus sp.	C										
Hydrobiomorpha casta	C										
Hydrochara sp.	C					0.5 ± 1.2	16.7	0.5 ± 1.5	11.1		
Tropisternus lateralis	C									2.7 ± 4.7	38.9
Hydrophilus triangularis	C										
Noteridae											
Mesonoterus addendus	P	0.7 ± 1.9	14.3	0.8 ± 2.5	11.1	0.5 ± 1.5	11.1				
Pronoterus semipunctatus	P			1.0 ± 2.3	16.7						
Suphisellus gibbulus	P	0.4 ± 1.4	9.5								
Psilodactylidae											
Anchytarsus bicolor	H										
Scirtidae: Helodidae											
Prionocyphon sp.	C									1.2 ± 2.9	16.7
Trichoptera											
Hydropsychidae											
Polycentropus sp.	F										
Hydroptilidae											
Oxyethira sp.	H	0.9 ± 2.4	14.3								
Lepidoptera											
Pyralidae	H							0.3 ± 1.0	11.1		
Diptera											
Ceratopogonidae	P	11.3 ± 21.7	57.1			8.0 ± 18.0	38.9	9.3 ± 22.9	33.3	3.8 ± 6.7	44.4
Chaoboridae	P			1.5 ± 2.8	27.8	2.7 ± 7.8	27.8	3.3 ± 9.9	16.7		
Chironomidae	*	51.7 ± 63.3	85.7	28.2 ± 32.5	83.3	43.3 ± 46.5	88.9	38.8 ± 46.9	72.2	64.3 ± 89.5	100.0
Culicidae	F					6.3 ± 13.0	44.4				
Dixidae	C									0.2 ± 0.7	5.6

Table 28. (Continued)

Macroinvertebrate taxonomy and feeding group classification		GS Natural Cypress (21 samples)		S-89 Natural Cypress (18 samples)		W-19 Impaired Cypress (18 samples)		S-63 Augmented Cypress (18 samples)		W-5 Augmented Cypress (18 samples)	
		Mean density per m^2 ± SD	Occurrence frequency (percent)	Mean density per m^2 ± SD	Occurrence frequency (percent)	Mean density per m^2 ± SD	Occurrence frequency (percent)	Mean density per m^2 ± SD	Occurrence frequency (percent)	Mean density per m^2 ± SD	Occurrence frequency (percent)
Sciomyzidae	P			0.2 ± 0.7	5.6	0.5 ± 1.5	11.1				
Stratiomyidae	C									0.3 ± 1.0	11.1
Tabanidae	P					0.2 ± 0.7	5.6			0.8 ± 1.7	22.2
Tanyderidae	C					0.2 ± 0.7	5.6	0.2 ± 0.7	5.6		
Tipulidae	C					1.3 ± 2.8	22.2	0.5 ± 1.2	16.7	0.7 ± 1.6	16.7
Mollusca											
Gastropoda											
Ampullariidae	S										
Pomacea paludosa											
Ancylidae	S										
Laevapex fuscus	S							5.2 ± 21.9	5.6	0.8 ± 2.0	16.7
Lymnaeidae	S										
Fossaria cubensis	S							4.5 ± 5.8	55.6		
Physidae	S										
Haitia cubensis	S							20.8 ± 37.8	66.7		
Planorbidae	S										
Gyraulus parvus	S							4.2 ± 10.1	16.7		
Micromenetus dilatus	S										
Planorbella duryi	S										
Planorbella scalaris	S										
Planorbella pivotivus	S									13 ± 3.1	22.2
Viviparidae	S										
Viviparus georgianus	S										
Bivalvia											
Sphaeriidae	F										
Musculium lacustre										0.7 ± 1.6	16.7

Like shredders, scrapers also are underrepresented in many southern wetlands (Haack and others, 1989; Batzer and others, 2005). Scrapers were represented in the present study principally by the abundant gastropods (snails) found at all four of the augmented sites (tables 27 and 28). Snails were not found at any of the natural (unaugmented) wetlands because calcium carbonate concentrations in the acidic surface waters were too low for shell formation. The number of species, frequency of occurrence, and density of snails in the present study were greater at the augmented marsh sites than the augmented cypress sites (tables 27 and 28). At W-5 Augmented Cypress, the amphipod *Hyalella azteca* was an abundant facultative scraper species (Merritt and others, 1999) that may thrive by scraping attached algae from the abundant Riccia mats where it was collected. These floating mats of vegetation not only provided a substrate for attachment of *Hyalella*, but also may have indirectly provided a food source as a surface for algal growth. Amphipods were also moderately abundant at W-19 Impaired Cypress, and submersed aquatic vegetation (*Utricularia* spp.) was present at this site as a substrate for these macroinvertebrates. Kushlan and Kushlan (1980) reported that amphipods were abundant at wetland sites where they were secure from predation, especially within vegetation mats. The occurrence of *Hyalella azteca*, however, may be limited by pH and available substrate. This species prefers neutral pH conditions and is not common in areas with a pH below 5.8 (Grapentine and Rosenberg, 1992); therefore, its abundance at W-5 Augmented Cypress (median pH 7.4) and W-19 Impaired Cypress (median pH 6.0) would be expected. The absence of *Hyalella azteca* at sites with circumneutral pH and abundant submersed aquatic vegetation, such as at the augmented marshes, cannot be explained on the basis of these factors alone.

Chironomidae (Diptera) were not identified below the family level in the present study. Consequently, the distribution of individuals in this family among functional feeding groups at the study wetlands could not determined.

Macroinvertebrates as Ecological Indicators in Wetlands

Macroinvertebrates can be used as biotic indicators of ecological condition in wetlands because they generally have well-understood life histories, established ecological requirements, a varying degree of sensitivity to stress, and are easily identified (Angeler and Garcia, 2005). Macroinvertebrate ecological indicators are widely used in the United States to monitor the effects of human-related stressors, including nutrient enrichment, contamination by metals, acidification related to mining, salinization, sedimentation, and vegetation removal (U.S. Environmental Protection Agency, 1990; 2001). Doherty and others (2000a) produced a comprehensive compilation of literature describing how specific stressors in inland freshwater wetlands of Florida may affect macroinvertebrate species assemblages. The University of Florida, under contract with the Florida Department of Environmental Protection, developed a series of wetland bioassessment documents to standardize methods and advance the understanding of wetlands in the State (Doherty and others, 2000b; Lane, 2000; Lane and others, 2003; Reiss and Brown, 2005). Those efforts include the development of a Wetland Condition Index (which incorporates macroinvertebrates) for isolated depression forested and herbaceous wetlands throughout Florida.

Ephemeroptera (mayflies) have been used as indicator species in some parts of the United States, and their absence is often interpreted as an indication of unfavorable environmental conditions. However, Ephemeroptera were found at all wetlands in this study, and both of the genera found (*Callibaetis* and *Caenis*) are common inhabitants of natural Florida wetlands that dry out seasonally (Berner and Pescador, 1988), including Everglades marshes (Rader, 1994). Moreover, they may be ideally adapted to these habitats because they are (1) tolerant of low oxygen conditions and low pH; (2) have short development times; and (3) produce multiple generations each year, allowing continuous recolonization if water is present. *Caenis* spp. and *Libellula* spp. (Odonata) are considered to be indicative of permanent standing water in Florida (Doherty and others, 2000b). In the present study, *Caenis* spp. were not found in the impaired wetlands, where water is intermittent, although *Libellula* spp. were found.

The numerical proportions of Diptera and Chironomidae (a family within Diptera) in macroinvertebrate communities have been used to describe and compare wetlands. Communities of Diptera with great similarity in species composition have been found in both natural and created flatwoods marshes in Florida that differ in their environmental conditions (Crisman and others, 1997; Evans and others, 1999), most likely because many species of aquatic Diptera tolerate a wide range of environmental conditions. In the present study, the mean proportion of Diptera to all other macroinvertebrates was substantially lower in W-3 Augmented Marsh (17 percent) and W-5 Augmented Cypress wetland (13 percent) than in any of the natural marshes (mean value 67 percent) or any of the natural cypress wetlands (mean value 64 percent) (figure 67). At Duck Pond Augmented Marsh and S-63 Augmented Cypress, Diptera made up about 40 percent of the total macroinvertebrate abundance. Diptera constituted 87 percent of the total invertebrate community at W-29 Impaired Marsh, and 45 percent at W-19 Impaired Cypress. Within the order Diptera, individuals in the families Chironomidae (figure 67), Chaoboridae, and Ceratopogonidae contributed most to the overall abundance of this insect order. In natural forested pond wetlands in Massachusetts (Brooks, 2000), Chironomidae also were dominant and their numerical dominance was greater in shorter hydroperiod wetlands. In longer hydroperiod wetlands in Massachusetts, the taxa richness of the entire macroinvertebrate community was greater, diminishing the relative importance of a single family such as Chironomidae.

The natural variability of macroinvertebrate communities in marsh and cypress wetlands in the present study was high, and may exceed the differences attributable to augmentation for many of the community metrics that were used in this study. Similarly high levels of inter-site and temporal variability in total density and taxa richness of macroinvertebrates also have been reported in other isolated wetlands in Florida and throughout the Southeast (Cowell and Vodopich, 1981; Leslie and others, 1997, 1999; Kratzer and Batzer, 2007). For each wetland type in the present study the two augmented wetlands did not resemble one another, although they also were often different from the natural wetlands of the same type. For example, taxa richness and the number of macroinvertebrate families collected were higher at Duck Pond Augmented Marsh than at the natural marshes, but were much lower at W-3 Augmented Marsh. These differences in the macro- invertebrate communities between the two augmented marshes probably reflected their dissimilar bathymetry and water depths. Likewise, mean macroinvertebrate density was similar in the two natural cypress wetlands, but was four times higher in one of the augmented cypress wetlands (W-5) than in the other (S-63).

Taxa richness in the unaugmented marsh (15-20 taxa) and cypress wetlands (13-20 taxa) in the present study was similar to reported taxa richness in natural marsh wetlands (14-17 taxa) and natural cypress wetlands (8-12 taxa) in Martin and St. Lucie Counties in southeastern Florida (Smock, 1995). The mean number of families (13-17) and the macro-invertebrate density (56-13 6 individuals/m^2) in unaugmented cypress wetlands in the present study were somewhat lower than the number of families (12-27) and the invertebrate density

(39-1,245 individuals/m^2) reported by Haack and others (1989) in a forested wetland in northern Florida, although the northern Florida wetland was a flow-through system instead of an isolated wetland. Leslie and others (1997; 1999) also reported higher densities of macroinvertebrates (1,127-5,320 individuals/ m^2) in pond cypress wetlands near Gainesville, Florida, than those found in the present study. Taxa richness in shallow, acidic, nutrient-rich Carolina bay marshes of the southeastern United States (Taylor and others, 1999) was much higher ($\geq$100 taxa) than taxa richness in marshes in the present study.

In the present study, unaugmented marshes had higher mean macroinvertebrate density (73-450 individuals/m^2) and taxa richness (15-20 taxa) than unaugmented cypress wetlands (56-136 individuals/ m^2; 13-20 taxa). A similar pattern of macroinvertebrate density and taxa richness was reported in natural limesink marsh and cypress wetlands in Georgia (Golladay and others, 1999; Battle and Golladay, 2001). Battle and Golladay (2001) suggest that the dense emergent vegetation and associated periphyton in the Georgia marshes provide more food resources and greater habitat availability for macroinvertebrates than in the forested wetlands.

Few studies have compared macroinvertebrates between augmented and natural wetlands. Data from an augmented cypress wetland in northern Florida (MacMahan and Davis, 1984) indicate that there is an overall decrease in species richness, number of individuals, and biomass of arthropods compared to the control (nonaugmented) wetland. A study by Berryman and Hennigar, Inc. (2000) compared 11 natural and augmented marsh and cypress wetlands in the northern Tampa Bay area, and found that the greatest number of macroinvertebrate species were found at a natural marsh and at an augmented marsh (W-3 Augmented Marsh), and the fewest number of species were found at several augmented cypress wetlands. Species diversity was highest in a natural marsh (2.6) and S-63 Augmented Cypress (2.1), and lowest (0.4-0.6) at other augmented cypress sites in that study. No relations between macroinvertebrate abundance and wetland augmentation were found in that study.

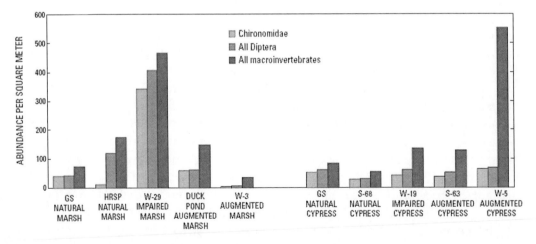

Figure 67. Abundance of Chironomidae, all Diptera, and all macroinvertebrates in marsh and cypress wetlands

Although macroinvertebrates have been reported to respond to changes in wetland hydroperiod (Batzer and others, 1999), differences in macroinvertebrate communities among different hydrologic groups were not apparent in the current study. Schneider (1999) reported that as the duration of standing water increased in vegetated ponds, macroinvertebrate taxa richness also increased, and invertebrate communities were most similar in ponds with similar hydroperiods. Short-duration ponds were the most variable in invertebrate community composition, and ponds with the longest flood duration were the least variable (Schneider, 1999). Small pond-cypress swamps in northern Florida are characterized by unpredictable changes in invertebrate abundance (Leslie and others, 1999), and variable patterns of drying and rewetting may be responsible for the lack of predictability in invertebrate populations in these wetlands. In natural limesink wetlands in southwest Georgia (Golladay and others, 1999), extended inundation at some sites caused short- term reductions in macroinvertebrate populations.

Because of the naturally occurring differences in macroinvertebrate density, diversity, and taxa richness within wetland types, a greater number of augmented and natural wetlands of each type are needed than in the present study before reliable conclusions can be made about the hydrologic effects of augmentation on ecologic conditions. Differences related to water quality, such as the presence or absence of gastropods and mollusks, were clearly evident in the current study, even with the small sample size used.

Tadpoles were collected incidentally in dip-net samples in the two cypress wetlands at Starkey Well Field (S-63 Augmented Cypress and S-68 Natural Cypress), as well as in all of the unaugmented and augmented marsh wetlands in the present study (table 29). Tadpoles were not collected in dip-net samples in GS Natural Cypress, W-5 Augmented Cypress, and W-19 Impaired Cypress. Hydroperiod has been found to regulate amphibian reproductive success in several wetlands near the study wetlands in the Starkey Well Field (Mushinsky and others, 2004), and the capture rate and species richness of larval frogs was higher in wetlands with longer hydroperiods. Most amphibians actually require small, ephemeral, fish-free wetlands to successfully reproduce (Sexton and Phillips, 1986; Brooks, 2000). In wetlands in the Morris Bridge Well Field, Guzy and others (2006) found no significant relation between the number of tadpole species and wetland hydroperiod, although the density of tadpoles was higher in wetlands unaffected by ground-water pumping than in any of the wetlands with hydroperiods shortened by ground-water pumping. A more systematic estimate of larval frog density and distribution would be required to determine correlations with flooding frequency and flooded extent in wetlands from the present study.

Fish also were collected incidentally in some dip-net samples in the present study (table 29). The presence of fish in wetlands requires either perennial standing water, small refugia in localized depressions, or seasonal interconnections to adjacent surface-water bodies. Fish were collected in GS Natural Marsh and both the augmented marshes, but not in HRSP Natural Marsh or W-29 Impaired Marsh. Because the natural and impaired marshes dry out periodically, fish populations disappear during those times, and opportunities for recolonization are limited to periods when these wetlands are connected to nearby water bodies (Euliss and others, 1999). GS Natural Marsh did have a wet-season connection to a nearby perennially flooded borrow pit, whereas W-29 Impaired Marsh and HRSP Natural Marsh had no such connection or source for fish recolonization. In the cypress wetlands, no fish were collected in GS Natural Cypress and W-19 Impaired Cypress. S-68 Natural Cypress and S-63 Augmented Cypress, which had fish present, both can have surface-water connections to nearby Cross Cypress Branch during periods of high rainfall, providing a seasonal source for fish recolonization. Similarly, W-5 Augmented Cypress is connected by surface flow during wet periods to the Cypress Creek system.

Studies have linked minimum wetland size, the presence of buffer areas, and proximity to other wetlands to the stability of wetland faunal communities (Amezaga and others, 2002), including birds (Haig and others, 1998), amphibians and reptiles (Semlitsch and Bodie, 2003), fish (Matthews, 1998), and macroinvertebrates (Bried and Ervin, 2006).

Habitat fragmentation of wetlands is a growing phenomenon, whereby a few wetlands are preserved but the landscape mosaic overall has fewer total wetlands. The more isolated a wetland is, the smaller the opportunity for near-by wetlands to serve as refugia or as sources of new colonization for all types of biota. Many groups of wetland organisms use the surrounding uplands for forage area and for completion of essential life-history stages. Disturbance in the upland area surrounding a wetland can interrupt these important processes. Further studies are needed to establish a scientific foundation for decisions related to the creation and maintenance of protective ecological buffers (Environmental Protection Commission of Hillsborough County, 2006; Taylor and others, 2007).

Wissinger (1999), in a synthesis of studies on macroinvertebrates in North American wetlands, cites hydroperiod, dissolved oxygen, salinity, pH, suspended sediment, and nutrient levels as the factors most often found to influence invertebrate abundance and community composition. Of these factors, only pH and hydroperiod were sufficiently different between natural and augmented wetlands in the present study to have a measurable influence on invertebrate communities. Wissinger (1999) noted that because hydroperiod can have many indirect effects (presence of predators, nutrient availability, vegetation heterogeneity, and water chemistry) it is generally difficult to separate the direct effects (drying and inundation) from those indirect effects. The ability of many macroinvertebrates to reproduce under a variety of conditions, colonize either from the air or by way of overland connections, and facultatively feed at different trophic levels indicates that ecosystem integrity in wetlands can be maintained across a range of conditions, and that invertebrate communities can be heterogeneous between sites, yet functionally similar and ecologically intact.

Overview of Wetland Ecology

Because the algae making up the periphyton community have short life cycles and respond rapidly to changing conditions, they are less influenced by water depth and hydrologic regime than are wetland vegetation and macroinvertebrates. If water disappears from a wetland, the periphyton ceases to grow and may enter a desiccated (dried) resting stage, often settling and accumulating in the moist bottom sediments (Stevenson and others, 1996). Many algae are adapted to pulsed hydroperiods and, depending on the extent and duration of dry periods, can recolonize rapidly from desiccated cells. Drawdown of water levels, either naturally or due to anthropogenic activities, concentrates dissolved nutrients that can stimulate subsequent periphyton growth when water returns. Reflooding can also mobilize previously unavailable nutrients from oxidized organic material in the wetland basin.

Table 29. Occurrence of Fish and Larval Amphibians (Tadpoles) in Study Wetlands

Wetland name	*Jordanella floridae*	*Fundulus seminolis*	*Heterandria formosa*	*Gambusia holbrooki*	Tadpoles
GS Natural Marsh				x	x
HRSP Natural Marsh					x
W-29 Impaired Marsh					x
Duck Pond Augmented Marsh	x		x	x	x
W-3 Augmented Marsh		x	x	x	x
GS Natural Cypress					
S-68 Natural Cypress		x		x	
W-19 Impaired Cypress					
S-63 Augmented Cypress		x		x	
W-5 Augmented Cypress			x		

Overall, periphyton biomass was greater in augmented wetlands than in natural and impaired wetlands of both types in this study. Median concentrations of nutrients (nitrogen and phosphorus) in the study wetlands did not exceed threshold concentrations that typically indicate nutrient enrichment in wetlands and, therefore, patterns of periphyton abundance related to nutrients could not be determined in the study. Diatom species abundance and distribution in the present study were related to differences in specific conductance, pH, and possibly to nutrients in the accumulated organic material. In studies of prairie wetlands (Mayer and Galatowisch, 1999), the high degree of natural variability in diatoms among sites made them a poor indicator of human activities.

Plant species richness was higher in augmented wetlands than in natural and impaired wetlands. Changes in flooding characteristics or water quality may have facilitated the establishment of additional plant species at individual sites. Plant biomass was higher in augmented marshes than in natural and impaired marshes. These differences were not related to measured nutrient concentrations, but may be related to nutrients released by decaying plant material and quickly absorbed by vegetation, promoting plant growth. Tree density was lower and the percentage of fallen and dead trees was higher in augmented and impaired cypress wetlands than in natural cypress wetlands, most likely because extended dry conditions prior to augmentation accelerated tree fall and altered hydrology, preventing germination of new trees.

The natural variability of macroinvertebrate communities in marsh and cypress wetlands was high and may exceed any differences attributable to augmentation for many community metrics used in this study. Similarly high levels of inter-site and temporal variability in total density and taxa richness of macroinvertebrates have been reported in other isolated wetlands in Florida and throughout the southeastern United States. Regarding wetland types, unaugmented marshes generally had higher macroinvertebrate density and taxa richness than unaugmented cypress wetlands. Generalizations about wetland hydrologic groups were more difficult to determine because there were few similarities in macroinvertebrate communities between the two augmented marshes, and also between the two augmented cypress wetlands. Because of the naturally occurring differences in macroinvertebrate density, diversity, and taxa richness between wetland types, a greater number of augmented and natural wetlands of each type are needed for consideration than in the present study before reliable conclusions can be made about the hydrologic effects of augmentation. Differences related to water quality, such as the presence or absence of gastropods and mollusks, were clearly evident in the current study, even with the small sample size used.

SUMMARY AND CONCLUSIONS

Understanding isolated wetlands over the spectrum of prevailing hydrologic conditions in west-central Florida required the development of sampling and analysis techniques that could be applied equivalently to two different types of wetlands (marsh and cypress) in three wetland groups with widely differing hydrologic regimes (natural, impaired, and augmented). Comparisons of wetland hydrology, water quality, and ecology indicated intrinsic differences between marshes and cypress wetlands in this study, as well as between natural wetlands and wetlands affected by environmental stresses including impaired water levels and ground-water augmentation. Results were used to characterize the hydrologic behavior of natural wetlands and then compare this behavior to wetlands affected by long-term ground-water withdrawals from large municipal well fields.

Collectively, five comparisons were considered. Natural marshes were compared to natural cypress wetlands to highlight possible hydrologic differences between the two wetland types. Augmented wetlands were compared to natural wetlands to infer the long-term consequences of augmentation. Impaired wetlands were compared to natural wetlands to assess the degree of impairment, and then compared to augmented wetlands to infer the extent of mitigation that was achieved. Recent and historical flooding conditions in each wetland group were compared to infer the effects of ground-water pumping and rainfall over time. Finally, the amount of water required to steadily augment a wetland was compared to the amount needed to refill it from dry conditions. Ecological comparisons of the wetlands based upon surveys of periphyton, vegetation, and macroinvertebrates were then used to explore the effect of these physical differences on wetland condition. In addition to being used for comparisons, the results from these 10 wetlands expand the available knowledge about isolated wetlands in general by documenting in detail the wetland flooding characteristics, wetland geologic framework and geochemistry, ground-water flow patterns around wetlands, and wetland water budgets.

Augmentation has maintained some of the functional capacity of the four augmented wetlands located within the well fields during the augmentation period (which began in the early 1980s). Without augmentation, the four augmented wetlands would have been dry during the majority of this period. The historical flooding pattern of W-29 Impaired Marsh illustrated the most optimistic flooding regime that could have been expected in the absence of augmentation: 20 percent or less of the total wetland area was inundated for most of the time, and entirely dry conditions prevailed for as much as 80 percent of the time. In addition, the soil moisture comparisons at the natural and impaired marshes, together with the hydrogeologic sections of the augmented wetlands, indicate that without augmentation, the water table would have been too deep below the wetlands to provide the soil moisture conditions necessary for aquatic algae, wetland plants, and freshwater macroinvertebrates to survive. Wetland plants would likely have been replaced with upland vegetation, as occurred at W-29 Impaired Marsh where slash pines became established throughout the marsh during prolonged dry conditions (Haag and others, 2005). Cypress tree mortality would have been widespread, as was evident in W-19 Impaired Cypress. Moreover, because both of the impaired wetlands were affected less severely by ground-water withdrawals than the four augmented wetlands prior to their augmentation, even more severe deterioration could have been expected.

The wetlands augmented with ground water are ecologically similar to the natural wetlands in many respects. Most of the biotic community measures in the augmented wetlands, including relative species abundance, taxa richness, and Shannon diversity were within the existing range for natural wetlands of the same type. The distribution of wetland periphyton species was related to pH and specific conductance, and differences related to nutrient concentrations were not distinct. Biomass of herbaceous vegetation was higher in augmented wetlands than in unaugmented wetlands, and may be related to availability of nutrients released from the accumulated partially decayed vegetation. The relative abundance of plant types (obligate, facultative wet, and facultative) was not substantially different among wetland groups, most likely because many of these plants have broad tolerances for water depth and grow across a gradient of hydrologic conditions. The occurrence of snails and mussels was confined to augmented sites where the concentration of calcium carbonate was sufficient for shell formation. With the exception of W-3 Augmented Marsh (where snails were abundant), the biomass and density of macroinvertebrates at augmented sites was within the range found at natural and impaired sites.

Isolated freshwater wetlands act as surface-water storage features in the landscape

The hydrology of augmented wetlands differed from the natural wetlands in several fundamental aspects, including the size of the flooded areas, residence times of water in the wetlands, leakage rates, the magnitude of runoff, and the water-table configuration. The relatively constant flooded area in three of the four augmented wetlands was well within the wetland perimeter, leaving the remainder of the wetland bottom subject to invasion by upland vegetation. Perennial standing water in augmented wetlands, however, increased their primary productivity compared to natural wetlands, as indicated by the higher vegetation and periphyton biomass. This greater primary productivity, combined with infrequent drying, probably accelerated the accumulation of organic material in all but S-63 Augmented Cypress, which repeatedly dried out. Radium-226 activities were not substantially elevated in the bottom sediment of augmented wetlands compared to natural wetlands.

Although augmentation practices could be refined to more closely mimic the flooded-area behavior of natural wetlands, the quantitative information needed to design a reliable system for doing this is lacking. The information described in the comparative analyses moves this goal closer by detailing the quantities and fate of the water flowing through augmented wetlands. Knowledge about the leakage quantities from a variety of augmented wetlands, the size of the recharge mounds, the change in the flooded area associated with changes in wetland stage, and the change in leakage quantities with changing levels in the Upper Floridan aquifer, can be used to size augmentation pipelines and allocate augmentation volume amounts during the year. For example, the augmentation experiment at W-5 Augmented Cypress demonstrated that, if pipelines are sized adequately, it is feasible to allow an augmented wetland to dry out completely for several weeks or months and to refill the wetland within several days. Drying provides ecological benefits because it allows organic material to dry, oxidize, and compact. Moreover, drying and refilling this wetland saved a substantial volume of water compared to uninterrupted augmentation over the same time period.

Having improved methods for comparing the hydrologic condition of natural and impaired wetlands will provide better evidence for defining wetland impairment and for refining mitigation goals for wetlands. For example, in addition to the current policy of augmenting wetland water levels to a minimum elevation, augmentation could be used to flood a minimum percentage of the total wetland area. The minimum percentage of inundated wetland area during both short and long time periods could be inferred by the recent and historical flooded-area duration of natural wetlands in the same region. Similarly, as a survey tool, impairment may be indicated if the distance of the potentiometric surface of the Upper Floridan aquifer below a wetland remains consistently outside the range observed in natural wetlands in the same region. Study results also indicate that preserving the greatest wetland area for a given amount of augmentation water may not always equate to conserving the largest number of individual wetlands. The augmentation experiment and water-budget results showed that linear leakage rates typically decreased as the size of the flooded area increased. This finding suggests, for example, that expanding the flooded area in an existing augmented wetland could be an efficient way to compensate for the loss of flooded area in wetlands that cannot effectively be rehydrated. Overall, augmentation may be required in fewer wetlands in the coming decade than the previous two decades, because the reduced ground-water pumping that was initiated in 2003 will raise potentiometric levels at the well fields, increasing wetland water levels and flooded area in numerous impaired and augmented wetlands. Less augmentation water would then be required to maintain augmented wetlands at their desired levels, especially at the leakiest sites such as Duck Pond Augmented Marsh and S-63 Augmented Cypress, where daily leakage rates were inversely correlated to Upper Floridan aquifer water levels.

Comparing wetland types indicated possible differences in geologic setting between marsh and cypress wetlands in this study. Considered collectively, the geologic material below marshes had lower leakance values than most cypress wetlands (with the exception of Duck Pond Augmented Marsh), indicating that marshes may occupy depressions with less permeable bed material than cypress wetlands. The two natural marshes leaked more slowly than the two natural cypress wetlands. The isotopic signature of water in marshes showed greater evidence of evapoconcentration than cypress wetlands, possibly because of higher evaporation rates and longer water residence times in marshes. The duration of flooding at the deepest point in natural marshes and natural cypress wetlands was similar, although more than half of the surface area of marshes was flooded more often than at cypress wetlands. Historically, natural cypress wetlands tended to exhibit extremes in the size of the flooded area, either nearly full or nearly dry, more often than the natural marshes.

The study results consistently showed that the isolated freshwater wetlands in this study act as surface-water storage features that receive rainfall and runoff from upland areas and slowly release this water as ground-water recharge to the surficial and Upper Floridan aquifers. Recharge mounds were mapped for 8 of the 10 wetlands using hydrogeologic data, and the recharge water altered the geochemistry of the surficial aquifer around and below the wetlands. Leakage rates below wetlands varied by a factor of 30, with augmented wetlands leaking fastest. In addition to increasing wetland leakage rates, ground-water withdrawals also reduce runoff to wetlands, which is an additional consequence of concern.

Runoff constituted a substantial component of wetland water budgets, even before it began generating stream flow between wetlands. Wetland hydrology evaluated from an overall watershed perspective is considered a priority for future studies. Data are needed to quantify the water stored in wetlands, the water flowing between individual wetlands during the wettest periods, and the accumulated flow exiting the watershed. Because isolated wetlands frequently act as headwaters to rivers, quantifying wetland hydrology on the watershed scale will expand the current understanding of both of these surface-water resources in Florida.

References Cited

Abtew, W. (1996). Evapotranspiration measurements and modeling for three wetland systems in South Florida: *Water Resources Bulletin* v. *32*, no. 3, p. 465-473.

Adamus, P. R., Stockwell, L. T., Clairain, E. J., Morrow, M. E., Rozas, L. P. & Smith, R.D. (1991). *Wetland Evaluation Technique (WET)*, Vol. *1*, Literature review and evaluation rationale: U.S. Army Corps of Engineers, Wetlands Research Program Technical Report WRP-DE-2.

Amezaga, J. M., Santamaria, L. & Green, A. J. (2002). Biotic wetland connectivity—Supporting a new approach for wetland policy: *Acta Oecologia*, v. *23*, p. 213-222.

Anderson, M. P. & Woessner, W. W. (1992). *Applied groundwater modeling*: Simulation of *flow and advective transport: New York*, Academic Press, 381 p.

Angeler, D. G. & Garcia, Gregorio (2005). Using emergence from soil propagule banks as indicators of ecological integrity in wetlands: Advantages and limitations: *Journal North American Benthological Society*, v. *24*, no. 4, p. 740-752.

Barr, G. L. (1993). Applications of ground penetrating radar methods in determining hydrogeologic conditions in a karst area, west-central Florida: U.S. Geological Survey Water- Resources Investigation Report 92-4141, 26 p.

Battle, J. & Golladay, S. W. (2001). Water quality and macroinvertebrate assemblages in three types of seasonally inundated limesink wetlands in southwest Georgia: *Journal of Freshwater Ecology*, v. *16*, no. 2, p. 189-207.

Batzer, D. P., Dietz-Brantley, S. E., Taylor, B. E. & DeBiase, A. E. (2005). Evaluating regional differences in macroinvertebrate communities from forested depressional wetlands across eastern and central North America: *Journal North American Benthological Society*, v. *24*, no. 2, p. 403-414.

Batzer, D. P., Rader, R. B. & Wissinger, S. A. (1999). Invertebrates in freshwater wetlands of North America: New York, John Wiley, 1100 p.

Batzer, D. P. & Wissinger, S. A. (1996). Ecology of insect communities in nontidal wetlands: *Annual Review of Entomology*, v. *41*, p. 75-100.

Bear, J. (1979). Hydraulics of groundwater: New York, McGraw-Hill, 567 p.

Beck, J. T. & Cowell, B. C. (1976). Life history and ecology of the freshwater Caridean shrimp, *Palaemonetes paludosus* (Gibbes): *American Midland Naturalist*, v. *96*, no. 1, p. 52-65.

Bedford, B. L., Walbridge, M. R. & Aldous, A. (1999). Patterns in nutrient availability and plant diversity of temperate North American wetlands: *Ecology*, v. *80*, p. 2151-2169.

Berner, L. & Pescador, M. L. (1988). *The mayflies of Florida (2d ed.):* Gainesville, University Presses of Florida.

Berryman & Hennigar, Inc. (1995). *Evaluation of groundwater augmentation of wetland and aquatic habitats: Clearwater*, Fla., Consultant report prepared for the West Coast Regional Water Supply Authority, 45 p.

Berryman & Hennigar, Inc. (2000). Phase II: Evaluation of groundwater augmentation of wetland and aquatic habitats: Clearwater, Fla., Report prepared for Tampa Bay Water, 95 p.

Bidlake, W. R., Woodham, W. M. & Lopez, M. A. (1996). *Evapotranspiration from areas of native vegetation in west- central Florida:* U.S. Geological Survey Water Supply Paper 2430, 35 p.

Biological Research Associates, Inc. & SDI Environmental Services, Inc. (2001). *Water budgets and consumptive use of groundwater used for augmentation of lakes and wetlands:* An analysis of nine augmented wetlands and lakes in the northern Tampa area: Brooksville, Consultant's report prepared for Southwest Florida Water Management District, 72 p.

Brenner, Mark, Schelske, C.L., and Kenney, W.F., 2004, Inputs of dissolved and particulate ^{226}Ra to lakes and implications for ^{210}Pb dating recent sediments: Journal of Paleolimnology, v. 32, p. 53-66.

Brenner, Mark, Schelske, C. L. & Whitmore, T. J. (1997). Radium-226 stratigraphy in Florida lake sediments as an indicator of human disturbance: *Verhein International Verein Limnologie*, v. *26*, p. 809-8 13.

Brenner, Mark, Smoak, J. M., Allen, M. S., Schelske, C. L. & Leeper, D. A. (2000). Biological accumulation of Radium-226 in a ground-water augmented Florida lake: *Limnology and Oceanography*, v. *45*, p. 710-715.

Brenner, Mark, Smoak, J. M., Leeper, D. A., Streubert, M. & Baker, S. M. (2007). Radium-226 accumulation in Florida freshwater mussels: *Limnology and Oceanography, v. 52*, no. 4, p.1614-1623.

Brenner, Mark & Whitmore, T. J. (1999). Paleolimnological reconstruction of water quality for Lakes Dosson, Halfmoon, and Round in Hillsborough County, Florida: January, 1999: Southwest Florida Water Management District report, 158 p.

Brenner, Mark, Whitmore, T. J., Riedinger-Whitmore, M. A., DeArmond, B. & others. (2006). Geochemical and biological consequences of groundwater augmentation in lakes of west-central Florida (USA): *Journal of Paleolimnology*, v. *36*, p. 371-383.

Bried, J. T. & Ervin, G. N. (2006). Abundance patterns of dragonflies along a wetland buffer: *Wetlands*, v. *26*, no. 3, p. 878-883.

Brinson, M. M. (1993). A hydrogeomorphic classification for wetlands: U.S. Army Corps of Engineers Wetlands Research Program technical report WRP-DE-4, 79 p.

Brooks, R. T. (2000). Annual and seasonal variation and the effects of hydroperiod on benthic macroinvertebrates of seasonal forest ("vernal") ponds in central Massachusetts, USA: *Wetlands*, v. *20*, no. 4, p. 707-715.

Browder, J. A., Gleason, P. J. & Swift, D. R. (1994). Periphyton in the Everglades: Spatial variation, environmental correlates, and ecological implications, *in* Davis, S.M., and Ogden, J.C., eds., Everglades: The ecosystem and its restoration: *Del Ray Beach, Fla.*, St. Lucie Press, p. 379-418.

Buono, A., Spechler, R. M., Barr, G. L. & Wolansky, R. M. (1979). Generalized thickness of the confining bed overlying the Floridan aquifer: U.S. Geological Survey Open-File Report 79–1171, 1 sheet, scale 1:50,000.

Burgess, G. (2004). *Identification key to native freshwater fishes of Peninsular Florida: Gainesville*, Fla. Accessed Sept. 20, 2004, at http://www.flmnh.edu/fish everglades/marshe s/fi shkeyedu.html

Campbell Scientific, Inc. (1996). *Instruction Manual for CS615 Water Content Reflectometer*: 12 p.

Carr, W. J. & Alverson, D. C. (1959). Stratigraphy of middle Tertiary rocks in part of west-central Florida: *U.S. Geological Survey Bulletin* 1092, p. 1–109.

Carter, V. (1978). *Wetland hydrology, water quality, and associated functions, in National Water Summary on Wetlands*: U.S. Geological Survey Water-Supply Paper 2425, p. 35-48.

CH$_2$M Hill. (1996). *Wetlands impact, mitigation, and planning- level cost estimating procedure: Technical memorandum E.1.F*: Gainesville, Fla., Technical report prepared for St. Johns River Water Management District, 185 p.

Cheal, F., Davis, J. A., Growns, J. E., Bradley, J. S. & Whittles, F. S. (1993). The influence of sampling method on the classification of wetland macroinvertebrate communities: *Hydrobiologia, v. 257*, p. 47–56.

Chen, E. & Gerber, J. F. (1990). Climate, *in* Meyers, R.L., and Ewel, J.E., eds., *Ecosystems of Florida:* Orlando, University of Central Florida Press, p. 11-34.

Choi, J. & Harvey, J. W. (2000). Quantifying time-varying ground-water discharge and recharge in wetlands of the northern Florida Everglades: *Wetlands*, v. *20*, no. 3, p. 500-511.

Clark, I. D. & Fritz, Peter. (1997). *Environmental isotopes in hydrogeology*: New York, Lewis Publishers, 328 p.

Cooney, P. & Allen, M. S. (2006). Effects of introduced groundwater on water chemistry and fish assemblages in central Florida lakes: *Hydrobiologia*, v. *556*, p. 279-294.

Cowardin, L. M., Carter, V., Golet, F. C. & LaRoe, E. T. (1979). *Classification of wetlands and deepwater habitats of the United States*: Washington, D.C., U.S. Fish and Wildlife Service report FWS/OBS-79-31, 131 p.

Cowell, B. C. & Vodopich, D. S. (1981). Distribution and seasonal abundance of benthic macroinvertebrates in a subtropical Florida lake: *Hydrobiologia*, v. *78*, p. 97-105.

Craft, C. B., Vymazal, J. & Richardson, C. J. (1995). Response of Everglades plant communities to nitrogen and phosphorus additions: *Wetlands,* v. *15*, no. 1, p. 258-271.

Craig, H. (1961). Standard for reporting concentrations of deuterium and oxygen-18 in natural waters: *Science*, v. *133*, p. 1833.

Crisman, T. L., Streever, W. J., Kiefer, J. H. & Evans, D. L. (1997). An evaluation of plant community structure, fish, and benthic meio- and macrofauna as success criteria for reclaimed wetlands: Gainesville, University of Florida, Florida Institute of Phosphate Research publication no. 03-086-135.

Daigle, J. J. (1991). Florida damselflies (Zygoptera): A species key to the aquatic larval stages: Tallahassee, *Florida Department of Environmental Regulation Technical Series* v. *11*, no. 1, 12 p.

Davis, J. H., Jr. (1946). *The peat deposits of Florida: Tallahassee*, Florida Geological Survey Bulletin 30.

Davis, S. M. & Ogden, J. C. (1994). Everglades: The ecosystem and its restoration: *Del Ray Beach, Fla.*, St. Lucie Press, 608 p.

DeArmond, B. S., Brenner, M., Kenney, W. F., Leeper, D. A., Smoak, J. M. & others. (2006). Radium-226 accumulation in sediments of a ground-water augmented lake near Tampa, Florida, USA: *Verhein International Verein Limnologie,* v. *29*, p. 1275-1279.

Deghi, G. S. (1984). Seedling survival and growth rates in experimental cypress domes, *in* Ewel, K.C., and Odum, H.T., eds., *Cypress Swamps:* Gainesville, University Presses of Florida, p. 141-144.

Demaree, D. (1932). Submerging experiments with *Taxodium*: *Ecology,* v. *13*, p. 258-262.

Dickson, R. E. & Broyer, T. C. (1972). Effects of aeration, water supply, and nitrogen source on growth and development of tupelo gum and bald cypress: *Ecology*, v. *53*, p. 626-634.

Dierberg, F. E. & Brezonik, P. L. (1984). Nitrogen and phosphorus mass balances in natural and sewage-enriched cypress domes: *Journal of Applied Ecology*, v. *20*, no. 1, p. 323-337.

Doherty, S. J., Cohen, M., Lane, C., Line, L. & Surdick, J. (2000a). *Biological criteria for inland freshwater wetlands in Florida: A review of technical and scientific literature (1990-1999):* Gainesville, University of Florida, Technical report prepared for the U.S. Environmental Protection Agency, variously paged.

Doherty, S. J., Lane, C. R. & Brown, M. T. (2000b). *Proposed classification for biological assessment of Florida inland freshwater wetlands:* Gainesville, University of Florida, Technical report prepared for the Florida Department of Environmental Protection, 33 p.

Duever, M. J., Carlson, J. E. & Riopelle, L. A. (1975). *Ecosystem analyses at Corkscrew Swamp*, *in* Odum, H.T., Ewel, L.C., Ordway, J.W., and Johnson, M.K., eds., Cypress wetlands for water management, recycling, and conservation: Gainesville, University of Florida, p. 627-725.

Eisenlohr, W. S., Jr. (1972). *Hydrologic investigations of prairie potholes in North Dakota, 1959-68*: U.S. Geological Survey Professional Paper 585-A, 102 p.

Environmental Protection Commission of Hillsborough County, Florida, (2006). *Developing scientifically-based ecological buffers to protect watersheds in Hillsborough County*, Florida: Technical memorandum, 23 p.

Epler, J. H. (1996). *Identification manual for the water beetles of Florida: Tallahassee, Florida Department of Environmental Protection*, variously paged.

Euliss, N. H., Wrubleski, D. A. & Mushet, D. M. (1999). *Wetlands of the prairie pothole region*, *in* Batzer, D.P., Rader, R.B., and Wissinger, S.A., eds., Invertebrates in freshwater wetlands of North America: New York, John Wiley, Ecology and Management, p. 471-514.

Evans, D. L. Streever, W. J. & Crisman, T. L. (1999). Natural flatwoods marshes and created freshwater marshes of Florida: Factors influencing aquatic invertebrate distribution and comparisons between natural and created marsh communities, *in* Batzer, D.P., Rader, R.B., and Wissinger, S.A., eds., Invertebrates in freshwater wetlands of North America: New York, John Wiley, *Ecology and Management*, p. 81-104.

Ewel, K. C. (1990). Swamps, *in* Meyers, R.L. and Ewel, J.J., eds., *Ecosystems of Florida*: *Orlando*, University of Central Florida Press, p. 28 1-322.

Ewel, K. C. & Odum, H. T., eds. (1984). *Cypress swamps:* Gainesville, University Presses of Florida.

Florida Department of Environmental Protection. (2004). Wetland evaluation and delineation program: Accessed June 16, 2004, at http://www.dep.stste.fl.us/water/wetlands delineation/vegindex.htm

Florida Department of State. (1994). Delineation of the landward extent of wetlands and surface waters, *in* Florida Administrative Code, chap. 62-340, sec. 62-340.450: Vegetative index.

Florida Legislature. (2007). 2007 Florida Statutes, Chapter 373, Part IV: Accessed April 7, 2008, at http://www.leg.state. fl.us/Statutes/index.htm

Focazio, M. F., Szabo, Z., Kraemer, T. F., Mullin, A. H. & others. (2001). Occurrence of selected radionuclides in ground water used for drinking water in the United States: A targeted reconnaissance survey, 1998: U.S. Geological Survey Water- Resources Investigations Report 00-4273, 40 p.

Freeze, R. A. & Cherry, J. A. (1979). *Groundwater:Englewood Cliffs*, N.J., Prentice-Hall, 604 p.

Freeman, L. A., Carpenter, M. C., Rosenberry, D. O., Rousseau, J. P. & others (2004). *Use of submersible pressure transducers in water-resources investigations: U.S. Geological Survey Techniques of Water Resources Investigations*, 08-A3, 52 p.

Frissel, M. J. & Koster, H. W. (1990). Radium in soil: IAEA Technical Report Series 310, International Atomic Energy Agency, Vienna.

Galehouse, J. S. (1971). Sedimentation analysis, *in* Carver, R.E., ed., *Procedures in sedimentary petrology: New York*, John Wiley, 69-94 p.

Gerla, P. J. (1992). The relationship of water-table changes to the capillary fringe, evapotranspiration, and precipitation in intermittent wetlands: *Wetlands*, v. *12*, no. 2, p. 91-98.

German, E. R. (2000). *Regional evaluation of evapotranspiration in the Everglades*: U.S. Geological Survey Water- Resources Investigations Report 00-42 17, 48 p.

Goldsborough, L. G. & Robinson, G. G. C. (1996). Pattern in wetlands, *in* Stevenson, R.J., Bothwell, M.L., and Lowe, R.L., eds., Algal ecology: *Freshwater and benthic systems:* New York, Academic Press, p. 77-117.

Golladay, S. W., Entrekin, Sally & Taylor, B. W. (1999). Forested limesink wetlands of southwest Georgia: Invertebrate habitat and hydrologic variation, *in* Batzer, D.P., Rader, R.B., and Wissinger, S.A., eds., Invertebrates in freshwater wetlands of North America: New York, John Wiley, *Ecology and Management*, p. 197-216.

GPI Southeast, Inc. (2006). Wetland plant zonation study summary report: Brooksville, Technical report prepared for the Southwest Florida Water Management District, 24 p.

Grapentine L., and Rosenberg, D., 1992, Responses of the freshwater amphipod *Hyalella azteca* to environmental acidification: *Canadian Journal of Fisheries and Aquatic Sciences*, v. *49*, p. 52-64.

Gunn, D. E. & Best, A. I. (1998). A new automated nondestructive system for high resolution multisensor core logging of open sediment cores: *Geo-Marine Letters*, v. *18*, no. 1, p. 70-77.

Guzy, J. C., Campbell, T. S. & Campbell, K. R. (2006). Effects of hydrological alterations on frog and toad populations at Morris Bridge Well Field, Hillsborough County, Florida: *Florida Scientist,* v. *69*, p. 277-287.

Haack, S. K., Best, G. R. & Crisman, T. L. (1989). Aquatic macroinvertebrate communities in a forested wetland: Interrelationships with environmental gradients, *in* Shirts, R.R., and Gibbons, J.W., eds., Freshwater wetlands and wildlife, 1989, CONF-8603 101, DOE Symposium Series No. 61: Oak Ridge, Tennessee, U.S. Department of Energy Office of Scientific and Technical Information, p. 437-454.

Haag, K. H. & Lee, T. M. (2006). *Flooding frequency alters vegetation in isolated wetlands*: U.S. Geological Survey Fact Sheet 2006-3 117, 4 p.

Haag, K. H., Lee, T. M. & Herndon, D. C. (2005). Bathymetry and vegetation in isolated marsh and cypress wetlands in the Northern Tampa Bay Area, 2000-2004: U.S. Geological Survey Scientific Investigations Report 2005-5109, 49 p.

Haig, S. M., Mehlman, D. W. & Oring, L. W. (1998). Avian movements and wetland connectivity in landscape conservation: *Conservation Biology*, v. *12*, p. 749-758.

Hancock, M. C. & Smith, D. A. (1996). *Northern Tampa Bay Water Resources Assessment Program*, Vol. *1*, Surfacewater/ground-water interrelationships: Brooksville, Southwest Florida Water Management District report, 468 p.

Hayashi, M., van der Kamp, G. & Rudolph, D. L. (1998). Water and solute transfer between a prairie wetland and adjacent uplands, 1. Water balance: *Journal of Hydrology*, v. *207*, p. 42-55.

Hazardous Substance & Waste Management Research, Inc. (2000). Human health risk assessment and preliminary ecological evaluation regarding potential exposure to Radium-226 in several central Florida lake ecosystems: Brooksville, Consultant's report prepared for the Southwest Florida Water Management District, 22 p.

Heard, W. H. (1979). Identification manual of the freshwater clams of Florida: Tallahassee, *Florida Department of Environmental Regulation Technical Series*, v. *4*, no. 2, 83 p.

Heimburg, K. F. (1976). *Hydrology of some north central Florida cypress domes: Gainesville*, University of Florida, M.S. thesis.

Heimburg, K. F. (1984). Hydrology of north-central Florida cypress domes, *in* Ewel, K.C., and Odum, H.T., eds., *Cypress Swamps:* Gainesville, University Presses of Florida, p. 72-82.

Hem, J. D. (1985). *Study and interpretation of the chemical characteristics of natural water*: U.S. Geological Survey Water-Supply Paper 2254, 263 p.

Hernandez, T., Nachabe, M., Ross, M. & Obeysekera, J. (2003). Modeling runoff from variable source areas in humid, shallow water table environments: *Journal American Water Resources Association*, v. *39*, no. 1, p. 75-85.

Hillsborough County Environmental Protection Commission. (2006). Developing scientifically-based ecological buffers to protect the watersheds in Hillsborough County, Florida: Technical Memorandum to the Hillsborough County Planning and Growth Management Department, January 25, 2006, 23 p.

Houlahan, J. E., Kelly, P. A., Makkay, K. & Findlay, C. S. (2006). The effects of adjacent land use on wetland species richness and community composition: *Wetlands*, v. *26*, no. 1, p. 79-96.

Jongman, R. H. G., Ter Braak, C. J. F. & van Tongeren, O. F. R. (1995). Data analysis in community and landscape ecology: *Great Britain*, Cambridge University Press, 321 p.

Kadlec, R. H. & Knight, R. L. (1996). *Treatment wetlands: Boca Raton*, Fla., Lewis Publishers, 936 p.

Kane, Richard. (2004a). *Water Resources Data—Florida, water year 2004*, Vol. *3A*: Southwest Florida surface water: U.S. Geological Survey Water-Data Report FL-04-3A.

Kane, Richard, (2004b). Water Resources Data—Florida, water year 2004, Vol. 3B: Southwest Florida ground water: U.S. Geological Survey Water-Data Report FL-04-3B.

Kane, Richard & Fletcher, W. L. (2002). *Water Resources Data—Florida, water year 2002*, Vol. *3A*, Southwest Florida surface water: U.S. Geological Survey Water-Data Report FL-02-3A.

Kane, Richard, Fletcher, W. L. & Lane, S. (2003). *Water Resources Data—Florida, water year 2003*, Vol. *3B*, Southwest Florida ground water: U.S. Geological Survey Water-Data Report FL-03-3B.

Kirkman, L. K., Golladay, S. W., LaClaire, L. & Sutter, R. (1999). Biodiversity in southeastern, seasonally ponded, isolated wetlands: Management and policy perspectives for research and conservation: *Journal of the North American Benthological Society*, v. *18*, no. 4, p. 533-563.

Klein, H., Armbruster, J. T., McPherson, B. F. & Freiberger, H. J. (1975). *Water and the south Florida environment*: U.S. Geological Survey Water-Resources Investigation 24-75.

Knowles, L., Jr., Phelps, G. G., Kinnaman, S. L. & German, E. R. (2005). Hydrologic response in karstic-ridge wetlands to rainfall and evapotranspiration, central Florida, 2001- 2003: U.S. Geological Survey Scientific Investigations Report 2005-5 178, 82 p.

Kowalski, K. P. & Wilcox, D. A. (2003). Differences in sedge fen vegetation upstream and downstream from a managed impoundment: *American Midland Naturalist*, v. *150*, p. 199-220.

Kratzer, E. B. & Batzer, D. P. (2007). Spatial and temporal variation in aquatic macroinvertebrates in the Okeefenokee Swamp, Georgia, USA: *Wetlands,* v. *27*, no. 1, p. 127-140.

Krebs, C. J. (1999). Ecological methodology (2d ed.): Menlo Park, Calif., Addison-Wesley Educational Publishers, 620 p.

Kruse, S. M., Grasmueck, M., Weiss, M. & Viggiano, D. (2006). Sinkhole structure imaging in covered karst terrain: *Geophysical Research Letters*, v. *33*, L16405, doi: 10. 1029/2006GL026975.

Kushlan, J. A. & Kushlan, M. S. (1980). The function of nest attendance in the American alligator (Crocodilia: Crocodylidae): *Herpetologicia,* v. *36*, p. 27-32.

LaBaugh, J. W. (1986). Wetland ecosystem studies from a hydrologic perspective: *Water Resources Bulletin.* v. *22*, p. 1-10.

LaBaugh, J. W., Winter, T. C., Adomaitis, V. A. & Swanson, G. A. (1987). Hydrology and chemistry of selected prairie wetlands in the Cottonwood Lake area, Stutsman County, North Dakota, 1979-82: U.S. Geological Survey Professional Paper 1431, 26 p.

Lane, C. R. (2000). *Proposed wetland regions for Florida freshwater wetlands*: Gainesville, Consultant's report prepared for the Florida Department of Environmental Protection, 112 p.

Lane, C. R. & Brown, M. T. (2007). Diatoms as indicators of isolated herbaceous wetland condition in Florida, USA: *Ecological Indicators*, v. *7*, no. 3, p. 521-540.

Lane, C. R., Brown, M. T., Murray-Hudson, M. & Vivas, M. B. (2003). The Wetland Condition Index (WCI): Biological indicators of wetland condition for isolated depressional herbaceous wetlands in Florida: Gainesville, Technical report prepared for the Florida Department of Environmental Protection, 149 p.

Lanesky, D. E., Logan, B. W., Brown, R. G. & Hine, A. C. (1979). A new approach to portable vibracoring underwater and on land: *Journal of Sedimentary Petrology*, v. *49*, p. 654-657.

Lee, T. M. (1996). Hydrogeologic controls on the groundwater interactions with an acidic lake in karst terrain, Lake Barco, Florida: *Water Resources Research*, v. *32*, no. 4, p. 831-844.

Lee, T. M. & Haag, K. H. (2006). Strength in numbers: Describing the flooded area of isolated wetlands: U.S. Geological Survey Fact Sheet 2006-3118, 4 p.

Lee, T. M. & Swancar, Amy. (1997). Influence of evaporation, ground water, and uncertainty in the hydrologic budget of Lake Lucerne, a seepage lake in Polk County, Florida: U.S. Geological Survey Water-Supply Paper 2439, 61 p.

Leslie, A. J., Crisman, T. L., Prenger, J. P. & Ewel, K. C. (1997). Benthic macroinvertebrates of small Florida pond cypress swamps and the influence of dry periods: *Wetlands,* v. *17*, p. 447-455.

Leslie, A. J., Prenger, J. P. & Crisman, T. L. (1999). *Cypress domes in north Florida: Invertebrate ecology and response to human disturbance*, in Batzer, D.P., Rader, R.B., and Wissinger, S.A., eds., Invertebrates in freshwater wetlands of North America: New York, John Wiley, Ecology and Management, p. 105-120.

MacMahan, E. A. & Davis, L. R. (1984). Density and diversity of microarthropods in manipulated and undisturbed cypress domes, *in* Ewel, K.D., and Odum, H.T., eds., Cypress Swamps: *Gainesville*, University Presses of Florida, p. 197-209.

Magee, T. K. & Kentula, M. E. (2005). Response of wetland plant species to hydrologic conditions: *Wetlands Ecology and Management*, v. *13*, p. 163-181.

Mao, L. M., Bergman, M. J. & Tai, C. C. (2002). Evapotranspiration measurement and estimation of three wetland environments in the Upper St. Johns River Basin, Florida: *Journal of the American Water Resources Association*, v. *35*, no. 5, p. 1271-1285.

Marella, R. L. (2004). Water withdrawals, use, discharge, and trends in Florida, 2000: U.S. Geological Survey Scientific Investigations Report 2004-5 151, 136 p.

Matheney, R. K. & Gerla, P. J. (1996). Environmental isotope evidence for the origins of ground and surface water in a prairie discharge wetland: *Wetlands*, v. *16*, no. 2, p. 109-120.

Matthews, W. J. (1998). Patterns in freshwater fish ecology, London, Chapman and Hall, 756 p.

Mayer, P. M. & Galatowitsch, S. M. (1999). Diatom communities as ecological indicators of recovery in restored prairie wetlands: *Wetlands*, v. *19*, no. 4, p. 765-774.

McPherson, B. F., Hendrix, G. Y., Klein, Howard & Tyus, H. M. (1976). The environment of south Florida—A summary report: U.S. Geological Survey Professional Paper 1011, 82 p.

Merritt, R. W. & Cummins, K. W. (1984). Introduction to the aquatic insects of North America (2d ed.): Dubuque, Iowa, Kendall/Hunt Publishing Company, 722 p.

Merritt, R. W., Higgins, M. J., Cummins, K. W. & Vandeneeden, B. (1999). The Kissimmee River-riparian marsh ecosystem, Florida, *in* Batzer, D.P., Rader, R.B., and Wissinger, S.A., eds., Invertebrates in freshwater wetlands of North America: New York, John Wiley, *Ecology and Management*, p. 55-80.

Merritt, R. W., Wallace, J. R., Higgins, M. J. & others. (1996). Procedures for the functional analysis of invertebrate communities of the Kissimmee River-floodplain ecosystem: *Florida Scientist*, v. *59*, no. 4, p. 216-274.

Metz, P. A. & Sacks, L. A. (2002). *Comparison of the hydrogeology and water quality of a ground-water augmented lake with two non-augmented lakes in northwest Hillsborough County*, Florida: U.S. Geological Survey Water Resources Investigations Report 02-4032, 74 p.

Millar, J. B. (1971). Shoreline-area ratio as a factor in rate of water loss from small sloughs: *Journal of Hydrology*, v. *14*, p. 259-284.

Miller, J. A. (1986). Hydrogeological framework of the Floridan aquifer system in Florida, and in parts of Georgia, Alabama, and South Carolina: U.S. Geological Survey Professional Paper 1403-B, 91 p.

Mitsch, W. J. (1984). Seasonal patterns of a cypress dome in Florida, *in* Ewel, K.C., and Odum, H.T., eds., *Cypress Swamps: Gainesville*, University Presses of Florida, p. 25-33.

Mitsch, W. J. & Gosselink, J. G. (2000). Wetlands: New York, Van Nostrand Reinhold, p. 920

Mortellaro, S., Krupa, S., Fink, L. & Van Horn, J. (1995). *Literature review on the effects of groundwater draw- down on isolated wetlands*: West Palm Beach, South Florida Water Management District Technical Publication no. 96-01, 44 p.

Mushinsky, H. R., McCoy, E. D. & Gonzalez, S. M. (2004). Measuring wetland health comparing vegetation and anurans as indicators: Brooksville, Technical report prepared for Southwest Florida Water Management District, 66 p.

Myers, R. L. & Ewel, J. J. (1990). *Ecosystems of Florida:Orlando*, University of Central Florida Press, 765 p.

National Oceanographic & Atmospheric Administration. (2007). Temperature, precipitation, drought data for Florida: NOAA Climate Division. Accessed July 17, 2007, at http://www1.ncdc.noaa.gov/pub/data/cirs/drd964x.pcp.txt

Newman, S., Schutte, J., Grace, J. B., Rutchey, K. & others. (1998). Factors influencing cattail abundance in the northern Everglades: *Aquatic Botany*, v. *60*, no. 3, p. 265-280.

O'Driscoll, M. A. & Parizek, R. B. (2003). The hydrologic catchment area of a chain of karst wetlands in central Pennsylvania: *Wetlands*, v. *23*, no. 1, p. 171-179.

Oudin, L., Michel, C. & Anctil, F. (2005). Which potential evapotranspiration input for a lumped rainfall-runoff model? Part 1—Can rainfall-runoff models effectively handle detailed potential evapotranspiration inputs?: *Journal of Hydrology*, v. *303*, p. 275-289.

Pennak, R. W. (1989). *Fresh-water invertebrates of the United States: Protozoa to Mollusca*: New York, John Wiley, 628 p.

Poiani, K. A. & Johnson, W. C. (2003). Simulation of hydrology and vegetation dynamics of prairie wetlands in the Cottonwood Lake area, *in* Winter, T.C., ed., Hydrological, chemical, and biological characteristics of a prairie pothole wetland complex under highly variable climate conditions—The Cottonwood Lake area, east-central North Dakota: U.S. Geological Survey Professional Paper 1675, p. 95-109.

Poiani, K. A., Johnson, W. C., Swanson, G. A. & Winter, T. C. (1996). Climate change and northern prairie wetlands: Simulations of long-term dynamics: *Limnology and Oceanography*, v. *41*, no. 5, p. 871-88 1

Porter, J. W. & Porter, K. G. (2002). The Everglades, Florida Bay, and Coral Reefs of the Florida Keys: *Boca Raton, Fla.,* CRC Press, 1000 p.

Potapova, M. & Charles, D. F. (2003). Distribution of benthic diatoms in U.S. rivers in relation to conductivity and ionic composition: *Freshwater Biology*, v. *48*, p. 1311-1328.

Rader, R. B. (1994). Macroinvertebrates of the northern Everglades: Species composition and trophic structure: *Florida Scientist*, v. *57*, p. 22–33.

Rader, R. B. & Richardson, C. J. (1994). Response of macro- invertebrates and small fish to nutrient enrichment in the Northern Everglades: *Wetlands,* v. *14*, p. 134-146.

Ramette, R. W. (1981). Limitations of experimental measurements, *in* Chemical equilibrium and analysis: Reading, Mass., Addison-Wesley, p. 49-82.

Rasmussen, A. K. & Pescador, M. L. (2002). A guide to the Megaloptera and Aquatic Neuroptera of Florida: Final report for Florida Department of Environmental Protection contract number WM71 5, 45 p.

Reed, P. B. (1988). National list of plant species that occur in wetlands: 1988-Florida: St. Petersburg, Florida National Wetlands Inventory, U.S. Fish and Wildlife Service, 140 p.

Reiss, K. C. & Brown, M. T. (2005). *The Florida Wetland Condition Index (FWCI): Developing biological indicators for isolated depressional forested wetlands*: Gainesville, Technical report prepared for the Florida Department of Environmental Protection, 168 p.

Reynolds, Smith & Hills, Inc. (2001). Final annual comprehensive report: Ecological and hydrological monitoring of the Cypress Creek Well Field and vicinity, Pasco County, Florida, Water Year 2000: Clearwater, Technical report prepared for Tampa Bay Water, variously paged.

Richardson, J. S. (2003). Identification manual for the dragonfly larvae (Anisoptera) of Florida: Tallahassee, Florida Department of Environmental Regulation, 114 p.

Riekerk, H. & Korhnak, L. V. (1992). Rainfall and runoff of Florida pine flatwoods: *Water, Air, and Soil Pollution,* v. *65*, p. 69-68.

Riekerk, H. & Korhnak, L. V. (2000). The hydrology of cypress wetlands in Florida pine flatwoods: *Wetlands*, v. *20*, no. 3, p. 448-460.

Rochow, T. F. (1994). The effects of water table level changes on fresh-water marsh and cypress wetlands in the Northern Tampa Bay region—A review: Brooksville, Southwest Florida Water Management District Technical Report 1994-1, 64 p.

Rochow, T. F. (1998). The effects of water table level changes on freshwater marsh and cypress wetlands in the northern Tampa Bay region—A Review: Brooksville, Southwest Florida Water Management District Technical Report 1998-1, 64 p.

Ryder, P. D. (1985). *Hydrology of the Floridan aquifer system in west-central Florida*: U.S. Geological Survey Professional Paper 1403-F, p. F1-F63.

Sacks, L. A. (2002). *Estimating ground-water inflow to lakes in central Florida using the isotope mass-balance approach*: U.S. Geological Survey Water-Resources Investigations Report 02- 4192, 47 p.

Sacks, L. A., Lee, T. M. & Tihansky, A. B. (1992). Hydrogeologic setting and preliminary data analysis for the hydrologic-budget assessment of Lake Barco, an acidic seepage lake in Putnam County, Florida: U.S. Geological Survey Water-Resources Investigations Report 91-4180, 28 p.

Sacks, L. A., Swancar, Amy & Lee, T. M. (1998). Estimatingground-water exchange with lakes using water budget and chemical mass-balance approaches for ten lakes in ridge areas of Polk and Highlands Counties, Florida: U.S. Geological Survey Water-Resources Investigations Report 98-4133, 52 p.

Schmidt, W. (1997). Geomorphology and physiography of Florida, *in* Randazzo, A.F., and Jones, D.S., eds., *The geology of Florida*: Gainesville, University Presses of Florida, p. 1-12

Schneider, D. W. (1999). Snowmelt ponds in Wisconsin— Influence of hydroperiod on invertebrate communities, *in* Batzer, D.P., Rader, R.B., and Wissinger, S.A., eds., Invertebrates in freshwater wetlands of North America: New York, John Wiley, Ecology and Management, p. 299-318.

Scott, T. M. (1988). The lithostratigraphy of the Hawthorn Group (Miocene) of Florida: Tallahassee, Florida Geological Survey Bulletin, 59, 148 p.

Semlitsch, R. D. & Bodie, J. R. (2003). Biological criteria for buffer zones around wetlands and riparian habitats for amphibians and reptiles: *Conservation Biology*, v. *17*, p. 1219-1228.

Sexton, O. & Phillips, C. (1986). A qualitative study of fish-amphibian interactions in three Missouri ponds: *Transactions of the Missouri Academy of Science*, v. *20*. p. 25-30.

Shaffer, P. W., Cole C. A., Kentula, M. E. & Brooks, R. P. (2000). Effects of measurement frequency on water-level summary statistics: *Wetlands*, v. *20*, no. 1, p. 148-161.

Shay, J. M., deGeus, P. M. & Kapinga, M. R. M. (1999). Changes in shoreline vegetation over a 50-year period in the Delta Marsh, Manitoba, in response to water levels: *Wetlands,* v. *19*, no. 2, p. 413-425.

Shjeflo, J. B. (1968). Evapotranspiration and the water budget of prairie potholes in North Dakota: U.S. Geological Survey Professional Paper 585-B, 49 p.

Sinclair, W. C. (1974). Hydrogeologic characteristics of the surficial aquifer in northwest Hillsborough County, Florida: Tallahassee, Florida Bureau of Geology Information Circular 86, 98 p.

Sinclair, W. C., Knutilla, R. L., Gilboy, A. E. & Miller, R. L. (1985). Types, features, and occurrence of sinkholes in the karst of west-central Florida: U.S. Geological Survey Water-Resources Investigations Report 85-4126, 81 p.

Smoak, J. M. & Krest, J. M. (2006). Sources of radium in a well-water-augmented Florida lake: *Journal of Environmental Radioactivity*, v. *89*, p. 102-114.

Smock, L. A. (1995). *Characterization of macroinvertebrate communities in isolated wetlands of south Florida*: West Palm Beach, Technical report prepared for the South Florida Water Management District, 32 p.

Southeastern Geological Society. (1986). *Hydrogeological units of Florida: Tallahassee*, Florida Bureau of Geology Special Publication 28, 9 p.

Southwest Florida Water Management District. (1999a). Northern Tampa Bay Phase II Scope of Work: Brooksville, 51 p.

Southwest Florida Water Management District. (1999b). Section 3.1 Palustrine Cypress Wetlands, *in* Report of the scientific peer review panel on the data, theories, and methodolo- gies supporting the minimum flows and levels rule for the Northern Tampa Bay area, Florida, August 3, 1999, 165 p.

Southwest Florida Water Management District. (2007). Environmental Resource Permit Applications with the Southwest Florida Water Management District, Part B: Basis of Review 3.2.7 Secondary Impacts: 127 p. Accessed October 26, 2007, at http://www.swfwmd.state.fl.us/rules/ files/erp_basis_of_review.pdf

Southwest Florida Water Management District & Tampa Bay Water. (2005). Wetland Assessment Procedure (WAP) instruction manual for isolated wetlands, March 2005: Brooksville.

Stevenson, R. J., Bothwell, M. L. & Lowe, R. L. (1996). *Algal ecology*: New York, Academic Press, 753 p.

Stevenson, R. J., McCormick, P. V. & Frydenborg, R. (2002). Methods for evaluating wetland condition: #11 Using algae to assess environmental conditions in wetlands: Washington, D.C., U.S. Environmental Protection Agency Report EPA-822-R-02-021.

Stewart, R. E. & Kantrud, H. A. (1972). Vegetation of prairiepotholes, North Dakota, in relation to quality of water and other environmental factors: U.S. Geological Survey Professional Paper 585-D, 36 p.

Sumner, D. M. (2001). Evapotranspiration from a cypress and pine forest subjected to natural fires, Volusia County, Florida, 1998-99: U.S. Geological Survey Water-Resources Investigations Report 01-4245, 56 p.

Sumner, D. M. (2006). Adequacy of selected evapotranspiration approximations for hydrologic simulation: *Journal of the American Water Resources Association*, v. *42*, no. 3, p. 699-711.

Sun, G., McNulty, S. G., Amatya, D. M. & others (2002). A comparison of the watershed hydrology of coastal forested wetlands and the mountainous uplands in the Southern U.S.: *Journal of Hydrology*, v. *263*, no. 1-4, p. 92-104.

Swancar, Amy (2006). Magnitude and variability of components of a central Florida lake water budget during recent climate extremes, 1996-2005: American Society of Civil Engineering 22nd Annual Water Resources Seminar, Orlando, Florida, April 7, 2006.

Swancar, Amy & Lee, T. M. (2003). Effects of recharge, Upper Floridan aquifer heads, and time scale on simulated groundwater exchange with Lake Starr, a seepage lake in central Florida: U.S. Geological Survey Water-Resources Investigations Report 02-4295, 53 p.

Swanson, G. A., Euliss, N. H., Jr., Hanson, B. A. & Mushet, D. M. (2003). Dynamics of a prairie pothole wetland complex: Implications for wetland management, *in* Winter, T.C., ed., Hydrological, chemical, and biological characteristics of a prairie pothole wetland complex under highly variable climate conditions—The Cottonwood Lake area, east-central North Dakota: U.S Geological Survey Professional Paper 1675, p. 55-94.

Sweeting, M. M. (1973). *Karst landforms: New York,* Columbia University Press, p. 362

Tampa Bay Water. (2000). Environmental management plan for the Tampa Bay Water central system well fields, March 4, 2000: Clearwater, 58 p.

Tampa Bay Water. (2004). *Optimized regional operations plan annual report July 2004*: Clearwater, Report prepared for Southwest Florida Water Management District, 36 p.

Taylor, A. K., Sprott, P. & Mazzotti, F. J. (2007). The vital link between land and water: The importance of uplands for protecting wetland functions. Accessed November 20, 2007, at http://edis.ifas.ufl.edu/UW095

Taylor, B. E., Leeper, D. A., McClure, M. A. & DeBaise, A. E. (1999). Carolina Bays: Ecology of aquatic invertebrates and perspectives on conservation, *in* Batzer, D.P., Rader, R.B., and Wissinger, S.A., eds., Invertebrates in freshwater wetlands of North America: New York, John Wiley, Ecology and Management, p. 167-196.

Thompson, F. G. (2004). An identification manual for the freshwater snails of Florida: Gainesville, Florida Museum of Natural History. Accessed August 3, 2004, at http://www.flmnh.ufl.edu/ natsci/MALACOLOGY/fl-snail/SNAILS1.htm

Thorp, J. H. & Covich, A. P. (1996). Ecology and classification of North American freshwater invertebrates: *San Diego, Calif.*, Academic Press, 911 p.

Tibbals, C. H. & Grubbs, H. F. (1982). Aquifer test results, Green Swamp area, Florida: U.S. Geological Survey Water-Resources Investigations Report 82-3 5, 29 p.

Tihansky, A. B. (1999). Sinkholes, west-central Florida, *in* Galloway, D., Jones, D.R., and Ingebritsen, S.E., eds., Land subsidence in the United States: U.S. Geological Survey Circular 1182, 177 p.

Tihansky, A. B., Arthur, J. D. & DeWitt, D. W. (1996). Sublake geologic structure from high-resolution seismic-reflection data from four sinkhole lakes in the Lake Wales Ridge, Central Florida: U.S. Geological Survey Open-File Report 96-224, 72 p.

Tiner, R. W. (1991). *The concept of a hydrophyte for wetland identification: Bioscience,* v. *41*, no. 4, p. 236-247.

Topp, G. C., Davis, J. L. & Annan, A. P. (1980). Electromagnetic determination of soil water content: Measurements in coaxial transmission lines: *Water Resources Research,* v. *16*, no. 3, p. 574-582.

Trommer, J. T., Sacks, L. A. & Kuniansky, E. L. (2007). Hydrology, water quality and surface- and ground-water interactions in the upper Hillsborough River watershed, west-central Florida: U.S. Geological Survey Scientific Investigations Report 2007-5 125, 52 p.

U.S. Army Corps of Engineers and South Florida Water Management District. (2000). *Comprehensive Everglades Restoration Plan Master Program Management Plan*: Jacksonville, Fla., variously paged.

U.S. Environmental Protection Agency. (1990). Impacts on quality of inland wetlands of the United States: A survey of indicators, techniques, and applications of community level biomonitoring data. Accessed September 23, 2005, at http:// www/epa.gov/0w0w/ wetlands/wqual/miv.html

U.S. Environmental Protection Agency. (1999). Cancer risk coefficients for environmental exposure to radionuclides: Federal Guidance Report no. 13, EPA/402-R-99-001.

U.S. Environmental Protection Agency. (2001). Indicators for monitoring biological integrity of inland, freshwater wetlands—A survey of North American Technical literature (1990-2000): U.S. Environmental Protection Agency Office of Water Wetlands Division (4502F), EPA843-R-01 -Fall 2001, variously paged.

U.S. Geological Survey. (2007). USGS Ground-Water Data for Florida: Accessed July 13, 2007, at http://waterdata.usgs.gov/ fl/nwis/gw

VanDam, H., Mertenes, A. & Sinkeldam, J. (1994). A coded checklist and ecological indicator values of freshwater diatoms from the Netherlands: *Netherlands Journal of Aquatic Ecology, v. 28*, p. 117-133.

Verdi, R. J., Tomlinson, S. A. & Marella, R. L. (2006). *The drought of 1998-2002: Impacts on Florida's hydrology and landscape*: U.S. Geological Survey Circular 1295, 34 p.

Wassenaar, L. I. (1990). Geochemistry, isotopic composition, origin, and role of dissolved organic carbon fractions in groundwater systems: Ontario, University of Waterloo, Ph.D. dissertation.

White, W. A. (1970). *The geomorphology of the Florida peninsula:Tallahassee*, Florida Bureau of Geology Bulletin 5, 164 p.

Wilcox, D. A. (1995). Wetland and aquatic macrophytes as indicators of anthropogenic hydrologic disturbance: *Natural Areas Journal, v. 15*, p. 240-248.

Wilcox, D. A., Apfelbaum, S. I. & Hiebert, R. D. (1984). Cattail invasion of sedge meadows following hydrologic disturbance in the Cowles bog wetland complex, Indiana Dunes National Lakeshore: *Wetlands, v. 4*, p. 115-128.

Wilde, F. D., Radtke, D. B., Gibs, J. & Iwatsubo, R. T. (1998).National field manual for the collection of water-quality data: U.S. Geological Survey Techniques of Water-Resources Investigations, book 9, chap. A1-A9, variously paged.

Wilson, W. L. & Garmen, M. K. (2002). Identification and delineation of sinkhole collapse hazards in Florida using ground penetrating radar and electrical resistivity imaging: Tampa, Fla., Subsurface Evaluations Inc. technical report. Accessed August 15, 2006, at http://www.dot.ca.gov/hq/esc/ geotech/gg/geophysics2002/ 114garman_sinkhole4.pdf

Winter, T. C. (1981). Uncertainties in estimating the water balance of lakes: *Water Resources Bulletin, v. 17*, no. 1, p. 82-114.

Winter, T. C. & Rosenberry, D. O. (1995). The interaction of ground water with prairie pothole wetlands in the Cottonwood Lake area, east-central North Dakota, 1979- 1990: *Wetlands, v. 15*, no. 3, p. 193-211.

Winter, T. C. & Woo, M. K. (1990). Hydrology of lakes and wetlands, *in* Wolman, M.G., and Riggs, H.C., eds., Surface water hydrology: Boulder, Colo., The Geological Society of America, p. 159-187.

Winter, T. C., Harvey, J. W., Franke, O. L. & Alley, W. M. (1998). Ground water and surface water: A single resource: U.S. Geological Survey Circular 1139, 79 p.

Wissinger, S. A. (1999). *Ecology of wetland invertebrates: Synthesis and applications for conservation and management, in* Batzer, D.P., Rader, R.B., and Wissinger, S.A., eds.,

Invertebrates in freshwater wetlands of North America: New York, John Wiley, Ecology and Management.

Wolansky, R. M. & Thompson, T. H. (1987). Relationship between ground water and surface water in the Hillsborough River Basin, west-central Florida, U.S. Geological Survey Water-Resources Investigations Report 87-4010, 58 p.

Wunderlin, R. P. (1998). Guide to vascular plants of Florida: Gainesville, University Press of Florida, 809 p.

Wunderlin, R. P. & Hansen, B. F. (2004). Atlas of Florida vascular plants: Tampa, Institute for Systematic Botany, University of South Florida. Accessed June 24, 2004, at http://www.plantatlas.usf.edu

Wilde, F. D., Radtke, D. B., Gibs, J. & Iwatsubo, R. T. (1998). National field manual for the collection of water-quality data: U.S. Geological Survey Techniques of Water-Resources Investigations, book 9, chap. A1-A9, variously paged.

Wilson, W. L. & Garmen, M. K. (2002). Identification and delineation of sinkhole collapse hazards in Florida using ground penetrating radar and electrical resistivity imaging: Tampa, Fla., Subsurface Evaluations Inc. technical report. Accessed August 15, 2006, at http://www.dot.ca.gov/hq/esc/ geotech/gg/geophysics2002/ 114garman_sinkhole4.pdf

Winter, T. C. (1981). Uncertainties in estimating the water balance of lakes: *Water Resources Bulletin*, v. *17*, no. 1, p. 82-114.

Winter, T. C. & Rosenberry, D. O. (1995). The interaction of ground water with prairie pothole wetlands in the Cottonwood Lake area, east-central North Dakota, 1979- 1990: *Wetlands,* v. *15*, no. 3, p. 193-211.

Winter, T. C. & Woo, M. K. (1990). Hydrology of lakes and wetlands, in Wolman, M.G., and Riggs, H.C., eds., *Surface water hydrology: Boulder, Colo.*, The Geological Society of America, p. 159-187.

Winter, T. C., Harvey, J. W., Franke, O. L. & Alley, W. M. (1998). *Ground water and surface water: A single resource*: U.S. Geological Survey Circular 1139, 79 p.

Wissinger, S. A. (1999). Ecology of wetland invertebrates: Synthesis and applications for conservation and management, in Batzer, D.P., Rader, R.B., and Wissinger, S.A., eds., Invertebrates in freshwater wetlands of North America: New York, John Wiley, Ecology and Management.

Wolansky, R. M. & Thompson, T. H. (1987). *Relationship between ground water and surface water in the Hillsborough River Basin, west-central Florida*, U.S. Geological Survey Water-Resources Investigations Report 87-4010, 58 p.

Wunderlin, R. P. (1998). Guide to vascular plants of Florida: Gainesville, University Press of Florida, 809 p.

Wunderlin, R. P. & Hansen, B. F. (2004). Atlas of Florida vascular plants: Tampa, Institute for Systematic Botany, University of South Florida. Accessed June 24, 2004, at http://www.plantatlas.usf.edu

GLOSSARY

aquatic — Living or growing in or on water.

aquifer — A geologic formation, group of formations, or part of a formation that contains sufficient saturated permeable material to yield significant quantities of water to wetlands, springs, and wells.

biomass — The amount of living plant or animal matter present in a particular habitat, usually expressed as weight-per-unit area.

confining unit — A body of impermeable or distinctly less permeable material stratigraphically adjacent to one or more aquifers that restricts the movement of water into and out of aquifers.

cypress wetland — A poorly drained to permanently wet depression dominated by cypress trees.

discharge area — An area that has surface-water levels that are lower than the surrounding water table, leading to an inflow of ground water.

emergent plants — Erect, rooted, herbaceous plants that may be temporarily to permanently flooded at the base, but that do not tolerate the prolonged inundation of the entire plant.

evapotranspiration — A process in which water is discharged to the atmosphere as a result of (1) evaporation from the soil and surface-water bodies, and (2) plant transpiration.

flood duration — The amount of time that a wetland or part of a wetland contains water.

flood frequency — The average number of times that a wetland or part of a wetland is flooded during a given period.

functional capacity — The ability of a wetland to carry out natural processes such as nutrient processing, water retention, and aquatic plant succession.

hydraulic head — The elevation above a common datum to which water rises in a tightly cased well. Synonymous with head.

hydrogeomorphic class (HGM) — Wetland classification system based on type of hydrologic conditions, local geomorphology, and climate.

hydroperiod — The seasonal pattern of the water level in a wetland.

isolated wetlands — Wetlands with no apparent surface-water connection to streams, rivers, estuaries, or the ocean.

karst — A region underlain by limestone that contains solution cavities and where the physical features of the land surface include large and small depressions.

marsh — A frequently to continually wet depression characterized by emergent herbaceous vegetation without trees.

overland flow — Nonchannelized sheet flow of surface water that usually occurs during and immediately following rainfall.

permeability — The capacity of soil or rock to conduct water flow.

potentiometric surface — The surface that represents the level to which water will rise in a tightly cased (sealed) well.

runoff — Nonchannelized surface-water flow.

seasonally flooded — Wetlands that are flooded for extended periods during the growing season and dry by the end of the growing season.

species richness — A count of the number of different species in a sample or group of samples.

stage — Wetland water level, in feet above a common datum.

swamp — A wetland dominated by trees or shrubs.

taxa richness — A count of the number of different taxa in a sample or group of samples. Used when identification to species is not possible. A taxon is a level of identification above the species level, such as genus.

well field — An area developed by a local or regional water authority where ground water is withdrawn from the aquifer and sent to a treatment and distribution system.

wetlands — Ecosystems characterized by the presence of shallow water or flooded soils for part of the growing season, plants adapted to a wet environment, and soil indicators of flooding (hydric soils).

wetland augmentation — The addition of water from an external source to increase the water level in a wetland.

wetland plant indicator categories:

obligate — Found in wetlands more than 99 percent of the time.

facultative wet — Found in wetlands 67 to 99 percent of the time.

facultative — Found in wetlands 34 to 66 percent of the time.

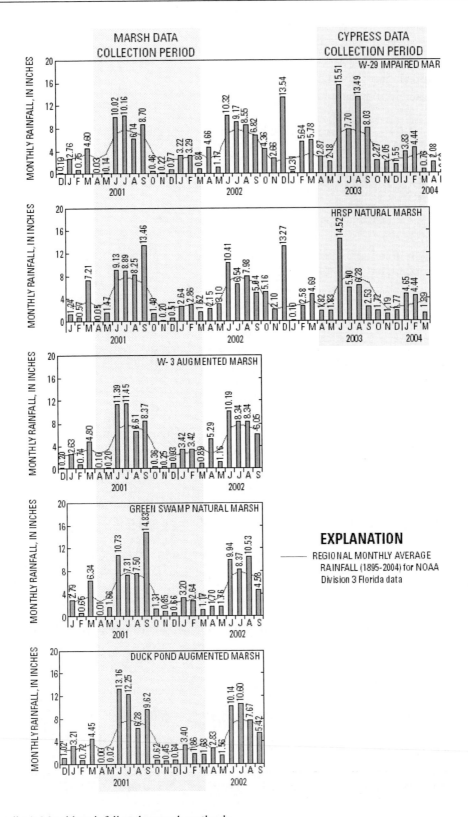

Appendix 1. Monthly rainfall at the marsh wetlands.

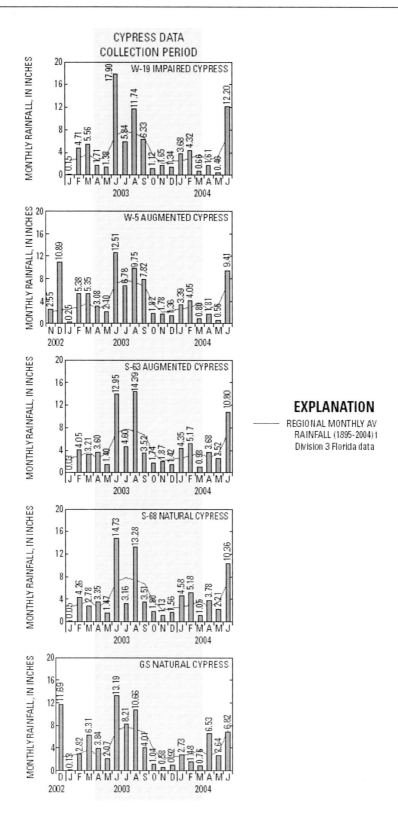

Appendix 2. Monthly rainfall inside the canopy at the cypress wetlands.

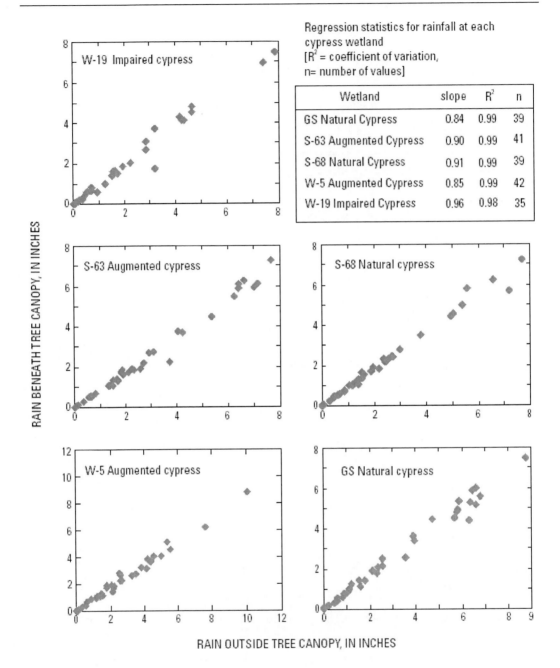

Appendix 3. Relation between rainfall measurements inside and outside of the tree canopy at the cypress wetlands.

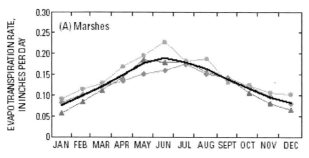

EXPLANATION

⎯▲⎯ Central Florida marshes, lysimeter, Mao and others (2002)
········· South Florida marshes, lysimeter, Abtew (1996)
⎯◆⎯ Everglades marshes, energy-budget method, German (2000)
━━━ Synthetic daily marsh wetland ET, in/d (Annual total ET is 48.35 in)

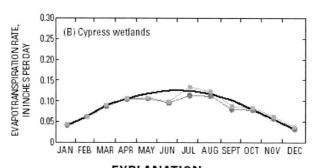

EXPLANATION

⎯✳⎯ Central Florida cypress wetland average ET, energy-budget, Sumner (2001)
········· Central Florida cypress wetland maximum daily ET, energy-budget, Sumner (2001)
━━━ Synthetic daily cypress wetland ET, in/d (Annual total ET is 40.63 in)

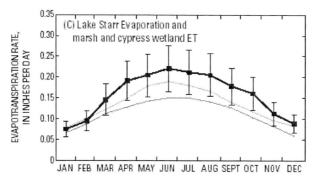

EXPLANATION

■ Monthly average daily energy budget rate, Lake Starr (Swancar, 2006)
━━━ Lake Starr daily evaporation interpolated from monthly average (Annual Total ET is 57.29 in)
········· Synthetic daily cypress wetland ET
········· Synthetic daily marsh ET
I Plus and minus 25 percent of the evaporation rate

Appendix 4. Evapotranspiration (ET) estimates for marsh and cypress wetlands.

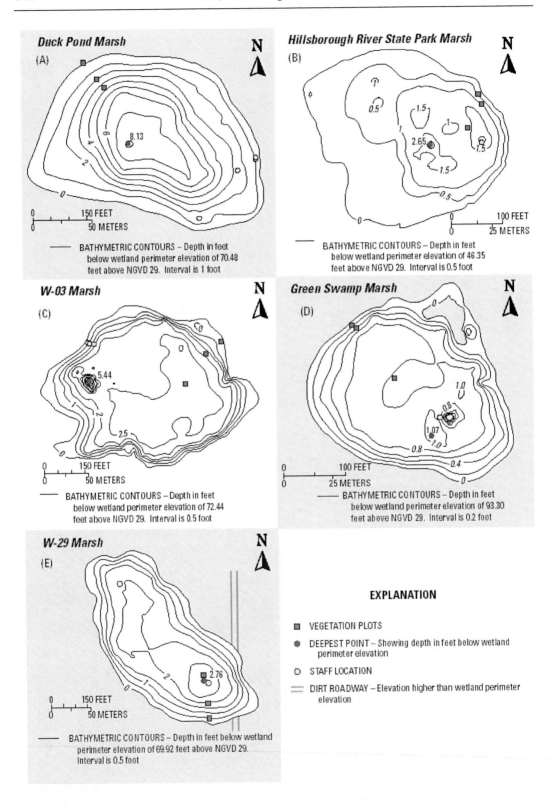

Duck Pond Marsh

(A)

N

8.13

0   150 FEET
0   50 METERS

— BATHYMETRIC CONTOURS – Depth in feet
   below wetland perimeter elevation of 70.48
   feet above NGVD 29. Interval is 1 foot

Hillsborough River State Park Marsh

(B)

N

0.5
1.5
1
2.65
1.5
1.5
0.5
0

0   100 FEET
0   25 METERS

— BATHYMETRIC CONTOURS – Depth in feet
   below wetland perimeter elevation of 46.35
   feet above NGVD 29. Interval is 0.5 foot

W-03 Marsh

(C)

N

5.44
2
2.5
0

0   150 FEET
0   50 METERS

— BATHYMETRIC CONTOURS – Depth in feet
   below wetland perimeter elevation of 72.44
   feet above NGVD 29. Interval is 0.5 foot

Green Swamp Marsh

(D)

N

0
1.0
0.8
1.07
1.0
0.8
0.4
0

0   100 FEET
0   25 METERS

— BATHYMETRIC CONTOURS – Depth in feet
   below wetland perimeter elevation of 93.30
   feet above NGVD 29. Interval is 0.2 foot

W-29 Marsh

(E)

N

2.76
1
2
0

0   150 FEET
0   50 METERS

— BATHYMETRIC CONTOURS – Depth in feet below wetland
   perimeter elevation of 69.92 feet above NGVD 29.
   Interval is 0.5 foot

EXPLANATION

▧ VEGETATION PLOTS

◆ DEEPEST POINT – Showing depth in feet below wetland
   perimeter elevation

○ STAFF LOCATION

▤ DIRT ROADWAY – Elevation higher than wetland perimeter
   elevation

Appendix 5. Continued on next page.

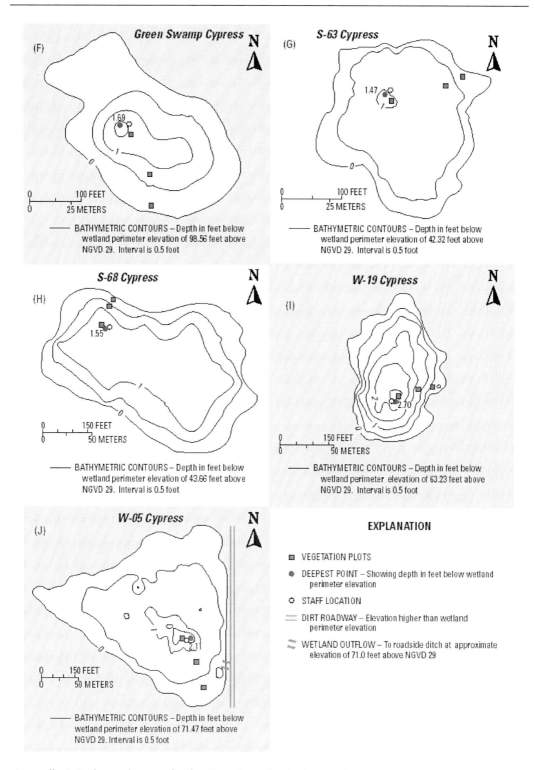

Appendix 5. Bathymetric maps for the 10 study wetlands showing location of vegetation plots (modified from Haag and others, 2005)

CONVERSION FACTORS, ACRONYMS, AND ABBREVIATIONS

Multiply	By	To obtain
Length		
inch (in.)	2.54	centimeter (cm)
inch (in.)	25.4	millimeter (mm)
foot (ft)	0.3048	meter (m)
mile (mi)	1.609	kilometer (km)
Area		
acre	4,047	square meter (m^2)
acre	0.4047	hectare (ha)
square mile (mi^2)	2.590	square kilometer (km^2)
Volume		
cubic foot (ft^3)	0.028316	cubic meter (m^3)
gallon (gal)	3.785	liter (L)
gallon (gal)	0.003785	cubic meter (m^3)
million gallons (Mgal)	3,785	cubic meter (m^3)
acre-foot (acre-ft)	1,233	cubic meter (m^3)
Flow rate		
gallon per minute (gal/min)	0.06309	liter per second (L/s)
gallon per day (gal/d)	0.003785	cubic meter per day (m^3/d)
inch per year (in/yr)	25.4	millimeter per year (mm/yr)
million gallons per day (Mgal/d)	0.04381	cubic meter per day (m^3/d)
Radioactivity		
disintegration per minute per gram (dpm/g)	0.45	picocurie per gram (pCi/g)
disintegration per minute per liter (dpm/L)	0.45	picocurie per liter (pCi/L)
Hydraulic conductivity		
foot per year (ft/yr)	0.3048	meter per year (m/yr)
Leakage		
inch per day (in/d)	2.54	centimeter per day (cm/d)
inch per hour (in/hr)	2.54	centimeter per hour (cm/hr)
Leakance		
foot per day per foot [(ft/d)/ft]	1	meter per day per meter
inch per year per foot [(in/yr)/ft]	83.33	millimeter per year per meter [(mm/yr)/m]
Temperature		
Celsius (°C)	°F = (1.8 × °C) + 32	Fahrenheit (°F)

Vertical coordinate information is referenced to National Geodetic Vertical Datum of 1929 (NGVD 29).

Horizontal coordinate information is referenced to the North American Datum of 1983 (NAD 83).

Elevation, as used in this chapter, refers to distance above the vertical datum.

Specific conductance is given in microsiemens per centimeter at 25 degrees Celsius (µS/cm at 25°C).

Concentrations of chemical constituents in water are given in milligrams per liter (mg/L).

All data and interpretive results in the Wetland Ecology section of the report use metric units. Terms for which definitions are provided in the Glossary are presented in boldface type.

ACRONYMS AND ADDITIONAL ABBREVIATIONS

ANC	acid neutralizing
cm^3/cm^3	cubic centimeter per cubic centimeter
δ	delta notation for isotopic composition
δD	delta deuterium
$\delta^{18}O$	delta oxygen-18
DOC	dissolved organic
g/cm^3	grams per cubic
GPR	ground penetrating
GS	Green Swamp
HRSP	Hillsborough River
mg/L	milligrams per liter
mg/m^2	milligrams per
$\mu g/cm^2$	micrograms per
mg/cm^2	milligrams per
µS/cm	microsiemens per centimeter
NWQL	National Water
SWFWMD	Southwest Florida
USGS	U.S. Geological

CHAPTER SOURCES

The following chapters have been previously published:

Chapter 1 – This is an edited, excerpted and augmented edition of a United States Department of the Interior, U.S. Geological Survey publication, Circular 1342, dated 2010.

Chapter 2 – This is an edited, excerpted and augmented edition of a Hydrology & Ecology of Freshwater Wetlands in Central Florida Appendix including maps showing the distribution of wetlands by type and pie diagrams showing the percent of each wetland type in each county in Central Florida, dated 2010.

Chapter 3 – This is an edited, excerpted and augmented edition of a United States Department of the Interior, U.S. Geological Survey publication, Professional Paper 1758, dated 2009.

INDEX

D